Section VI

Gases

by Todd Bennett

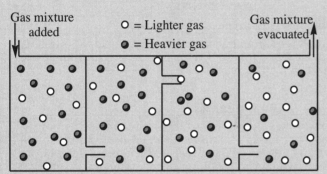

Gas mixture is richer in the heavier gas on the left side of the tube

Gas mixture is richer in the lighter gas on the right side of the tube

The BERKELEY R·E·V·I·E·W®

Specializing in MCAT Preparation

Gases Section Goals

 Know the definition of a gas and the terms associated with gases.

You must know what an ideal gas and a real gas are. Understand the following terms used to describe a gas system: pressure, volume, concentration, density, temperature, moles, molecules, collision frequency, and mean free path.

 Have a solid understanding of the kinetic theory of gases.

Be able to recite a viable description of gases at the microscopic level using the kinetic theory of gases. Know that gases move about their environment in a random fashion, and that they frequently collide with other gas particles and the walls of the container. Know that the momentum of heavier gases is greater than the momentum of lighter gases. Know that the velocities of each gas particle sum to zero for a gas in a stationary, closed container.

 Know the proper applications of the various gas laws.

Know hen to use Avogadro's, Boyle's, and Charles's laws from the variables presented in the question. Have an understanding of the experimental conditions required to use each law. Recognize the shape of the graphs that show the relationships between the variables of each gas law.

 Be able to distinguish between a real gas and an ideal gas.

An ideal gas is composed of molecules that occupy no volume and exhibit no intermolecular forces. A real gas is just what the name implies, a gas made up of real molecules that do occupy volume and exhibit intermolecular forces. The pressure and volume of a real gas are therefore different from those of an ideal gas. The Van der Waals equation (which you should understand but not memorize) shows the relationship betweenideal variables and real variables for a gas.

 Be able to determine the partial pressure of a gas within a mixture.

The total pressure of a system is the sum of the individual pressures (partial pressures) of all of the component gas particles. The partial pressure due to one component in the mixture can be determined by multiplying the mole fraction of the component by the total pressure of the system. You must be able to convert between different pressure units.

 Understand the relationship between speed, mass, and temperature for a gas.

You must know the effect of a particle's mass on its velocity. Lighter gases travel at a faster rate than heavier gases. The velocity of a gas particle is inversely proportional to the square root of its mass. You must know the effect of temperature on velocity. At higher temperatures, gases travel at a faster rate. The velocity of a gas particle is directly proportional to the square root of the temperature.

 Understand the concepts of effusion and effusion rate, infusion, and diffusion.

Effusion is the process by which gas molecules pass from within a container to the outside through pores in the container wall. The rate of effusion depends on the velocity of the gas molecules, the number of pores in the material, and the size of the pore relative to the size of the molecule. When gases enter a container through a pore, the process is referred to as *infusion*. When a gas particle moves from a region of higher concentration to a lower concentration, the process is known as *diffusion*.

Gases and Gas Laws

The gas phase, from the macroscopic perspective, is defined as the state of a closed system in which molecules have no definite shape and no definite volume. From the microscopic perspective, the molecules are freely moving particles traveling through space, where the kinetic energy associated with each particle is greater than the potential energy of intermolecular forces. The gas phase is the first of three phases of matter that we shall address. Gases differ from liquids in that liquids have a definite volume, and the molecules in a liquid are in continuous contact with neighboring molecules. Gases differ from solids in that solids have a definite volume and definite shape, and the molecules in a solid undergo no translational motion and are in continuous contact with neighboring molecules. Of the three common phases of matter (solid, liquid, and gas), the gas phase has the largest amount of kinetic energy and the greatest entropy. To reach the gas phase, energy must be added to the molecules within a system that is not already in the gas phase. It is essential to understand a gas from both the macroscopic and microscopic perspectives.

Macroscopic View of a Gas: A gas assumes the shape and volume of its container. Gases are compressible and must be contained on all sides to hold them in place. Gases are described by the macroscopic variables pressure, concentration, temperature, and volume. Chemists treat gases as if they are composed of inert spheres that occupy no molecular volume. This is a basic assumption of the ideal gas law. Most calculations involving gases are based on the ideal gas equation ($PV = nRT$). There are two common types of calculation questions about gases that you may encounter on the MCAT 1) the before-and-after questions about the effect of changes on a gas system and 2) the straightforward type using $PV = nRT$. Calculation questions requiring you to find a precise value are few, but conceptual relationships can be determined from calculations as well. The first style of question is better understood as an application of one of the gas laws (Avogadro's, Boyle's or Charles's laws). For instance, if the temperature increases in a sealed, rigid container, what changes? This is another way of asking how a change in temperature affects the pressure of a gas, assuming constant volume and moles. Rather than memorize gas laws, know qualitatively how one variable in the ideal gas equation affects another.

Microscopic View of a Gas: Gases consist of individual molecules or atoms that are randomly moving about the space within a container. The particles are in contact only during collisions. This concept is known as the *kinetic theory of gases*. Gases can be described by the microscopic variables of collision frequency, mean free path, and mean velocity. The fact that microscopic behavior involves interactions between gas particles implies that the molecules do in fact occupy a small volume and they are capable of exhibiting intermolecular forces (both attractive and repulsive). The strength of these forces varies with distance. Gases exist as real gases, which are approximated as obeying ideal behavior when they do not interact. Ideal gas behavior is best simulated at low pressure (fewer collisions between molecules and minimal forces between molecules) and high temperature (at high temperature, molecules have the energy to overcome intermolecular forces). Under these conditions, the forces acting between gas molecules become negligible. This is the basis of the kinetic theory of gases.

The behavior of a gas is predictable in terms of the variables that describe the gas system. We use the ideal gas law to predict the effects of changes on gas systems. Although there are no ideal gases, the approximation is still rather close.

Terminology and Concepts

Gas Phase Definitions

The terms used to describe a gas can be broken down into categories of macroscopic and microscopic. We can consider either the system as a whole (macroscopic perspective), or the individual particles that constitute the system (microscopic perspective). Each of the macroscopic properties has a microscopic equivalent. Table 6.1 lists the macroscopic and corresponding microscopic properties that describe the state of a gas system.

Macroscopic Measurements	Microscopic Measurements
Pressure (P; standard unit is atm.)	Collision frequency and collision force
Volume (V; standard unit is liters)	Mean free path
Moles (n; standard unit is moles)	Molecules
Temperature (T; standard unit is K)	Average kinetic energy

Table 6.1

It is imperative to have a well-developed glossary in your memory by the time you take the MCAT. Organize the terms in a manner such that one definition helps you to recall additional definitions. The definitions of selected terms from Table 6.1 are:

Gas Pressure: Gas pressure is defined as the force per unit area exerted by a gas through collisions against a defined area of the container wall. As the gas molecules collide more frequently with the container walls or increase their force during collisions with the walls, the gas pressure increases. The gas pressure depends on the number of gas particles, the volume of the container, and the temperature of the gas system. The standard unit for pressure is atmospheres.

Collision Frequency: The collision frequency is defined as the rate at which molecules in the gas system collide with each other and with the wall of the container. The collision frequency can be increased in one of three ways: increasing the temperature (energy of the gas system), increasing the concentration of gas particles, or reducing the mean free path. All of these changes result in an increase in the number of collisions experienced by a molecule within the system in a given period of time.

Collision Force: The collision force is defined as the force exerted by a gas particle during a collision between it and the container wall. It is based on impulse, so both greater momentum and a shorter time of contact increase the force of impact. The collision force can be increased by increasing the temperature (energy of the gas system), because greater temperature imparts greater velocity, and thus greater momentum, to each particle.

Volume: The volume of a gas is defined as the region within the walls of a container. The actual volume that a gas molecule can occupy (the real volume) is the volume of the container minus the volume of the other gas molecules, because no two gas molecules can occupy the same point in space at the same time. The volume of a gas in an open environment is undefined, because the container holding the gas is also undefined. The standard unit of volume is liters.

Concentration: The concentration of a gas is the number of gas particles per unit volume in a container. A gas is assumed to be homogeneous, so a sample from anywhere in the container may be used to determine the gas concentration. As more molecules of gas are added to a system, or as the volume of the container is decreased, the gas becomes more concentrated. This means that as a gas is compressed, it becomes more concentrated.

Mean Free Path: The mean free path is defined as the average distance a particle can travel before colliding with another particle. Although it isn't the same thing, it can be thought of as the average distance between gas particles at any given time. It is the microscopic equivalent of concentration. If the concentration of a gas remains constant, then the average distance between any two particles within the container also remains constant.

Temperature: Temperature is a measure of the total kinetic energy of a system. If each particle in the system has greater energy, then the system has a larger amount of total energy, and thus the system must have a higher temperature. Temperature can be measured in degrees Celsius or Kelvin, although Kelvin is the better measurement to use when working with gases.

Average Kinetic Energy: The average kinetic energy of a system refers to the mean energy of a particle in that system. As the energy of each particle in the system increases, the average kinetic energy of the system increases, thereby resulting in an increased temperature.

Example 6.1
Which statement below accurately describes the relationship between temperature and energy?
A. Temperature quantifies the energy of a system.
B. Energy quantifies the temperature of a system.
C. Temperature is independent of energy.
D. Temperature is variable, while energy is constant.

Solution
Temperature is a measurement of the average kinetic energy of a system. The best answer is choice **A**. A thermometer is used to determine the temperature of a system. The way a thermometer works is based on the kinetic theory of gases. The thermometer is an evacuated closed column that is partially filled with a pure liquid, preferably of low volatility (such as mercury). Gases collide with the outside of the evacuated glass casing that contains the non-volatile liquid. The energy from these collisions is transferred through the glass walls and into the liquid. A sufficient number of collisions can increase the vibrational energy of the liquid in the container and force the liquid to expand, thereby causing the height of the column of liquid to rise. This implies that the density of a liquid is inversely proportional to its temperature, because as the temperature rises, the volume of a liquid increases (the liquid is expanding). Because the density of water does not change uniformly (it increases from 0°C to 4°C and then decreases from 4°C to 100°C), it is impractical to use it in thermometers. In addition, the range of temperatures over which water exists as a liquid is too small. The liquid chosen to fill a thermometer must have a large temperature range between its freezing point and boiling point. In most thermometers, the liquid used is mercury. In other thermometers, a non-volatile alcohol tinted with a red dye is used.

Kinetic Molecular Theory of Gases

The kinetic molecular theory of gases takes a microscopic view of the component molecules (or atoms) that make up a gas. Four assumptions associated with this theory with which we shall concern ourselves are the following:

1. Particles are so small compared to the distances between particles (internuclear distances) that their volumes are negligible (assumed to be zero).

2. Particles move in straight lines. The direction of a particle's motion is changed only by its collision with either another molecule or the walls of the container. The collisions are said to be elastic (no energy is dissipated), and momentum is conserved.

3. Particles are in constant random translational motion. Gas pressure is caused by collisions of the particles against the walls of the container.

4. Gas molecules exhibit no intermolecular forces. This is to say that the particles neither attract nor repel one another.

Figure 6-1 shows the random pathway of one gas particle over time, according to the rules of the kinetic molecular theory of gases. If the kinetic energy of the particle increases, the particle's speed increases, so it collides more frequently with the wall. Because it is moving faster, it collides with greater momentum, so impulse increases. The result on the macroscopic level is that the force per unit area exerted against the walls increase, meaning pressure is greater. The kinetic theory of gases explains macroscopic observations using principles derived from a microscopic model.

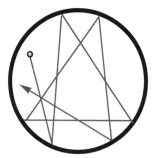

The particle moves until it collides with the wall. In a real system, the particle would also collide with other particles present in the container.

Figure 6-1

When there are many gas particles in the container, collisions between particles become more common than collisions with the wall. However, the presence of more particles in the container also results in a greater number of collisions with the walls, so the pressure of the system increases as particles are added to the system. When there are particles of different masses in a mixed gas, heavier particles move more slowly, hence they exhibit lower collision frequencies. However, because they have a greater mass and only slightly reduced speed, they collide with greater force (momentum).

As a general rule, lighter gas molecules have greater average speeds (and greater collision frequencies) than heavier ones, but less momentum (and thus less collision force). Because pressure depends on both collision frequency and collision force, gas particles of different masses exert the same pressure. On the macroscopic level, this means that pressure is the same under identical conditions for all ideal gases, independent of their molecular mass. A good example is to compare helium and nitrogen. The reason they have the same pressure at the same temperature is because they have the same kinetic energy (mv^2 term). The molecule with greater mass has less speed. The average speed is inversely proportional to the square root of the mass.

Example 6.2
In a rigid, closed container, how does an increase in temperature affect the gas particles in the system?
A. The mean free path increases.
B. The collision force decreases.
C. The collision frequency increases.
D. The particle momentum decreases.

Solution
The fact that the container is rigid means that the volume remains constant. Because it is a closed system, the moles of gas do not change (matter can neither enter nor exit a closed system). The concentration remains constant, so the mean free path does not change. This eliminates choice A. The mean free path is the average distance a particle travels between collisions. It can also be thought of as the average distance between particles at any given instant. Because the volume of the container does not change, and the moles of gas do not change, the concentration (density of gas) does not change. This means that the particles are the same distance apart, so the mean free path does not change. According to the equation $PV = nRT$, if the temperature of the system increases while volume and moles remain constant, the pressure must increase. This means that collision force, collision frequency, or both must have increased. As temperature increases, the velocity of the particles increases (the kinetic energy increases in terms of velocity). With an increase in velocity, the particles travel the distance between collisions at a greater rate, so they collide more frequently. Because the particles have greater velocity, they have greater momentum, so the collision force increases. The result is that the collision force and collision frequency both increase, so choice B is eliminated and choice **C** is the best answer. At greater velocity, the particles have greater momentum, so choice D is eliminated.

Boltzmann's Distribution
In a gas system, not all particles have the same kinetic energy. There is instead a random distribution of energies, known as *Boltzmann's distribution*. Figure 6-2 shows a Boltzmann's distribution of kinetic energy for the particles in a gas system at two different temperatures (total energies). The mean kinetic energy does not correspond to the apex of the curve, but to a point slightly to the right of the apex. This is because the energy distribution graph is skewed to the right. As temperature increases, each particle gains kinetic energy, shifting the distribution to the right. In Figure 6-2, T_2 is greater than T_1.

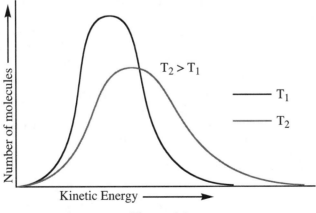

Figure 6-2

Ideal Gases

An ideal gas is a theoretical gas that obeys the following three conditions:

1. The molecules exhibit no intermolecular forces.
2. The molecules occupy no microscopic volume (are point masses).
3. All collisions are perfectly elastic.

Because real molecules cannot meet the constraints of the ideal gas, an ideal gas is strictly theoretical. Gases are closest to ideal at high temperature (having more kinetic energy to overcome intermolecular forces), low pressure (interacting minimally with one another), and when the system is composed of small, inert particles. The most ideal gas is helium (which has the smallest particles of any substance known and which exhibits negligible intermolecular forces). To verify these conditions, consider a phase diagram. When pressure is small and temperature is large, the state of matter is gaseous, far from the other phases in the phase diagram.

The ideal gas law was the result of empirical observations, such as noting that the volume of a gas is inversely proportional to its pressure, volume is directly proportional to temperature, and volume is directly proportional to moles. From these relationships, Equation 6.1 (a composite formula) was derived.

$$V \propto \frac{n \cdot T}{P} \qquad \text{(6.1)}$$

Equation 6.1 can be converted into Equation 6.2 by introducing a constant.

$$V = k \frac{n \cdot T}{P} \qquad \text{(6.2)}$$

Equation 6.2 can be manipulated to yield: $P \cdot V = k \cdot n \cdot T$, which in essence is Equation 6.3, where the constant is R, rather than k. Ideal gases obey Equation 6.3, the ideal gas equation.

$$PV = nRT \qquad \text{(6.3)}$$

where P is pressure, V is volume, n is moles, T is temperature, and R is the ideal gas constant of $0.0821 \; L \cdot atm \cdot mole^{-1} \cdot K^{-1}$.

In the best of all possible worlds, all gases would be ideal. But real gases make up 100% of all gases, so there are no ideal gases. However, while there are no ideal gases, we can make calculations for gases that are ideal and then adjust for our errors. The ideal gas law produces answers close enough to the exact values for real gases that we can use it in everyday practice. Deviations from ideality are approximated, and rough corrections are made to determine the conditions for a real gas. For example, as volume decreases, gases behave less ideally. This is because the actual size of the molecules does not change, so the percent of the volume occupied by the molecules increases. The molecules interact more and are limited in the free space they can occupy.

Ideal gas problems are straightforward, plug-and-chug in their purest form. Ideal gas questions also encompass the before-and-after case questions associated with gas laws. As you approach these problems, isolate the value that you are looking for and solve for it in terms of the other variables. Be sure to use the correct units. It is easy to forget to use kelvins. What you must do is observe what remains constant when you consider a system.

$$PV = nRT \quad \therefore \quad R = \frac{PV}{nT}, \text{ so } \frac{P_1 V_1}{n_1 T_1} = \frac{P_2 V_2}{n_2 T_2}$$

Cancel out the terms that are constant, and isolate the variables. Three examples of commonly used variations of the gas laws are:

If P and T constant: $\dfrac{V_1}{n_1} = \dfrac{V_2}{n_2}$.

If n and T are constant: $P_1V_1 = P_2V_2$.

If n and P constant: $\dfrac{V_1}{T_1} = \dfrac{V_2}{T_2}$.

Example 6.3

Given that the pressure of a twentieth of a mole of gas is 0.82 atm. at 27°C, what is its volume?

A.　1.50 liters
B.　1.72 liters
C.　22.4 liters
D.　50.0 liters

Solution

Isolating the volume term (V) in the ideal gas equation yields: $V = \dfrac{nRT}{P}$.

Substituting given values yields:

$$V = \frac{0.05 \text{ moles} \times 0.0821 \text{ L·atm·mole}^{-1}\cdot\text{K}^{-1} \times 300 \text{ K}}{0.82 \text{ atm.}} = \frac{0.05 \times 0.0821 \text{ L} \times 300}{0.82}$$

$$V = 0.05 \times 0.1 \times 300 \text{ L} = 0.05 \times 30 \text{ L} = 0.5 \times 3 \text{ L} = 1.5 \text{ L.}$$

The best answer choice is choice **A**.

Example 6.4

If a gas occupies 618 mL at STP, what is its volume at 50.4°C and 1.22 atm?

A.　895 mL
B.　732 mL
C.　600 mL
D.　512 mL

Solution

At STP, the pressure is 1.00 atm. and the temperature is 0°C. This means that the pressure increases from 1.00 atm. to 1.22 atm., and the temperature increases from 273 K to 323.4 K. An increase in pressure reduces the volume of the gas. An increase in temperature increases the volume. The change in pressure and change in temperature have opposite effects on the volume in this question, so the change in volume should be minimal. This makes choice **C** the most likely answer. However, to be certain, we need to do the math.

$$\text{Given: } \frac{P_1V_1}{n_1T_1} = \frac{P_2V_2}{n_2T_2} \text{ w/ } n_{constant} \Rightarrow \frac{P_1V_1}{T_1} = \frac{P_2V_2}{T_2}$$

$$V_2 = \left(\frac{P_1}{P_2}\right)\left(\frac{T_2}{T_1}\right)\cdot V_1 = \left(\frac{1.00}{1.22}\right)\left(\frac{323.4}{273}\right)\cdot 618 \text{ mL} \approx \left(\frac{4}{5}\right)\left(\frac{13}{11}\right)\cdot 618 \text{ mL}$$

$$V_2 \approx \frac{52}{55} \times 618 \text{ mL} \approx 600 \text{ mL}$$

The best answer choice is choice **C**.

Real Gases

There is no such thing as an ideal gas; all gases are real gases. An ideal gas is said to have molecules that occupy no space and exert no force upon one another. A real gas exhibits intermolecular forces (i.e., the molecules attract or repel one another), has particles of microscopic volume that transfer energy upon collision. The degree to which a real gas deviates from ideal behavior has to do with the magnitude of the intermolecular forces and the size of the particles. The Dutch chemist J. D. van der Waals studied real gases and developed corrections to the ideal gas law to explain real gas behavior. His name was given to the weak intermolecular forces between particles of a gas.

Deviations in pressure are due mainly to the intermolecular forces. For instance, if the gas particles exhibit attractive forces, the system implodes to a small degree. The result is that gas particles collide less frequently with the walls of the container, so the observed pressure (P_{obs}) is less than ideal pressure. This means that a correction term must be added to the observed pressure to make it equal the ideal pressure. This is shown as Equation 6.4 below:

$$P_{ideal} = P_{observed} + a\,\frac{n^2}{V^2} \tag{6.4}$$

where a is an empirical value for each gas, n is the number of moles of gas, and V is the volume of the container. It is easiest to think of a as being an *attraction coefficient*. When the particles repel, the value of a is negative.

Example 6.5
Which of the following types of gases has a negative a term?

A. Polar
B. Nonpolar
C. Hydrophobic
D. Ionized

Solution
The first step is to determine what this question seeks. It is asking for a negative a term, which is associated with particles in the gas phase that repel one another. The question can be reworded to read, "In what type of gas do the particles repel one another?" Choices B and C are the same answer worded differently, so both should be eliminated. Polar particles have attractive forces, so choice A is eliminated. An ionized gas is generated when an electron is removed from the valence shell of the gas atom or molecule. The particles of an ionized gas carry a positive charge, so they repel one another. This makes choice **D** the best answer.

Deviations in volume are due to the fact the molecules have volume. Because they have volume on the microscopic level, the actual *free space* (space not occupied by molecules) is less than the volume of the container. The bigger the molecules, the greater the volume they occupy, thus the greater the deviation. The more molecules, the greater the volume they occupy, thus the greater the deviation. The free space (ideal volume) is found by taking the container volume and subtracting the volume of the molecules. This means that the ideal volume (volume of empty space) is equal to the difference between the volume of the container and the volume of the particles. This is shown as Equation 6.5 below.

$$V_{ideal} = V_{container} - nb \tag{6.5}$$

where b is an empirical value for each gas and n is the number of moles of gas.

The greater the number of gas particles, the more volume the molecules occupy. This accounts for the n in the equation. Think of b as being a *bigness coefficient* (despite there being no such word as "bigness"). All particles have some volume, so b values are always positive.

Example 6.6
Which of the following gases has the greatest b term?

A. Methane
B. Ethane
C. Ethene
D. Ethyne

Solution
The first step is to determine what the question is asking for. It is asking for the largest b term, which is associated with the largest molecule. Methane has only one carbon, so choice A is eliminated. Choice C is eliminated, because ethene (C_2H_4) is in the middle of a sequence that starts with ethane (C_2H_6) and ends with ethyne (C_2H_2). The largest molecule can never be in the middle of a sequence like this. Because ethane has the most hydrogen atoms and has sp^3-hybridization, it is the largest molecule of the choices. Choice **B** is the best.

Combining the deviation in pressure and the deviation in volume leads to the real gas equation, also known as the *van der Waals equation*. Substituting the corrected terms for pressure and volume into the ideal gas equation derives the van der Waals equation, Equation 6.6.

$$\left(P_{observed} + a\frac{n^2}{V^2}\right)(V_{container} - nb) = nRT \qquad \textbf{(6.6)}$$

The value of the a term can be either positive or negative, because intermolecular forces are both attractive and repulsive. If the molecules attract one another, the pressure is reduced from ideal behavior, so a correction term must be added to $P_{observed}$. This means that the sign of a must be positive for attraction. The b term is always positive, because molecules have positive volume. Understand the deviation and be able to predict its effect on a real gas. Attractive forces, for instance, make the volume of a real gas less than the volume of an ideal gas.

Example 6.7
What are the a and b terms for an ideal gas?

A. $a = 1; b = 1$
B. $a = 1; b = -1$
C. $a = 0; b = 1$
D. $a = 0; b = 0$

Solution
When both a and b are zero, both of the correction terms in Equation 6.6 are zero, and thus drop out. This leaves us with $PV = nRT$, the ideal gas equation, indicating that choice **D** is the best answer. An ideal gas has no intermolecular forces, so the attraction coefficient is zero (the a value is zero.) The particles of an ideal gas occupy no microscopic volume, so the bigness coefficient is zero (the b value is zero.) This confirms that choice **D** is the best answer.

Example 6.8

For an inert real gas, if you were to reduce the pressure to half of its original value, then what would the final volume (V_f) relative to the initial volume (V_i) be?

A. $\frac{1}{2}V_i$ - a little bit

B. $\frac{1}{2}V_i$ + a little bit

C. $2V_i$ - a little bit

D. $2V_i$ + a little bit

Solution

When pressure is cut in half, the ideal gas law predicts that volume should double. However, because only the space between molecules increases, while the molecules remain the same size, the increase in volume is not as large as predicted by the ideal gas law. This makes choice **C**, $2V_i$ - a little bit, the best answer. The "little bit" term is attributed to the size of the molecules. Figure 6-3 shows this using hypothetical numbers.

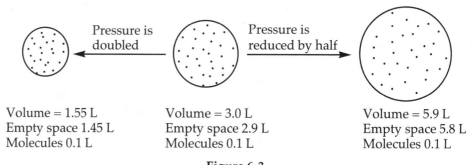

Volume = 1.55 L   Volume = 3.0 L   Volume = 5.9 L
Empty space 1.45 L   Empty space 2.9 L   Empty space 5.8 L
Molecules 0.1 L   Molecules 0.1 L   Molecules 0.1 L

Figure 6-3

Assume we have a 3.0 L container filled with a gas. Also assume that if the particles of the gas were compacted together, then their volume would be 0.10 L. When the dimensions of the container change, only the empty space changes, not the actual size (volume) of the molecules. When the container expands, the size of the molecules will still be 0.1 L. This means that when the pressure is cut in half, the volume doesn't quite double, but is $2V_i$ - a little bit. The value for our hypothetical system is 5.9 L. If the pressure were doubled, the volume wouldn't be reduced by exactly one-half, either. The new volume would be $\frac{1}{2}V_i$ + a little bit, as shown in Figure 6-3. The best answer is choice **C**.

Figure 6-3 shows that the microscopic volume of the molecules does not change. The size of an atom can change only when its radius is increased (by exciting its electrons to occupy a higher energy orbital with a greater radius). Note also in our example that when the pressure was increased (doubled), the volume decreased, but not all the way down to one-half of its original value. When the pressure was reduced by one-half, the volume increased, but not all the way up to double the original value. It may be easier to remember that **the change is never as large as you think it is** (i.e., what it is predicted to be according to the ideal gas law) when dealing with a real gas. Corrections to the ideal gas law should be intuitive for the most part.

Gas Laws

Applying Gas Laws

There are three common gas laws to know: Avogadro's law, Boyle's law, and Charles's law--the A, B, and C laws of gases. They all stem from the ideal gas law. It is possible to deduce them by solving for R in the equation $PV = nRT$, canceling out any terms that remain constant, and equating the values for before and after the change in the system. If you find yourself getting confused about which gas law refers to what, try creating a simple story about how each scientist might have made his discovery: Avogadro was into counting big numbers, so his law focuses on the number of molecules. Therefore, Avogadro's law deals with the relationship between moles of gas and volume. Big Boy Boyle sat on his lunch and smashed it (decreased the volume of his sandwich), by increasing the pressure on it. Therefore, Boyle's law deals with the relationship between pressure and volume. Good ol' Chuck overheated his popcorn and it scattered all over (increased its volume). Therefore, Charles's law deals with the relationship between temperature and volume. These descriptions may seem juvenile, but if they help you recall the gas laws by name, then they are worth it. For solving any gas questions, it is critical that you use temperature in terms of kelvins; otherwise, you will encounter much sadness and dismay.

As mentioned earlier, all of the gas laws, in conjunction with the ideal gas law, lead to the following relationship:

$$\frac{P_1 V_1}{n_1 T_1} = \frac{P_2 V_2}{n_2 T_2}$$

This relationship is the foundation in physics for the operation of any system that generates air flow, whether it is a human lung or a mechanical ventilator. One type of ventilator is an accordion-like apparatus used to maintain uniform respiration (circulation of air) through the lung of patients during their recovery from many kinds of medical problems that affect breathing, such as a collapsed lung.

The four steps in the normal cycle of a human lung are shown in Figure 6-4.

Step 1: The diaphragm contracts and the thoracic cavity expands, increasing the volume of the lung.

$$V_{lung} \uparrow, P_{lung} \downarrow \text{ so that } P_{internal} < P_{external}$$

Step 2: Air flows into the lung through the trachea.

$$n_{air} \uparrow, P_{lung} \uparrow \text{ until } P_{internal} = P_{external}$$

Step 3: The diaphragm relaxes and the thoracic cavity contracts, decreasing the volume of the lung.

$$V_{lung} \downarrow, P_{lung} \uparrow \text{ so that } P_{internal} > P_{external}$$

Step 4: Air flows out from the lung through the trachea.

$$n_{air} \downarrow, P_{lung} \downarrow \text{ until } P_{internal} = P_{external}$$

Figure 6-4

The workings of a ventilator are similar to these steps, but it has one-way valves. Air flows in both direction through the trachea, but ventilators typically have inlet and outlet tubes. (If you are taking the course, a ventilator is presented in one of the passages in the gases section of your in-class general chemistry passage collection.)

Avogadro's Law

According to Avogadro's law, the empirical relationship between the volume of a gas system and moles of the gas within the system, is that as the moles of the gas increase, the volume of the gas increases, if the temperature and the pressure remain constant. This really is just a common-sense observation. For instance, if you add more gas to a balloon, the balloon gets larger. You prove Avogadro's law every time you blow up a balloon. Figure 6-5 depicts this phenomenon in a schematic fashion.

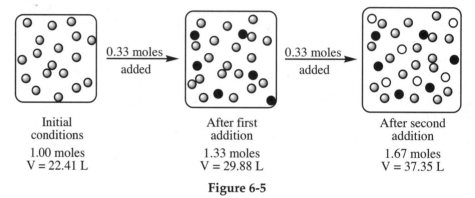

Initial conditions	After first addition	After second addition
1.00 moles	1.33 moles	1.67 moles
V = 22.41 L	V = 29.88 L	V = 37.35 L

Figure 6-5

Example 6.9

When 0.15 moles of helium gas are added to a piston containing 0.82 moles of another gas, by what percent does the total volume increase?

- **A.** 6.4%
- **B.** 14.4%
- **C.** 18.3%
- **D.** 25.0%

Solution

Moles of gas are being added to a closed system that can expand, so the moles increase, and the initial internal pressure equals the final internal pressure. This means that the addition of moles of gas increases the volume, making Avogadro's law applicable. The conclusion of Avogadro's law is that $V = k \cdot n$. The conditions are isothermal and isobaric, so the following relationship applies:

$$\frac{V_1}{n_1} = \frac{V_2}{n_2}$$

In this question, the moles increase from $n_1 = 0.82$ to $n_2 = 0.97$. The question asks for the percent increase in volume, which is equal to the percent increase in moles. The percent change is the difference divided by the original value. The math is shown below:

$$\%\text{change} = \frac{V_2 - V_1}{V_1} = \frac{n_2 - n_1}{n_1} = \frac{0.97 - 0.82}{0.82} = \frac{0.15}{0.82}$$

To approximate the answer:

$$\frac{0.15}{0.82} > \frac{0.15}{1.00} = 0.15, \text{ so increase} > 15\% \text{ AND } \frac{0.15}{0.82} < \frac{0.15}{0.75} = 0.20, \text{ so increase} < 20\%$$

The increase is between 15% and 20%, so the best answer is choice **C**. The math could have been solved relatively closely as follows:

$$\frac{0.15}{0.82} = \frac{0.15 + 0.03 + 0.003}{0.82 + 0.164 + 0.0164} = \frac{0.183}{1.0004} \approx 18.3\%$$

Boyle's Law

Boyle's law applies under isothermal conditions in a closed container. According to Boyle's law, when the external pressure is increased on a gas within a flexible container, the volume decreases in a manner that is inversely proportional to the pressure increase. That is, volume and pressure are inversely proportional to one another. This is true for ideal and real gases, although real gases deviate from ideal behavior as the conditions become more extreme. Once the volume stops changing, the internal pressure again equals the external pressure. The overall result is that as the volume of the container decreases, the pressure of the gas within the container increases. Boyle demonstrated the relationship between gas volume and gas pressure with an experiment that varied the volume of a gas in a closed, glass tube. He poured mercury into the open end of a J-shaped tube, as shown in Figure 6-6. As more liquid was added in, the height of the column of mercury rose, so that it exerted a greater pressure on the gas in the closed end of the tube, causing the gas to compress. Boyle observed that it became more difficult to compress the gas as its volume continued to decrease. This is because the repulsion between molecules increases as they are pushed closer together. Figure 6-6 shows three stages of the experiment.

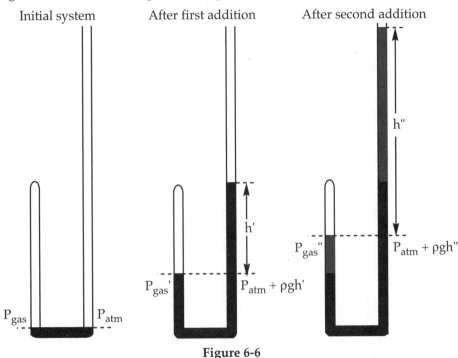

Figure 6-6

Step 1: Initially, just enough of the mercury is added to isolate the two sides of the J-shaped tube. Mercury is ideal for this purpose, because gases are generally insoluble in Hg. Initially: $P_{gas} = P_{atm}$

Step 2: Additional mercury is poured into the J-shaped tube. The mercury distributes itself unequally due to gas pressure now being greater than atmospheric pressure. After first addition: $P_{gas}' = P_{atm} + \rho gh'$

Step 3: More mercury is added to the J-shaped tube. The difference between gas pressure and atmospheric pressure is even more significant. h is larger. After second addition: $P_{gas}'' = P_{atm} + \rho gh''$

If a hole were poked in the glass at the top of the closed-end side of the tube after the last addition, gas would escape from the hole, because the internal pressure exceeds the atmospheric pressure. The mercury would flow from the side with higher mercury to the side with less mercury, until both sides of the tube were level. This would result in the equilibrating of gas pressures ($P_{gas} = P_{atm}$).

An experiment you can conduct to demonstrate Boyle's law for yourself is to observe gas bubbles as they rise through water. At lower depths, water pressure on the bubble is greater due to the force exerted by the water above. As a bubble ascends, the external pressure acting on it is reduced (because the total weight of water above it is steadily decreasing), and consequently the bubble expands as it rises. Consider a 1.00-liter air-filled rubber ball that is submerged below the surface of a lake to a depth of thirty feet. At thirty feet, the pressure due to the column of water is approximately one atmosphere. With each subsequent drop of thirty feet, the total pressure on the ball increases by one atmosphere. Table 6.2 shows the relationship between volume, depth, and pressure.

Volume (liters)	Depth (feet)	Pressure (atm)
1.00	at surface	1.00
0.50	-30	2.00
0.33	-60	3.00
0.25	-90	4.00

Table 6.2

Notice that the pressure changes by uniform increments, while the volume does not. This means that the volume change varies with pressure. It can be concluded that a gas becomes less compressible as the pressure increases. This means that a gas can expand most when it is at low pressure. Scuba divers, for instance, are at greatest risk for developing air embolisms during ascent, as they near the surface. During their entire ascent, near the surface is where the volume of gas undergoes the greatest percent change with changing pressure. Figure 6-7 is a graph relating pressure and volume at constant temperature, for two distinct temperatures. The graph shows two asymptotic curves.

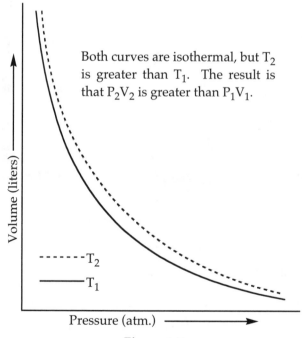

Both curves are isothermal, but T_2 is greater than T_1. The result is that P_2V_2 is greater than P_1V_1.

Figure 6-7

Example 6.10
If the pressure of a gas in a 1.250-L container is initially 0.872 atm., what is the pressure if the volume of the container is increased to 1.500 L, assuming temperature does not change?

A. 0.667 atm.
B. 0.726 atm.
C. 1.046 atm.
D. 1.333 atm.

Solution
The conclusion one draws from Boyle's experiment is that $PV = k$. This means that if the system remains closed and isothermal (constant temperature), then $P_1V_1 = P_2V_2$. Because the volume increases, the pressure must decrease. This eliminates choices C and D. It is given in the question that P_1 is 0.872 atm., V_1 is 1.250 L, and V_2 is 1.500 L. The answer is found mathematically as follows:

$$P_1V_1 = P_2V_2 \therefore P_2 = \frac{P_1V_1}{V_2} \Rightarrow P_2 = P_1\left(\frac{V_1}{V_2}\right)$$

The initial pressure (P_1) must be multiplied by a factor less than 1.0 to obtain the final pressure (P_2). Some calculation is necessary to decide between choices A and **B**.

$$P_2 = \frac{(0.872)(1.25)}{1.50} = \frac{(0.872)(5)}{6} \cong \frac{(0.9)(5)}{6} = 0.15(5) = 0.75$$

The value is just less than 0.75, so the best answer is choice **B**.

Example 6.11
The volume of a ballast bulb at sea level is 1.00 liters. If you dive 66 feet below the surface with the bulb, and the temperature of the water surrounding you does not change much, what is the approximate new volume of the bulb? (For every 33 feet you descend, water pressure increases by 1.00 atmospheres).

A. 3.00 liters
B. 2.00 liters
C. 0.50 liters
D. 0.33 liters

Solution
At sea level, air pressure on the bulb is 1.00 atm. At 66 feet below the surface, the pressure is 3.00 atm., which includes 2.00 atm. for the column of water directly above the bulb and 1.00 atm. for the column of air directly above the water. Because the pressure has tripled, the volume must decrease by a factor of three. This means that the final volume is about 0.33 liters, choice **D**.

Charles's Law

Charles's law states that if the temperature of a gas is increased at constant pressure (isobaric conditions) and constant moles (closed system), then its volume increases proportionally. This means that volume is directly proportional to temperature. Just as with Boyle's law, Charles's law is true for both ideal and real gases. The deviation from ideal behavior is more substantial as the volume of the gas decreases, because the molecules interact to a greater extent at short distances. Charles's law can be demonstrated rather easily by carrying out an experiment with a piston holding a known quantity of gas. A piston is chosen because the volume change is predictable and easily measured. With a piston, volume changes in only one dimension. Demonstrating Charles's law using a balloon has its problems, because the volume of a balloon changes in all directions, making the change in volume difficult to measure. Also, a balloon has a different restoring force at different volumes. If the volume of the balloon system were to be measured using displacement of a liquid into which it is fully submerged, the pressure on the balloon would vary.

According to Charles's law, the relationship between volume and temperature is that as the temperature of the gas increases, the volume of the gas increases, if the system remains closed and the pressure remains constant. Figure 6-8 illustrates the system experiment that demonstrates Charles's law.

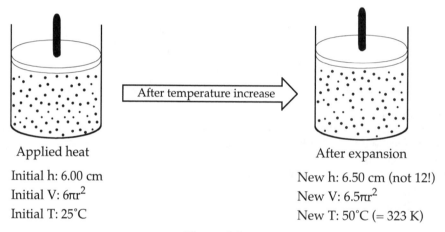

After temperature increase

Applied heat

Initial h: 6.00 cm

Initial V: $6\pi r^2$

Initial T: 25°C

After expansion

New h: 6.50 cm (not 12!)

New V: $6.5\pi r^2$

New T: 50°C (= 323 K)

Figure 6-8

It is critical that you consider the temperature in kelvins when applying Charles's law. The applied heat can be from many different sources. Typical sources include a heating coil (thermal energy generated by resistance of electrical flow through a wire), a Bunsen burner (thermal energy generated by combustion), and IR radiation (thermal energy generated by the release of an IR photon upon relaxation). In the example in Figure 6-8, the new volume is found by multiplying the initial volume times the ratio of the new temperature (323) to the initial temperature (298). The factor is roughly 325 divided by 300, which is equal to 13 divided by 12. If the temperature of the gas in the piston were lowered to 0°C, then the new height of the piston would be 5.50 cm. Figure 6-9 shows the graph of volume as a function of temperature over a range of temperatures that spans the three common phases of matter. The graph ceases to be linear at lower temperatures, because the gas undergoes a phase change to become a liquid, and the liquid becomes a solid. As Figure 6-9 indicates, expansion of a gas is more significant than expansion of either a liquid or a solid. When heated by small increments, liquids and solids expand only slightly.

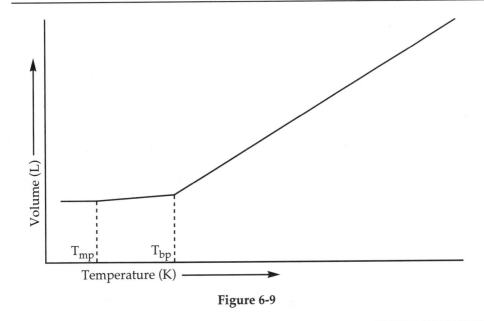

Figure 6-9

Example 6.12
If the volume of a piston filled with an inert gas is 4.31 L at 25°C, then what is the new volume occupied by the gas, after it is heated to 50°C, assuming the system experiences no net change in pressure?

A. 3.98 L
B. 4.31 L
C. 4.67 L
D. 8.62 L

Solution
The conclusion of Charles's law is that $V = k \cdot T$. This means that if the system remains closed and isobaric (constant pressure), then $T_2 V_1 = T_1 V_2$. Because the temperature increases, the volume must increase. This eliminates choices A and B. It is given in the question, that V_1 is 4.31 L, T_1 is 298 K, and T_2 is 323 K. The answer is found mathematically as follows:

$$\frac{V_1}{T_1} = \frac{V_2}{T_2} \therefore V_2 = \frac{V_1 T_2}{T_1} \Rightarrow V_2 = V_1\left(\frac{T_2}{T_1}\right)$$

The initial volume (V_1) must be multiplied by a factor greater than 1.0 to obtain final volume (V_2). Math is necessary to decide between choices **C** and D.

$$V_2 = \frac{(323 \text{ K})(4.31 \text{ L})}{298 \text{ K}} = \frac{323}{298}(4.31 \text{ L}) \cong \frac{325}{300}(4.31 \text{ L}) = \frac{13}{12}(4.31 \text{ L})$$

$$8.62 \text{ L} > \frac{13}{12}(4.31 \text{ L}) > 4.31 \text{ L}$$

The final volume is greater than 4.31 L, but far less than 8.62 L, so the best answer is choice **C**. Forgetting to convert degrees Celsius into kelvins would erroneously lead you to select choice D.

Gas System Properties

Partial Pressure

A gas system can be composed of one pure gas or it can be composed of a mixture of gases. Within a mixture of gases, each component gas can be treated separately from other components. The particles can migrate to any position within the system, so each component gas occupies the same volume. But they are independent particles. The notion of *partial pressure* stems from the concept that you may treat different components of a gaseous mixture independently. Partial pressure is the independent pressure exerted by a gas within a mixture. For instance, each gas in an equal molar mixture of three gases has a partial pressure that equals one-third that of the total pressure of the system. Consider the system in Figure 6-10, where the three components are theoretical gases X, Y, and Z.

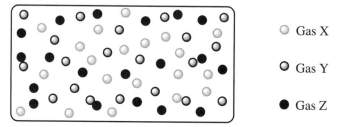

Figure 6-10

The idea that the mixture is a composition of the individual gases leads to the idea that the total number of moles of gas in a mixture is the sum of the individual moles of each separate gas. This is shown in Equation 6.7.

$$n_{total} = \sum n_i = n_a + n_b + n_c + ... \qquad (6.7)$$

(where i refers to each component gas within the mixture, and a, b, and c are arbitrary components)

The gases are in the same container, so they are at the same temperature and in the same volume. Because each gas is only a fraction of the total moles, it must also be a fraction of the total pressure. The total pressure of gas is the sum of all the individual partial pressures of each gas. Equation 6.8 shows this relationship, which is similar to the relationship for moles.

$$P_{total} = \sum P_i = P_a + P_b + P_c + ... \qquad (6.8)$$

Equation 6.8 can be used to find the total pressure of a mixture of gases from the partial pressures of its constituents. Example 6.13 illustrates how this is done.

Example 6.13

What is the total pressure of a mixture created by adding 0.15 moles He*(g)* to a 5.0-L flask that contains 570 torr of N_2*(g)* and 0.20 atm. Ar*(g)* at 125°C?

A. 1.10 atm.
B. 1.33 atm.
C. 1.61 atm.
D. 1.93 atm.

Solution

First off, everything must be converted to the same units. The units in the answer choices are atm; so we should convert everything to atm. 570 torr cleanly converts to 0.75 atm; so there are 0.75 atm. $N_2(g)$. To get the pressure of $He(g)$, you must employ the formula $PV = nRT$.

$$P_{He} = \frac{n \cdot R \cdot T}{V} \approx \frac{(0.15)(0.082)(400)}{5.00} = \frac{(15)(0.082)(4)}{5} = 12 \times 0.082 = 0.984 \text{ atm.}$$

The total pressure is: $P_{total} = P_{He} + P_{Ar} + P_{N_2} = 0.98 + 0.20 + 0.75 = 1.93$ atm. The best answer is choice **D**.

To determine the partial pressure of a component in the mixture, you must know the mole percentage of the gas in the vessel (referred to as the *mole fraction*). The partial pressure of a component is directly proportional to its mole fraction. This relationship is shown in Figure 6-11, for the three gases in Figure 6-10.

$$\frac{n_x}{n_{total}} = \frac{P_x}{P_{total}} \qquad \frac{n_y}{n_{total}} = \frac{P_y}{P_{total}} \qquad \frac{n_z}{n_{total}} = \frac{P_z}{P_{total}}$$

Figure 6-11

Given that the pressure fraction of a component in the system equals its mole fraction, the partial pressure of one component can be determined from knowing its mole fraction and the total pressure of the system. Equation 6.9 below is used to calculate the partial pressure from the total pressure.

$$\frac{P_i}{P_{total}} = \frac{n_i}{n_{total}} \quad \therefore P_i = \frac{n_i}{n_{total}} P_{total} = X_i P_{total} \qquad \text{(6.9)}$$

P_i is the partial pressure of an arbitrary component i, n_i is the moles of an arbitrary component i, and X_i is the mole fraction of that component.

Equation 6.9 is used to obtain a partial pressure from the total pressure. Example 6.14 illustrates how this is done.

Example 6.14

What is the partial pressure due to nitrogen in a balloon at STP that contains 1.00 moles helium, 1.25 moles nitrogen, and 1.75 moles argon?

A. 125 torr
B. 238 torr
C. 267 torr
D. 500 torr

Solution

Use Equation 6.9 to solve this problem, because the partial pressure of nitrogen is found by multiplying the mole fraction of nitrogen by the total pressure. At STP, the total pressure of the system is 760 torr. The number of total moles of gas in the system is $1.00 + 1.25 + 1.75$, which is 4.00. The mole fraction due to nitrogen is 1.25 divided by 4, which is 31.25 %. One-fourth of 760 is 190 torr, so the partial pressure due to nitrogen is greater than 190. This eliminates choice A. One-third of 760 is 253.3 torr, so the partial pressure due to nitrogen is less than 253.3. This eliminates choices C and D. The best answer is choice **B**. If you want to confirm this by math, 31.25% of 760 = 76 + 76 + 76 + 7.6 + 1.9 = 237.5 torr.

Manometers

Because a gas has no definite shape and no definite volume, it assumes the shape and volume of the container in which it is present. As the dimensions of the container are altered, so are the properties of the gas. A gas may be compressed or expanded by moving the walls of the container. Likewise, the walls of the container can be moved by adding or removing gas (think of blowing up a balloon). If the container is not flexible, then the pressure increases or decreases. Gas pressure is measured in units called torrs, where 1 torr is the pressure necessary to raise mercury by 1 mm in an evacuated column. A column of mercury is used to measure gas pressure, because mercury has a high density and it doesn't compress easily. This means that only a significant change in gas pressure on a column of mercury produces a noticeable and measurable difference in the height of the column.

Figure 6-12 shows measurements of gas pressure using a manometer. In each case, atmospheric pressure is compared to the pressure within a column. In systems I and II, the column is evacuated, so the initial pressure inside the column before mercury is added to either system is zero. Atmospheric pressure forces the mercury up into the evacuated column. Because there is less atmospheric pressure in the mountains than at sea level, the mercury does not rise as high in column II as it does in column I. In each case, the mercury in the tube remains at a fixed point once the force of gravity cancels the force exerted by the atmospheric pressure. In system III, the column is open to the atmosphere, so the pressure in the column equals the pressure exerted on the base.

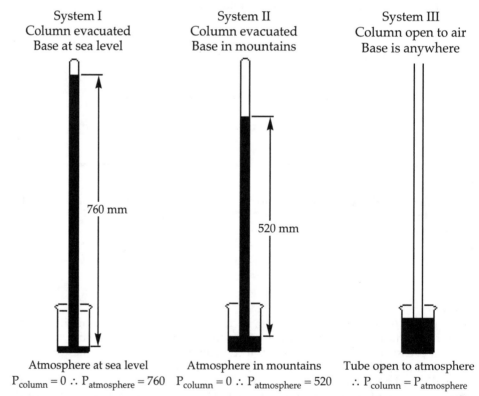

System I
Column evacuated
Base at sea level

System II
Column evacuated
Base in mountains

System III
Column open to air
Base is anywhere

760 mm

520 mm

Atmosphere at sea level
$P_{column} = 0 \therefore P_{atmosphere} = 760$

Atmosphere in mountains
$P_{column} = 0 \therefore P_{atmosphere} = 520$

Tube open to atmosphere
$\therefore P_{column} = P_{atmosphere}$

Figure 6-12

Systems I and II of Figure 6-12 show the pressure difference between a closed system in the column and the atmosphere. Manometers may also be used where the two sides of a mercury-filled U-tube are connected to two different closed containers. When both columns of the manometer are exposed to different pressures, there is a height difference between the two columns of mercury.

Figure 6-13 shows a manometer under different conditions with respect to system pressure. One end of the manometer is connected to a closed system. The other end is open to the atmosphere. The pressure difference between the gas in the system and the atmosphere can be measured. Knowing the atmospheric pressure allows us to determine the pressure of the system.

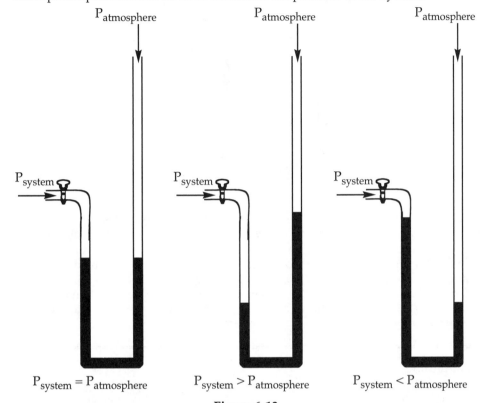

Figure 6-13

The difference in heights between the two columns can be used to measure the difference in the two pressures. The correlation between column height and pressure can be derived from the equilibrium relationship between gravitational force and the force exerted on the mercury by the pressure difference. The force pulling the mercury down is gravity ($F = mg$). The force pushing the mercury up is the pressure of the gas multiplied by the cross sectional area of the mercury ($F = PA$). As long as the mercury remains stationary, then the two forces are equal, meaning that $PA = mg$. The mass of the mercury in the column is the density of the mercury (ρ) multiplied by the volume of the mercury (V). Thus, column pressure is determined by Equation 6.10, derived as follows:

$$F_{up} = F_{down} \Rightarrow PA = mg = \rho Vg \therefore P = \rho g\frac{V}{A} = \rho gh$$

$$\Delta P = \rho g \Delta h \qquad\qquad \textbf{(6.10)}$$

The pressure difference between any connected columns can be determined using Equation 6.10, where Δh is the difference in height between the columns, and ΔP is the difference in pressure between the columns. For instance, if the gas pressure is known for one of two columns (we usually know that an open column has atmospheric pressure exerted on it), then the pressure of the second column can be determined by adding the difference in pressure between the two columns to the known pressure (atmospheric pressure in this case.) This is a common lab practice for gas phase reactions and reactions that require an inert environment (such as nitrogen gas or argon gas). Manometers are an easy way to monitor the pressure of a system while keeping it closed.

In Figure 6-14 below, the application of Equation 6.10 to a manometer system is demonstrated.

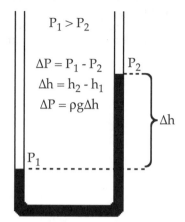

Figure 6-14

The pressure applied to the left side of the manometer (P_1) is greater than the pressure applied to the right side of the manometer (P_2), forcing the liquid to rise higher in the column on the right. The difference in pressure between the two sides of the manometer is proportional to the difference in the heights of the liquid in each column. When the liquid is mercury, each mm difference is referred to as a *torr*. Mercury is chosen, because it is the densest liquid, so gas does not readily diffuse through mercury. A closed system connected to a mercury manometer remains a closed system.

Example 6.15
What is the pressure in atmospheres of a column of gas in a closed tube above mercury if the height difference at sea level between a connected column of mercury open to the atmosphere and the closed column above mercury is 317 mm?

A. $317/760$ atm.

B. $443/760$ atm.

C. $760/443$ atm.

D. $317/443$ atm.

Solution
The height difference of 317 mm means that the pressure difference is 317 torr. The atmospheric pressure at sea level is 760 torr, so the gas pressure in the column is 443 torr (760 - 317). The conversion from torr to atm. involves dividing by a factor of 760 torr per atm. This makes choice **B** the best answer. As the question is worded, the pressure difference is provided, but the relative pressures are not mentioned. The pressure could also be 1077 torr (760 + 317), but this value is not listed as an answer choice.

Gas Motion

Gas Speed and Velocity

As a general rule in chemistry, we are concerned with particle speed rather than particle velocity, because we are generally interested in the energy of the system. The speed of a particle is dependent on both its mass and the temperature. The rate at which a gas particle travels is directly proportional to the square root of the temperature and inversely proportional to the square root of its mass. By equating the equations for kinetic energy of a gas to one another ($\frac{1}{2}mv^2$ to $\frac{3}{2}RT$), it is possible to determine the root mean square speed of a monatomic gas, both in an absolute manner and relative to another gas. The derivation of Equation 6.11, used to calculated the root mean square speed of a particle, is shown below:

$$\text{Kinetic energy} = \tfrac{1}{2}mv^2 \text{ and also} = \tfrac{3}{2}RT \;\therefore\; \tfrac{1}{2}mv^2 = \tfrac{3}{2}RT$$

$$\text{Because } \tfrac{1}{2}mv^2 = \tfrac{3}{2}RT, \; v^2 = \frac{3RT}{m}, \text{ so } \mu_{rms}{}^2 = \frac{3RT}{m}$$

$$\mu_{rms} = \sqrt{\frac{3RT}{m}}, \text{ where } \mu_{rms} \text{ is the root mean square speed}$$

$$\mu_{rms} = \sqrt{\frac{3RT}{m}} \qquad\qquad (6.11)$$

Example 6.16
What is the root mean square speed of neon atoms at 27°C?

- A. 19.3 m/s
- B. 211 m/s
- C. 612 m/s
- D. 1018 m/s

Solution
This question requires the use of Equation 6.11. Because scientists employ the MKS system, the mass must be in terms of kilograms, and the temperature must be in units of kelvins. The mass of one mole of neon is 0.020 kg and the temperature is 300 K. The solution is as follows:

$$\mu_{rms} = \sqrt{\frac{3RT}{m}} = \sqrt{\frac{3(8.314)(300)}{0.020}} = \sqrt{\frac{(8.314)(9 \times 10^2)}{2 \times 10^{-2}}} \approx \sqrt{\frac{8 \times 9}{2} \times 10^4}$$

$$\sqrt{\frac{8 \times 9}{2} \times 10^4} = \sqrt{36 \times 10^4} = 6 \times 10^2 = 600 \; \frac{m}{s}$$

The speed of neon at 27°C is slightly more than 600 meters per second, so the best answer is choice C.

It is also possible to determine the relative speeds of two gases using the energy relationship. The speed of a particle is inversely proportional to the square root of its mass, so the lighter the gas, the faster it travels at a given temperature. This leads to Graham's law for gas flow, which is listed below as Equation 6.12.

$$\frac{v_2}{v_1} = \sqrt{\frac{m_1}{m_2}} \qquad\qquad (6.12)$$

The speed of a gas particle is designated as v.

It is also possible to determine the relative speeds for particles of the same gas at two different temperatures. The speed of a particle is directly proportional to the square root of the temperature, so the greater the temperature, the faster a gas travels. This is summarized in Equation 6.13

$$\frac{v_2}{v_1} = \sqrt{\frac{T_2}{T_1}} \qquad\qquad \textbf{(6.13)}$$

Example 6.17
What is the speed of a gas particle at 125°C, if it has a speed of 100 m/s at 25°C?

A. 500 m/s
B. 223 m/s
C. 133 m/s
D. 114 m/s

Solution
The speed is greater at higher temperatures. This doesn't help, because all of the answer choices are greater than 100 m/s. To determine the exact value, the temperature must be converted to kelvins. The temperature increase is from 298 to 398, which means the temperature is 1.33 times greater. Because it is a square root function, the speed increases by a factor of $\sqrt{1.33}$, which when multiplied by 100 m/s yields a value less than 133 m/s. Only choice **D** is possible.

Diffusion
With diffusion, gas particles exhibit net flow from a region of higher concentration to a region of lower concentration until the concentration is essentially uniform throughout the container. A gas can diffuse as quickly as the gas travels. This means that lighter gases diffuse faster than heavier gases. Diffusion involves flow in all directions, until a barrier impedes the pathway. Unlike effusion and infusion, it involves no pores through which gases pass. Diffusion describes the dispersion of a particular gas through a container and is concentration-dependent, proceeding most rapidly when the mean free path is larger and the average kinetic energy is greater.

Example 6.18
Which of the following gases stinks up a room the fastest, if they are all released simultaneously?

A. SO_3
B. C_2H_6S
C. $C_4H_{10}S$
D. H_5C_6NCS

Solution
Stinking up the room the fastest results from having the greatest rate of diffusion. The rate of diffusion depends on the speed of each gas. They are all under same conditions of temperature, mean free path, and volume, so the only factor affecting their speeds that differs between the answer choices is their molecular mass. The lightest gas has the greatest average speed, and thus stinks up the room fastest. The lightest gas is C_2H_6S, choice **B**.

Effusion and Infusion

Effusion is the process of gas escaping from the region within a container to the environment outside of the container through pores (often microscopic pores) in the container's walls. The faster the molecules move, the more often they collide with the walls, and thus the more often they can pass through the pores. The more concentrated the species, the more frequently they interact with the pores, and thus the faster they effuse. The pore size has some effect on the effusion rate of a contained gas, when it is about the same size as the diameter of the gas molecule. The relative effusion rates of two or more gases can be determined by comparing the relative concentrations and speeds of the molecules.

Infusion is the reverse of effusion and involves a gas entering a container through the pores of its walls. The faster the molecules move, the more often the molecules pass through the pores and thus the faster the molecules can enter. The same rules that apply to effusion are also valid for infusion.

Example 6.19
If the rate of effusion for nitrogen gas is initially 17.5 mL/min, what is the initial rate of effusion for carbon dioxide under identical conditions?

A. 14.0 mL/min
B. 16.0 mL/min
C. 19.4 mL/min
D. 21.9 mL/min

Solution
The relative effusion rates for the two gases are equal to the relative average speeds for the two gases. Nitrogen is lighter than carbon dioxide, so it has a greater average speed and thus rate of effusion, resulting in an effusion rate for CO_2 less than 17.5 mL/min. This eliminates choices C and D. The effusion rates for the two gases are compared in the following way:

$$\frac{\text{Effusion Rate}_{\text{Nitrogen}}}{\text{Effusion Rate}_{\text{Carbon Dioxide}}} = \frac{\sqrt{3RT/m_{N_2}}}{\sqrt{3RT/m_{CO_2}}} = \frac{\sqrt{m_{CO_2}}}{\sqrt{m_{N_2}}} = \frac{\sqrt{44}}{\sqrt{28}} = \sqrt{1.571} \approx 1.25$$

The rate of effusion for N_2 is 1.25 times greater than the rate of effusion for CO_2. This means that the rate of effusion for CO_2 is 0.80 times the rate of effusion for N_2, which is (0.80)(17.5) = 14.0 mL/min, making choice **A** the best answer.

Effusion and infusion are defined in terms of direction rather than concentration, but the rates of both effusion and infusion are affected by concentration. Effusion and infusion can occur with or against a concentration gradient. When effusion rate exceeds infusion rate, there is a net flow of gas out of a system. When infusion rate exceeds effusion rate, there is a net flow into the system.

The gas flow speed affects the rate at which particles migrate through their container. Migration is a general term for motion in any direction, which takes into account diffusion, effusion, and infusion. Diffusion, effusion, and infusion exhibit similar trends. The rate of diffusion, effusion, or infusion for any gas is directly proportional to its average speed, which is inversely proportional to the square root of its mass. We assume that the pore size of a gas container has an equal (often minimal) effect on the effusion rate or infusion rate for a gas.

Isotopic Enrichment

Isotopic enrichment is a process by which isotopes are distributed in a non-uniform manner. Relative effusion rates can be exploited to separate isotopes from one another. Because the rate of effusion for a gas varies with its atomic mass, the different masses associated with different isotopes allow for isotopes to be separated after migration through several pores. A typical example involving the enrichment of deuterium from hydrogen is shown in Figure 6-15.

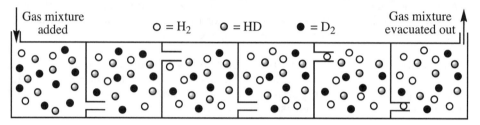

Figure 6-15

The lightest molecule is H_2, so it travels the fastest. It is in highest concentration in cells to the right. The heaviest molecule is D_2, so it travels the slowest. It is in lowest concentration in cells to the right. To obtain an enriched sample of deuterium, the last gas to escape from the tube is collected. Figure 6-16 shows the distribution of speeds for a hydrogen-deuterium mixture that has equal mole fractions of H_2, HD, and D_2.

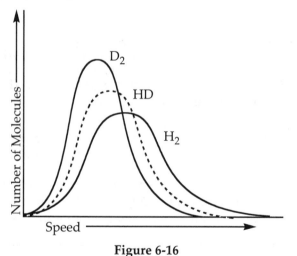

Figure 6-16

Chemistry teaches you to handle the pressure!

Gases
Passages

13 Passages

100 Questions

Suggested schedule:

I: After reading this section and attending lecture: Passages I, III, IV, & VII
Grade passages immediately after completion and log your mistakes.

II: Following Task I: Passages II, V, VI, & IX, (29 questions in 37 minutes)
Time yourself accurately, grade your answers, and review mistakes.

III: Review: Passages VIII, X - XIII and Questions 94 - 100
Focus on reviewing the concepts. Do not worry about timing.

Gases Study Passages

Gases Scoring Scale

Raw Score	MCAT Score
84 - 100	13 - 15
66 - 83	10 - 12
47 - 65	7 - 9
34 - 46	4 - 6
1 - 33	1 - 3

Passage I (Question 1 - 6)

The behavior of an ideal gas obeys the law $PV = nRT$, where P is pressure, V is volume, n is the moles, and T is the temperature (in kelvins). The equation only approximates the behavior of real gases, but well enough to predict relationships between real gases. A researcher chooses three gases to study the effect of varying pressure on gas behavior, specifically the relationship between PV and P. Figure 1 shows the results obtained in the experiment.

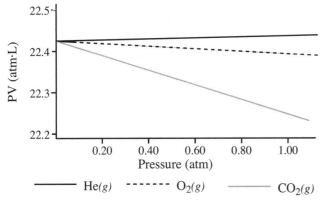

Figure 1

The data show slight deviations from ideal gas behavior at relatively standard pressures. Deviations are attributed to both attractive and repulsive forces in the gas phase. Table 1 lists PV vs. P for helium gas, oxygen gas, and carbon dioxide gas, respectively, obtained in a second experiment.

Pressure	$P_{He}V_{He}$	$P_{O_2}V_{O_2}$	$P_{CO_2}V_{CO_2}$
1.00	22.44	22.39	22.26
25.0	22.89	21.70	8.76
50.0	23.40	20.97	10.11
100.0	24.32	20.07	11.25
200.0	26.36	20.13	13.58
400.0	30.27	23.01	18.23

Table 1

Deviations from ideal behavior are compounded under extreme conditions, but near standard conditions, the molar volume for almost any gas is approximately 22.41 liters. Table 2 lists the molar volume of some common gases at STP (1.00 atm and 273.15 K).

Gas	Molar Volume (L)
Ar	22.395
CO_2	22.261
H_2	22.435
He	22.436
N_2	22.404
NH_3	22.081
O_2	22.396

Table 2

1. Which of the following does NOT account for deviations from ideal behavior in a real gas?

   A. A real gas is composed of molecules that have a measurable volume.

   B. There are attractive forces between molecules.

   C. There are repulsive forces between molecules.

   D. Gases are not uniform, so the pressure against the walls of the container does not accurately reflect the pressure of the system.

2. What is true about the interactions between gas molecules at higher pressures?

   A. The interactions are reduced, because the molecules collide less frequently.

   B. The interactions are reduced, because the molecules collide more frequently.

   C. The interactions are increased, because the molecules collide less frequently.

   D. The interactions are increased, because the molecules collide more frequently.

3. Which of these experimental gases shows no change in behavior as pressure is increased across an extreme range?

   A. Helium only

   B. Oxygen only

   C. Both oxygen and helium

   D. Both oxygen and carbon dioxide

4. How does the molar volume of ammonia gas compare to that of an ideal gas?

   A. It is larger than ideal, due to attractive forces.

   B. It is larger than ideal, due to repulsive forces.

   C. It is smaller than ideal, due to attractive forces.

   D. It is smaller than ideal, due to repulsive forces.

5. What is the expected molar volume of carbon dioxide gas at 75 atm.?

   A. 0.097 liters

   B. 0.142 liters

   C. 10.63 liters

   D. 11.22 liters

6. Under which of the following conditions does a real gas behave MOST like an ideal gas?

   A. High temperature and high pressure

   B. High temperature and low pressure

   C. Low temperature and high pressure

   D. Low temperature and low pressure

Passage II (Questions 7 - 14)

The kinetic molecular theory of gases is employed to explain the behavior of an ideal gas. It is, in essence, the theoretical perspective of an ideal gas on the microscopic level. The postulates of the kinetic molecular theory of gases as they relate to the particles of an ideal gas are as follows:

1. The particles are so small, compared to the distances between them, that the volume of the individual particles can be assumed to be negligible.

2. The particles are in constant random motion. The collisions of the particles with the walls of the container are responsible for the pressure exerted by the gas.

3. The particles are assumed to exert no force upon each other; they are assumed neither to attract nor repel one another.

4. The average kinetic energy of the particles is assumed to be directly proportional to the temperature of the gas in units of kelvins.

The kinetic theory of gases serves to explain temperature and pressure on the microscopic level. While it does not hold true for real gases, it is a good model for an ideal gas. Real gases exert force upon one another, and their particles have a finite volume.

As the properties of an ideal gas change, the particles are assumed to remain uniform. For instance, the average kinetic energy of a gas increases as it is heated, but the size of each atom remains the same and the bonds remain in place. This is to say that the particles are not altered by physical changes.

7. For a closed system in a 1.00-L sealed piston, what is observed when the temperature of the system increases?

    A. The number of molecules of gas increases.
    B. The average kinetic energy remains constant.
    C. The mean free path increases.
    D. The average molecular momentum remains constant.

8. For an inert gas system in a sealed rigid glass container, what occurs when the average kinetic energy of molecules increases?

    A. Collision frequency increases, while collision force decreases.
    B. Collision force increases, while collision frequency decreases.
    C. Both mean free path and collision force increase.
    D. Both collision frequency and collision force increase.

9. As temperature of a gas system in a closed flask decreases from 20°C to 10°C, the average speed of the component gas molecules:

    A. increases slightly.
    B. remains the same.
    C. decreases slightly.
    D. decreases substantially.

10. What is observed over time if a mixture of H_2 and D_2, initially at 50% by moles H_2, undergoes effusion through a small pore in the container?

    A. P_{H_2} decreases; X_{D_2} decreases.
    B. P_{H_2} increases; X_{D_2} decreases.
    C. P_{D_2} decreases; X_{D_2} increases.
    D. P_{D_2} increases; X_{D_2} increases.

11. Which of the following gases has the GREATEST momentum, if they are all under identical conditions of temperature and pressure?

    A. Helium
    B. Neon
    C. Nitrogen
    D. Sulfur dioxide

12. Which of the following graphs best describes the collision frequency as the number of particles in a sealed glass container increases?

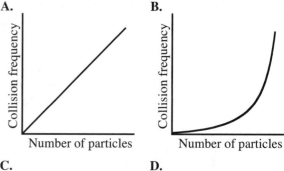

A.

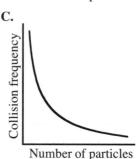

C.

B.

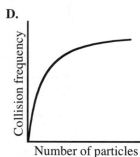

D.

13. Which of the following is an expected behavior of a gas, according to the kinetic molecular theory of gases?

   A. The gas has an infinitely high boiling point.
   B. Molecular gases show different behavior than atomic gases.
   C. The average velocity of a particle doubles when temperature doubles.
   D. The pressure exerted by a gas is independent of the shape of its container.

14. A gas differs from a liquid in all of the following ways EXCEPT:

   A. a liquid has a definite volume while a gas does not.
   B. particles in a liquid are always in contact with one another, while particles in a gas are never in contact with one another.
   C. a gas is more compressible than a liquid.
   D. an object is more buoyant in a gas than a liquid.

Passage III (Questions 15 - 22)

A researcher sets up a salt water tank (see Figure 1, below) with a depth of fifty feet to study Boyle's Law. An air-filled rubber ball is fitted with a thin metal ring around its circumference, positioned slightly on the lower side of the ball. The ball is placed in the tank of salt water, which is maintained at 25°C. At the base of the tank is an adjustable magnetic field that is used to submerge the ball to selected depths. The displacement of the water in the tank is measured to determine the volume of the ball.

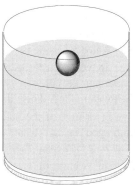

Adjustable Magnet

Figure 1

Floating on the surface, the ball is 50% submerged before the magnetic field is applied. The initial volume of the ball is 36.00 liters, but as it descends towards the bottom of the tank, its volume gradually decreases. The volume of the elastic ball is measured at the several depths. Table 1 lists the values for the ball's changing gas volume.

Depth (ft)	Pressure (atm)	Volume (L)
5	1.16	31.14
10	1.31	27.41
15	1.47	24.43
20	1.63	22.07
25	1.78	20.21
30	1.94	18.54
35	2.09	17.20
40	2.25	16.02
45	2.41	14.97
50	2.56	14.11

Table 1

Note: A pressure of 1.00 atm. is required to raise a column of pure water 32.6 ft.

15. The ball experiences its greatest change in volume during which segment of its descent?

   A. From 0 to 7 feet below the surface
   B. From 7 to 14 feet below the surface
   C. From 14 to 21 feet below the surface
   D. From 21 to 28 feet below the surface

16. At what depth will the ball neither rise nor sink if the magnetic field is turned off?

   A. Between 0 and 10 feet below the surface
   B. Between 10 and 20 feet below the surface
   C. Between 20 and 30 feet below the surface
   D. Between 30 and 40 feet below the surface

17. If fresh water were used rather than salt water, how would the results be affected?

   A. The change in volume of the ball would be greater when submerged in salt water than fresh water, because salt water is less dense than fresh water.
   B. The change in volume of the ball would be less when submerged in salt water than fresh water, because salt water is less dense than fresh water.
   C. The change in volume of the ball would be greater when submerged in salt water than fresh water, because salt water is denser than fresh water.
   D. The change in volume of the ball would be less when submerged in salt water than fresh water, because salt water is denser than fresh water.

18. For a ball that is filled with an ideal gas and immersed in fresh water, and that is initially 25% submerged before the magnetic field is applied, at what depth will the ball no longer be buoyant?

   A. At depths between 0 and 32 feet below the surface
   B. At depths between 32 and 64 feet below the surface
   C. At depths between 64 and 96 feet below the surface
   D. At depths greater than 96 feet below the surface

19. For a ball that is initially 60% submerged, what is observed when compared to the ball in Figure 1, under the same experimental conditions?

   A. The depth at which the density of the ball equals the density of surrounding water is below -32 feet, because the ball is less dense than the original ball in the experiment.
   B. The depth at which the density of the ball equals the density of surrounding water is above -32 feet, because the ball is less dense than the original ball in the experiment.
   C. The depth at which the density of the ball equals the density of surrounding water is below -32 feet, because the ball is denser than the original ball in the experiment.
   D. The depth at which the density of the ball equals the density of surrounding water is above -32 feet, because the ball is denser than the original ball in the experiment.

20. What has no direct effect on the volume of the ball?

   A. The external pressure
   B. The moles of gas in the ball
   C. The temperature of the water
   D. The magnetic field strength

21. If more salt were added to the water in the tank in Figure 1, what would be observed?

   A. The ball would rise, and a stronger magnetic, B, field would be required to submerge the ball below the surface.
   B. The ball would rise, and a weaker magnetic, B, field would be required to submerge the ball below the surface.
   C. The ball would sink, and a stronger magnetic, B, field would be required to submerge the ball below the surface.
   D. The ball would sink, and a weaker magnetic, B, field would be required to submerge the ball below the surface.

22. The compressibility of a gas is GREATEST when:

   A. the moles are high and the volume is low.
   B. the moles are high and the volume is high.
   C. the moles are low and the volume is high.
   D. the moles are low and the volume is low.

Passage IV (Questions 23 - 28)

Charles's law states that when the temperature of a gas within a closed system is increased, the volume of the gas increases proportionally, if the moles of gas and pressure remain constant. To demonstrate this law, a student sets out to observe the change in volume of a gas within a cylinder. The cylinder contains a heating coil that can be set by adjusting the voltage. As the voltage is increased, the current through the wire increases, causing more heat to be released from the coil. The change in volume of the piston is measured by the change in its height. Table 1 shows the data collected by the student for an unknown gas.

Temp	Height	Volume
10°C	6.00 cm	150.0π cm^3
20°C	6.21 cm	155.3π cm^3
30°C	6.42 cm	160.6π cm^3
40°C	6.64 cm	165.9π cm^3
50°C	6.85 cm	171.2π cm^3
60°C	7.06 cm	176.5π cm^3
70°C	7.27 cm	181.8π cm^3
80°C	7.48 cm	187.1π cm^3
90°C	7.70 cm	192.4π cm^3
100°C	7.91 cm	197.7π cm^3
110°C	8.12 cm	203.0π cm^3
120°C	8.33 cm	208.3π cm^3

Table 1

The data from the experiment show little deviation from ideal behavior. Equation 1 below represents Charles's law:

$$\frac{V_{initial}}{T_{initial}} = \frac{V_{final}}{T_{final}}$$

Equation 1

The volume can be expressed in any metric units, but the temperature must be measured in kelvins.

23. What is the volume of the unknown gas at 150°C?

   A. 219.9π cm^3

   B. 222.0π cm^3

   C. 224.2π cm^3

   D. 227.6π cm^3

24. What is the volume of a heated gas in a closed, flexible bulb at 27°C, if it had an initial volume of 7.0 liters at 7°C, and if the heating of the gas was carried out under isobaric conditions.

   A. 6.53 liters

   B. 7.20 liters

   C. 7.50 liters

   D. 27.0 liters

25. As you drive, what happens to the pressure in your car tire?

   A. It decreases, because your tire cools down and pressure decreases with decreasing temperature.

   B. It increases, because your tire cools down and pressure increases with decreasing temperature.

   C. It decreases, because your tire heats up and pressure decreases with increasing temperature.

   D. It increases, because your tire heats up and pressure increases with increasing temperature.

26. Charles's law states which of the following?

   A. At constant volume, as the pressure of a gas increases, the temperature decreases.

   B. At constant volume, as the temperature of a gas increases, the pressure increases.

   C. At constant temperature, as the pressure of a gas increases, the volume decreases.

   D. At constant pressure, as the temperature of a gas increases, the volume increases.

27. How can it be explained that the volume of the particles in the experiment at -15°C is a value less than 20 cm^3?

   A. Ideal behavior applies only to gases between 0°C and 100°C.

   B. The gas condenses into a liquid at a temperature slightly greater than -15°C.

   C. The gas condenses into a liquid at a temperature slightly less than -15°C.

   D. When the temperature of a gas is very low, its molecules get small enough to effuse out of the container.

28. In a system of three gas components (water, oxygen, and nitrogen), where water has a partial pressure of 22.1 torr and the percentage of oxygen gas is 20.9%, what is the partial pressure due to the third component (nitrogen), if the total pressure is 762 torr?

   A. 159.3 torr

   B. 444.4 torr

   C. 580.6 torr

   D. 719.0 torr

     GO ON TO THE NEXT PAGE

Boyle's law is based on the observation of a closed gaseous system at constant temperature. The conclusion is that when the system is closed so that moles of gas are held constant, the pressure varies inversely with the volume, if the temperature remains constant. Boyle's law is stated below:

As the pressure exerted on a gas in a closed system is increased, the volume of the system decreases in a linear fashion, if the temperature and moles of gas are held constant.

Summary: $P \uparrow : V \downarrow$ with n_c and T_c

To prove this, a researcher directs a constant stream of argon gas into a bent glass tube sealed at one end. The argon stream displaces the air in the tube, because argon is heavier than air. The system remains relatively pure in argon even though the tube is open at the other end to the air. The researcher then pours enough mercury into the tube barely to fill the bend in the tube. Once the mercury reaches a level where the gas in the left side of the tube is isolated, the height of the gas is measured to be 10 cm in the left side of the tube. The researcher next adds enough mercury to the open end of the tube to create a difference of 76 cm between the heights of the columns on the left and right side (this is the first addition of mercury to the tube). The height of the gas in the left side is then measured to be 5 cm. Mercury is again added to the right side, so that the difference in heights is now 152 cm. The height of the gas in the left side of the tube is found to be 3.3 cm. The stages are drawn in Figure 1:

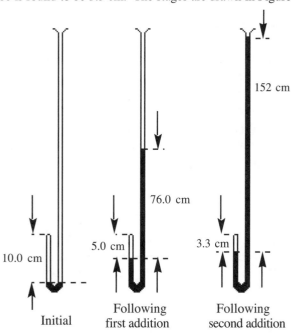

Figure 1

Every 760 mm of height in a mercury column exerts a gravitational force that when applied over a unit area equals 1.00 atm of pressure. This is independent of the radius of the column. If a less dense liquid is used, a greater height in the column is required to exert 1.00 atm of pressure.

In a second experiment, the researcher adds 1.000 grams of pure oxygen gas to a cylinder that can expand. The system is a closed system and the temperature is held constant by submerging the unit into a oil bath. Changes in the volume of the cylinder are determined by observing the level of a plunger connected to the top wall of the cylinder. The volume of the cylinder is proportional to its height, so the volume can be determined from the height of the plunger according to $V = \pi r^2 h$.

Table 1 shows the data collected at -78°C, 0°C, and 59°C. Figure 2 is a graphical representation of the data listed in Table 1.

-78°C		0 °C		59°C	
P (atm)	V (L)	P (atm)	V (L)	P (atm)	V (L)
0.25	2.029	0.25	2.841	0.25	3.455
0.50	1.014	0.50	1.420	0.50	1.727
0.75	0.6788	0.75	0.9466	0.75	1.139
1.00	0.5068	1.00	0.7095	1.00	0.8628
2.00	0.2532	2.00	0.3545	2.00	0.4311
3.00	0.1685	3.00	0.2359	3.00	0.2869
4.00	0.1264	4.00	0.1769	4.00	0.2151
5.00	0.1010	5.00	0.1414	5.00	0.1720

Table 1

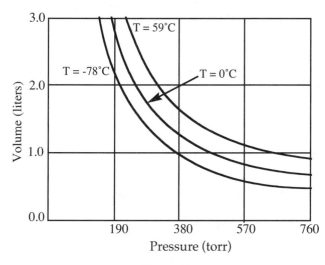

Figure 2

29. According to the graph in Figure 2, what can be said about the volume of 1.000 gram of oxygen gas at room temperature and 0.50 atm. of pressure?

   A. The volume is less than 1.01 liters.

   B. The volume is greater than 1.01 liters, but less than 1.42 liters.

   C. The volume is greater than 1.42 liters, but less than 1.71 liters.

   D. The volume is greater than 1.71 liters.

     GO ON TO THE NEXT PAGE

30. What would be observed if a liquid less dense than mercury were used in the J-tube in the first experiment?

A. The argon gas in the left side of the tube would compress less, and thus the height of the column of gas would be greater than what was observed with mercury in the manometer.

B. The argon gas in the left side of the tube would compress more, and thus the height of the column of gas would be less than what was observed with mercury in the manometer.

C. The argon gas in the left side of the tube would compress the same amount as with mercury, and thus the height of the column of gas would be the same as what was observed with mercury in the manometer.

D. The argon gas in the left side of the tube would compress more, and thus the height of the column of gas would be greater than what was observed with mercury in the manometer.

31. If a gas made up of molecules rather than atoms were substituted for argon gas in the first experiment, what should be observed for the heights of the gas in the left side of the tube in each of the trials?

A. 100 mm, 53 mm, 35 mm

B. 100 mm, 53 mm, 31 mm

C. 100 mm, 47 mm, 35 mm

D. 100 mm, 47 mm, 31 mm

32. If the temperature of a gas enclosed in a flexible container were increased from 25°C to 50°C while the pressure on the system were increased from 0.5 atm. to 1.0 atm., then what would happen to the volume of the system?

A. The volume would increase, because the effect of increasing pressure is greater than the effect of increasing temperature in this example.

B. The volume would increase, because the effect of increasing temperature is greater than the effect of increasing pressure in this example.

C. The volume would decrease, because the effect of increasing pressure is greater than the effect of increasing temperature in this example.

D. The volume would decrease, because the effect of increasing temperature is greater than the effect of increasing pressure in this example.

33. What would the volume of 2.000 grams of oxygen gas be at 0°C, if the pressure were 1.00 atmosphere?

A. 0.71 liters

B. 1.00 liters

C. 1.42 liters

D. 2.84 liters

34. According to the findings of the first experiment, one atmosphere of pressure when applied to an open column of mercury would raise the height of the mercury in the column by what amount?

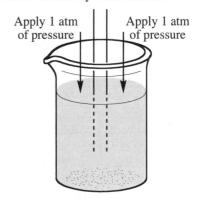

Apply 1 atm of pressure   Apply 1 atm of pressure

A. 5 centimeters

B. 10 centimeters

C. 76 centimeters

D. 152 centimeters

35. When mercury is added to a J-tube containing argon gas in uniform 100.0-mL increments, the change in volume decreases with each subsequent addition. How is this best explained?

A. The argon gas becomes more dense with each addition of mercury, so the particles become harder to compress.

B. The argon gas becomes less dense with each addition of mercury, so the particles become harder to compress.

C. The mercury becomes more dense with each addition, so the pressure exerted by mercury increases with each addition.

D. The mercury becomes less dense with each addition, so the pressure exerted by mercury increases with each addition.

The circulation of vital gases through the body starts in the lung, where large volumes of gas are exchanged between the body and the atmosphere. The volume of the lung can be broken down into four distinct volumes and dead space. There is the *tidal volume*, which is the volume of gas inspired or expired in a normal breath. There is the *inspiratory reserve volume*, which is the volume that can be inspired beyond the tidal volume, invoked during periods of exercise and strained breathing. There is the *expiratory reserve volume,* which is the volume of air that can be expired after the expiration of the tidal volume. There is the *residual volume*, which is the volume of gas that remains in the lungs after maximal expiration. Finally, there is dead space. There is the *physiological dead space*, which is the volume of the lung that does not eliminate carbon dioxide, and there is *anatomic dead space*, which is the volume of the conducting airways (about 150 mL in the average adult).

The breathing cycle is regulated by changes in the internal pressure of the lung. The ideal gas law can explain operation of the lung. The pressure change is caused by expansion and relaxation of the thoracic cavity. At rest, alveolar pressure is equal to atmospheric pressure. As defined in physiology, this is zero pressure. The interpleural pressure is negative, due to the tendency for the lung to collapse and chest cavity to expand. The onset of normal inspiration is a result of contraction of the inspiratory muscles, in particular the diaphragm. When the diaphragm contracts, the abdominal contents are forced downward, and the thorax expands. This increases the volume of the lung, making the alveolar pressure negative (sub-atmospheric).

Expiration is normally a passive process, resulting from the relaxation of inspiratory muscles back to rest. The lung and chest system is elastic, so after active inspiration, where it is expanded from its resting state, the system relaxes back to its resting state. This decreases lung volume, making the alveolar pressure positive (super-atmospheric). Air flows out of the lung as a result of this pressure difference. The amount of gas exchanged in one cycle of normal breathing is the tidal volume. As some of the definitions imply, there is also facilitated breathing, where inspiration is greater than normal and expiration is an active process.

36. Inspiration into the lung is BEST explained by:

- **A.** Archimedes' principle.
- **B.** Bernoulli's principle.
- **C.** Boyle's law.
- **D.** Charles's law.

37. What is true during expiration?

- **A.** Lung pressure is less than atmospheric pressure.
- **B.** Lung pressure is greater than atmospheric pressure.
- **C.** The thoracic cavity is contracted more than normal.
- **D.** Lung volume is at its smallest point.

38. At a low altitude with a low ambient temperature, what is true of atmospheric air?

- **A.** It has a lower partial pressure of $O_{2(g)}$, but the same mole fraction of $O_{2(g)}$ as normal air.
- **B.** It has a higher partial pressure of $O_{2(g)}$, but the same mole fraction of $O_{2(g)}$ as normal air.
- **C.** It has both a lower partial pressure and lower mole fraction of $O_{2(g)}$ as normal air.
- **D.** It has both a higher partial pressure and higher mole fraction of $O_{2(g)}$ as normal air.

39. What is observed during normal expiration?

- I. Total lung volume is less than tidal volume.
- II. Internal pressure exceeds external pressure.
- III. The mole fraction of CO_2 is less than in normal air.

- **A.** I only
- **B.** II only
- **C.** I and II only
- **D.** II and III only

40. What is NOT true as the diaphragm contracts?

- **A.** Internal pressure is less than external pressure.
- **B.** Partial pressure of carbon dioxide decreases.
- **C.** Lung volume is less than it is at rest.
- **D.** Air temperature in the lungs remains relatively constant.

41. For lungs with a tidal volume of 400 mL and a total volume following normal expiration of 1200 mL, how does internal pressure change to cause inspiration?

- **A.** It increases by 33%.
- **B.** It increases by 25%.
- **C.** It decreases by 25%.
- **D.** It decreases by 33%.

42. Why do scuba divers experience different breathing patterns underwater than on land?

- **A.** Air is more concentrated, so they breathe more O_2.
- **B.** Air underwater behaves more like an ideal gas.
- **C.** Air viscosity is greatly reduced underwater.
- **D.** Air in the anatomic dead space has a reduced partial pressure of CO_2 underwater.

43. The air flow associated with the lung moves:

- **A.** at a decreasing rate during a normal breath.
- **B.** at an increasing rate during a normal breath.
- **C.** at a constant rate during a normal breath.
- **D.** in a sinusoidal fashion during a normal breath.

Nuclear reactors requiring uranium use the isotope ^{235}U as fuel. Naturally occurring uranium is only 0.72% ^{235}U, with the majority of the uranium being the ^{238}U isotope. For a reactor to run efficiently, the uranium should be at least 3% ^{235}U. To enrich the sample with ^{235}U, the uranium is converted to the hexafluoro species (UF_6), a white solid at room temperature. The uranium hexafluoride compound is heated to its sublimation point, and the gas is allowed to effuse through tiny pores between a series of connected containers. With each effusion, the vapor becomes enriched with the ^{235}U species, because the lighter compound effuses faster, according to Graham's law. The relative rates of $^{235}UF_6$ and $^{238}UF_6$ are determined as follows:

$$\frac{v_{235}UF_6}{v_{238}UF_6} = \sqrt{\frac{mass_{238}UF_6}{mass_{235}UF_6}} = \sqrt{\frac{352}{349}} = \sqrt{1.00858} = 1.004$$

Figure 1

Because the average speed of the U-235 species is 0.4% greater than the U-238 species, the effusion rate of the U-235 species is 0.4% faster. This is assuming that the diameters of the $^{235}UF_6$ and $^{238}UF_6$ molecules are equivalent, which is valid because the only difference between the two isotopes of uranium is three neutrons. Only charged particles affect the radius of an atom. By carrying out successive effusions, the uranium can be enriched up to the necessary 3%. Once this is complete, the UF_6 is converted back to uranium metal.

44. As the diameter of a gas molecule increases, its effusion rate:

- **A.** decreases, because the molecule is hindered when passing through the pore.
- **B.** decreases, because the molecule collides with the pore more often.
- **C.** increases, because the molecule is hindered when passing through the pore.
- **D.** increases, because the molecule collides with the pore more often.

45. What can be said about the reactivity of fluorine gas (F_2) with U-235 and U-238?

- **A.** Fluorine gas reacts more readily with U-238, because it is heavier.
- **B.** Fluorine gas reacts more readily with U-235, because it is lighter.
- **C.** Fluorine gas reacts with U-235 and U-238 equally, because the extra neutrons do not significantly affect the chemical reactivity.
- **D.** Fluorine gas reacts with U-235 and U-238 equally, because the extra protons do not significantly affect the chemical reactivity.

46. Assuming that the molecular diameters are insignificant, which of the following compounds would effuse roughly twice as fast as UF_6?

- **A.** SO_2
- **B.** SO_3
- **C.** PF_3
- **D.** Xe

47. All of the following affect the effusion rate of a gas EXCEPT:

- **A.** the size of the molecule relative to the pore.
- **B.** the temperature of the gas.
- **C.** the presence of isotopes in the compounds.
- **D.** the concentration of the species outside of the container.

48. What is the mass percent of uranium-235 in $^{235}UF_6$?

- **A.** Less than 50%
- **B.** Between 50% and 60%
- **C.** Between 60% and 70%
- **D.** Greater than 70%

49. If UCl_6 were used instead of UF_6, the difference in effusion rates for the two uranium isotopes would be:

- **A.** greater than 0.4%, so fewer filtering chambers (pores) would be needed to enrich the sample.
- **B.** less than 0.4%, so fewer filtering chambers (pores) would be needed to enrich the sample.
- **C.** greater than 0.4%, so more filtering chambers (pores) would be needed to enrich the sample.
- **D.** less than 0.4%, so more filtering chambers (pores) would be needed to enrich the sample.

50. Which of the following pairs of gas molecules would be the MOST difficult to separate using the successive effusion technique?

- **A.** O_2 and N_2
- **B.** H_2 and Ne
- **C.** CO_2 and SO_2
- **D.** CO and C_2H_4

Passage VIII (Questions 51 - 57)

Air safety bags are standard features on new cars. These bags function through rapid gas generation. Because they are safety features, air bags must use a non-toxic gas that does not oxidize readily. Nitrogen gas is ideal because of its inert chemical behavior. The Reaction 1 is employed by airbags to produce nitrogen gas (N_2) rapidly.

$$2 \, NaN_3(s) \longrightarrow 2 \, Na(l) + 3 \, N_2(g)$$

Reaction 1

Sodium azide decomposes quickly to fill a 60.0 liter air bag in approximately 20 milliseconds. To proceed at this rate, the reaction must be run at 350°C. To maintain this temperature, Reaction 2 is employed.

$$6 \, Na(l) + Fe_2O_3(s) \longrightarrow 3 \, Na_2O(s) + 2 \, Fe(s)$$

Reaction 2

Once the air bag is filled, it must deflate rapidly. To accommodate this, there are small pores in the material to allow the gas to effuse out. If the bag remained inflated, vision would be hindered. The rate of effusion depends on the average speed of the molecules. The root mean square speed, μ_{rms}, of a gas is calculated using Equation 1.

$$\mu_{rms} = \sqrt{\frac{3kT}{m}}$$

Equation 1

where k is Boltzmann's constant, T is for temperature (measured in kelvins), and m is for mass (measured in kg).

51. What can be said about the thermodynamics of Reaction 1 and Reaction 2?

 A. Entropy increases in Reaction 1; Reaction 2 is endothermic.
 B. Entropy increases in Reaction 1; Reaction 2 is exothermic.
 C. Entropy decreases in Reaction 1; Reaction 2 is endothermic.
 D. Entropy decreases in Reaction 1; Reaction 2 is exothermic.

52. As the nitrogen gas cools from 350°C to room temperature:

 A. its pressure increases, and the kinetic energy of the gas increases.
 B. its pressure increases, and the kinetic energy of the gas decreases.
 C. its pressure decreases, and the kinetic energy of the gas increases.
 D. its pressure decreases, and the kinetic energy of the gas decreases.

53. If the average speed of a gas at 25°C is exactly 100.0 m/sec, then at 125°C the approximate average speed would be which of the following values?

 A. 115 m/sec
 B. 133 m/sec
 C. 224 m/sec
 D. 500 m/sec

54. An air safety bag fills at a rate of 100 moles/sec. After 10 milliseconds, what is the volume of the gas in the bag at 31°C? (At 31°C, gas is 25 L/mole)

 A. 2.5 liters
 B. 22.4 liters
 C. 25 liters
 D. 250 liters

55. If an air bag were filled with argon gas, helium gas, and nitrogen gas, which of the following relationships accurately describes the relative rates of effusion for each gas from the air bag?

 A. $He > N_2 > Ar$
 B. $N_2 > He > Ar$
 C. $He > Ar > N_2$
 D. $Ar > N_2 > He$

56. In a mixture of 50 grams nitrogen gas with 50 grams carbon dioxide at STP, the partial pressure attributed to carbon dioxide would be which of the following values?

 A. 50 torr
 B. 296 torr
 C. 380 torr
 D. 464 torr

57. What can be said about the average speed of neon gas at 25°C compared to argon gas at 25°C?

 (Ne has mass = 20 g/mole)

 (Ar has mass = 40 g/mole)

 A. Ne gas is twice as fast as Ar gas.
 B. Ne gas is 1.4 times as fast as Ar gas.
 C. Ar gas is 1.4 times as fast as Ne gas.
 D. Ar gas is twice as fast as Ne gas.

Passage IX (Questions 58 - 63)

Effusion is defined as the flow of a gas from the inside of a container to the outside of a container through a pore in the wall of the container. The size of the pore can range from microscopic (barely greater then the diameter of the gas particles) to macroscopic (as is the case with a valve). The rate at which a gas effuses depends on the velocity of the gas, the total area of the pores relative to the surface area of the container, and the concentration of the gas in the container.

A researcher sets out to study effusion using inert gases, so that intermolecular forces are minimal. The apparatus used is two unequal spheres connected by a tube with a porous valve. The left sphere (Region I) has a radius, r_1, while the right sphere (Region II) has a radius, r_2. Region II is triple the volume of Region I, as shown in Figure 1.

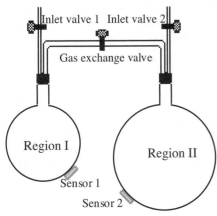

Figure 1

Region I is initially charged with equal moles of helium, nitrogen, and argon, at 25°C. Region II is evacuated. The exchange valve is set to allow gas exchange. The vessels are made of a polymer that is essentially pore-free for the lifetime of the experiment. Figure 2 shows the pressure of each gas in Region I over time.

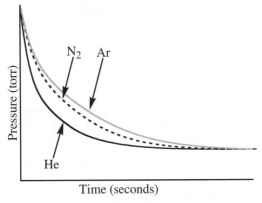

Figure 2

58. What is true once equilibrium has been established?

- **A.** The mole fraction of helium is lowest in Region I.
- **B.** The mole fraction of argon is greatest in Region II.
- **C.** The moles of nitrogen are greatest in Region I.
- **D.** The moles of helium are greatest in Region II.

59. What occurs in Region II, once the gas exchange valve is opened?

- **A.** Helium partial pressure grows rapidly, reaching the greatest partial pressure once at equilibrium.
- **B.** Helium partial pressure grows rapidly, reaching the smallest partial pressure once at equilibrium.
- **C.** Argon partial pressure grows slowly, but reaches the same partial pressure as helium once at equilibrium.
- **D.** Argon partial pressure grows rapidly, but reaches the same partial pressure as helium once at equilibrium.

60. Which of the following statements must be TRUE with regard to the system shown in Figure 1?

- I. The final pressure in Region II is three times as great as in Region I.
- II. At equilibrium, the mole fraction of helium is the same in Region I as the mole fraction of argon in Region II.
- III. Increasing the temperature would increase the rate of effusion and increase the equilibrium partial pressures, but it would not change the mole fractions at equilibrium.

- **A.** II only
- **B.** III only
- **C.** I and II only
- **D.** II and III only

61. All of the following can increase the effusion rate EXCEPT:

- **A.** opening the valve to a greater area.
- **B.** increasing the temperature of the system.
- **C.** increasing the volume of the system.
- **D.** increasing the partial pressure of a component.

62. How would hydrogen compare to the gases in Figure 2?

- **A.** It would have the steepest drop initially, reaching equilibrium before the other gases.
- **B.** It would have the flattest drop initially, reaching equilibrium after the other gases.
- **C.** It would be identical to the graph for helium.
- **D.** It would be between the graphs for nitrogen and argon.

63. How does the rate of diffusion change with time?

- **A.** It decreases for helium and increases for argon.
- **B.** It increases for helium and decreases for argon.
- **C.** It decreases for all three gases.
- **D.** It increases for all three gases.

A researcher carries out a series of reactions under standard conditions, in a round-bottom flask connected to a manometer. The line from the flask to the manometer is fitted with a valve that opens to the environment. The following four reactions take place in the reaction vessel:

$$HI(g) + Ba(NO_3)_2(aq) \longrightarrow BaI_2(s) + HNO_3(aq)$$

Reaction 1

$$KHCO_3(aq) + HCl(aq) \longrightarrow KCl(aq) + H_2O(l) + CO_2(g)$$

Reaction 2

$$AgNO_3(aq) + NaCl(aq) \longrightarrow NaNO_3(aq) + AgCl(s)$$

Reaction 3

$$Cl_2(aq) + Zn(s) \longrightarrow ZnCl_2(aq)$$

Reaction 4

The change in pressure is found by observing the difference in heights of mercury in the two columns of the manometer. The two columns have the same internal radius. The reaction apparatus is shown in Figure 1 below:

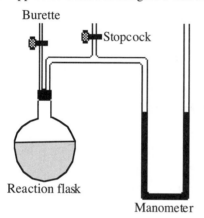

Figure 1

The data for each reaction are calculated using the ideal gas equation for the vapor in the system. The vapor pressure of water at 25°C is 27.2 torr. The pressure for each reaction is recorded along with the resting volume of the system. The volume of the gas space following the reaction is approximated as the original volume plus any positive or negative correction for the manometer. For a reaction in which the volume increases, for instance, the change in volume is the cross-sectional area of the manometer core times the height change.

64. Which of the reactions would result in an increase in the height of the mercury column on the right of side of the U-tube?

A. Reactions 1 and 2

B. Reaction 2 only

C. Reactions 1, 3, and 4

D. Reaction 4 only

65. Once the system is at equilibrium, if the right column of the manometer is higher than the left column of the manometer, then:

A. $P_{system\ at\ equilibrium} > P_{system\ initially}$; when the stopcock is opened, the net flow of gas is out.

B. $P_{system\ at\ equilibrium} < P_{system\ initially}$; when the stopcock is opened, the net flow of gas is out.

C. $P_{system\ at\ equilibrium} > P_{system\ initially}$; when the stopcock is opened, the net flow of gas is in.

D. $P_{system\ at\ equilibrium} < P_{system\ initially}$; when the stopcock is opened, the net flow of gas is in.

66. For a reaction that results in only a small change in volume, what type of tube in the atmospheric side of the manometer yields the MOST accurate reading?

A. One with a very dense liquid and a large bore radius

B. One with a liquid of low density and a large bore radius

C. One with a very dense liquid and a small bore radius

D. One with a liquid of low density and a small bore radius

67. What is the role of the stopcock in the middle line?

A. To equilibrate the two sides of the manometer before the reaction begins

B. To measure the pressure inside of the flask

C. To measure the pressure outside of the flask

D. To prevent pressure buildup inside the flask through one-way venting

68. As the bore radius of both tubes in a manometer is reduced, how is height of the fluid in the column in the atmospheric side affected?

A. If the radius decreases by half, the height increases by a factor of four.

B. If the radius decreases by half, the height increases by a factor of two.

C. If the radius decreases by half, the height does not change.

D. If the radius decreases by half, the height decreases by a factor of four.

69. Which of the following is the BEST liquid to use in the manometer for a system that produces a large quantity of gas?

A. Mercury

B. Water

C. Ethanol

D. Glycerol

70. For an endothermic reaction that neither consumes nor produces gases, what is observed after reaction?

A. The left column rises initially until the solution temperature falls to 4°C, then the left column begins to drop.

B. The left column rises initially until the solution freezes, then the left column remains constant.

C. The left column drops initially until the solution temperature falls to 4°C, then the left column begins to rise.

D. The left column drops initially until the solution freezes, then the left column remains constant.

Passage XI (Questions 71 - 78)

A researcher fills a balloon with a mixture of nitrogen gas (20% by volume) and helium gas (80% by volume) and then seals it. The balloon is used to transport sampling devices into the atmosphere to collect gases at various altitudes. It is filled to a total internal pressure of 760.0 torr at 27°C and a volume of exactly 24.63 liters. The balloon contains exactly one mole of total gases. It is allowed to rise to a height of 20,000 feet, where the atmospheric pressure is measured to be 507 torr (0.67 atm.) and the temperature is -3°C (270 K). The balloon carries a basket aloft containing equipment to monitor the atmospheric conditions. The balloon is released early in the morning and returns to the ground at night, where it is 7°C and the pressure is 760 torr.

In addition to sealed balloons, hot-air balloons may also be used. Drawn in Figure 1 below is a hot-air balloon with an attached basket.

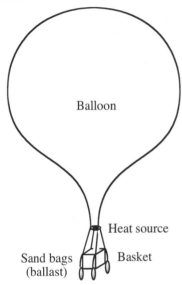

Balloon

Heat source

Sand bags (ballast)

Basket

Figure 1

Hot-air balloons demonstrate the principle of buoyancy. Hot air is less dense than the surrounding air, so when hot air displaces cold air in the balloon, it becomes less dense than the surrounding medium. Hot air rises to the top of the balloon, as shown in Figure 2. This lowers the center of mass for the system.

Figure 2

43

GO ON TO THE NEXT PAGE

71. What is the volume of the sealed balloon at 20,000 feet, where the temperature is -3°C and pressure is 507 torr?

    A. 14.78 liters
    B. 18.24 liters
    C. 33.25 liters
    D. 41.05 liters

72. What is the density of helium gas at STP?

    A. 0.18 grams/liter
    B. 0.36 grams/liter
    C. 1.00 grams/liter
    D. 4.00 grams/liter

73. As a hot-air balloon is lifting off, which point in the drawing below accurately reflects its center of mass?

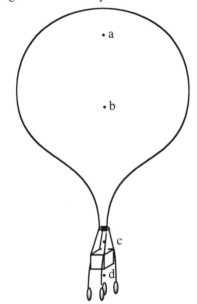

    A. Point a
    B. Point b
    C. Point c
    D. Point d

74. The relative rate of effusion from a balloon (with 50% He and 50% N_2) for helium compared to nitrogen would be which of the following?

    A. 7 times faster for helium
    B. $\sqrt{7}$ times faster for helium
    C. $\sqrt{7}$ times faster for nitrogen
    D. 7 times faster for nitrogen

75. Which of the following statements BEST describes the buoyancy of a hot-air balloon under varying conditions?

    A. The balloon is most buoyant on a hot day, because the surrounding air is denser than on a cold day.
    B. The balloon is most buoyant on a hot day, because the surrounding air is less dense than on a cold day.
    C. The balloon is most buoyant on a cold day, because the surrounding air is denser than on a hot day.
    D. The balloon is most buoyant on a cold day, because the surrounding air is less dense than on a hot day.

76. What is the partial pressure of $N_{2(g)}$ at 507 torr and 7°C?

    A. 102 torr
    B. 133 torr
    C. 157 torr
    D. 608 torr

77. Which of the following formulas can be used to calculate the molecular weight of a gas, where the mass of the gas in grams is represented by (g)?

    A. $\dfrac{gPV}{RT}$
    B. $\dfrac{gVT}{PR}$
    C. $\dfrac{gRP}{TV}$
    D. $\dfrac{gRT}{PV}$

78. How many moles of helium gas are in the balloon, if the pressure is reduced to .507 atm. and the temperature is reduced to -3°C?

    A. 0.48 moles He
    B. 0.80 moles He
    C. 1.08 moles He
    D. 1.20 moles He

                                       GO ON TO THE NEXT PAGE

Passage XII (Questions 79 - 86)

Chlorocarbons are a class of compounds composed of chlorine, carbon, and hydrogen, and *fluorocarbons* are a class of compounds composed of fluorine, carbon, and hydrogen. Both classes of molecules consist of polar compounds, for the most part. Their polarity affects their physical properties, such as boiling point, so they are often used as refrigerants. Because of their strong intermolecular forces, neither class of compounds acts like an ideal gas. An ideal gas obeys Equation 1:

$$PV = nRT$$

Equation 1

where P is pressure in atm., V is volume in liters, n is the number of moles of particles, R is the ideal gas constant 0.0821 L·atm·mole^{-1}·K, and T is temperature in kelvins.

When comparing a real gas to an ideal gas, deviations in pressure and volume are taken into account. The corrected terms, when substituted into Equation 1, yield Equation 2:

$$\left(P + a\frac{n^2}{V^2}\right) \times (V - nb) = nRT$$

Equation 2

where a is an empirical value related to the strength of the attractive intermolecular forces, and b is an empirical value related to the size of the molecule.

In general, bigger molecules have greater b values. Deviations from ideal behavior decrease as the mean free path increases. This deviation is attributed to reduced interactions caused by the increased average distance between particles. As the volume of the container increases, the space that is occupied by the particles becomes insignificant.

79. In a flask initially filled with equal moles of methane, fluoromethane, chloromethane, and bromomethane, which gas has the GREATEST mole fraction after a short duration of time, if each gas is allowed to effuse from the flask?

A. Methane
B. Fluoromethane
C. Chloromethane
D. Bromomethane

80. The b-value for 1,1-difluoroethane is:

A. half of the b-value for 1,1-dichloroethane.
B. slightly less than the b-value for 1,1-dichloroethane.
C. slightly more than the b-value for 1,1-dichloroethane.
D. twice as large as the b-value for 1,1-dichloroethane.

81. The a-value for a halocarbon increases proportionally with:

A. molecular mass.
B. nucleophilicity.
C. boiling point.
D. polarity.

82. What is the volume of 1.00 moles of CH_3F at 25°C and 1.00 atm.?

A. 20.17 L
B. 22.41 L
C. 24.24 L
D. 32.17 L

83. What does NOT decrease as the pressure exerted on a gas system in a piston increases?

A. Volume
B. Compressibility
C. Mean free path
D. Gas concentration

84. What is TRUE when comparing CH_2F_2 to CH_2Br_2 under identical conditions?

I. The diffusion rate of CH_2F_2 is greater than the diffusion rate of CH_2Br_2.

II. The collision impulse of CH_2F_2 is greater than the collision impulse of CH_2Br_2.

III. The average kinetic energy of CH_2F_2 is greater than the average kinetic energy of CH_2Br_2.

A. I only
B. I and II only
C. I and III only
D. I, II, and III

85. Which of the following gases has the GREATEST a-value?

A. Chloromethane
B. Fluoromethane
C. Methane
D. 1,2-Difluoroethane

86. Which of the following gases is MOST ideal?

A. 1,1-Difluoroethane
B. Difluoromethane
C. Fluorine
D. 1,2-Difluoropropane

45 **GO ON TO THE NEXT PAGE**

A balloon filled with enough helium floats in the air surrounding it, because its *countermass* exceeds its mass. The countermass is the mass of the surrounding medium that is displaced by the balloon, and it is found by multiplying the volume of air displaced by the balloon times the density of the medium. Helium is lighter than all gases except hydrogen, and it has the smallest molecular size of any gas known. Because of its low mass and small molecular size, helium effuses rapidly from a balloon. The restoring force of the rubber from which the balloon is made provides a driving force for effusion to exceed infusion. As the helium effuses, the volume of the balloon is decreased, reducing the countermass. Eventually, the mass of the balloon exceeds the countermass, and the balloon is no longer buoyant.

The effusion rate depends on the temperature and mass of the gas, and on the size of the gas particles relative to the size of the pores in the container's walls. The temperature and mass affect effusion rate, because they affect the average speed of the gas particles. Equation 1 shows the relationship of gas speed (v) to temperature (T) and mass (m):

$$v \propto \sqrt{\frac{T}{m}}$$

Equation 1

To study the average speed of a gas, particle flow in one direction through a vacuum is observed. The apparatus shown in Figure 1 is used to generate such conditions.

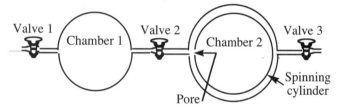

Figure 1

The system is completely evacuated, and a gas sample is injected into Chamber 1. The cylinder is then set in motion and Valve 2 is opened briefly, allowing gas to flow into Chamber 2. A sensor in Valve 3 detects collisions. Chamber 2 is re-evacuated, and the process is repeated with the cylinder spinning at a different rate. The goal of each adjustment is to determine the spin rate that causes the greatest collision frequency at the detector. It is assumed that the gas is passing straight through Chamber 2 at this spin rate. Under such conditions, the diameter and period of the spin are used to determine the speed of the gas particles.

87. A balloon filled with which of the following gases would require the GREATEST minimum volume to float in air?

   A. Ammonia
   B. Helium
   C. Hydrogen
   D. Methane

88. In the experiment illustrated by Figure 1, how must the spin rate of the cylinder be adjusted when nitrous oxide (44 grams/mole) is replaced by methane (16 grams/mole) to get the same results?

   A. It must be slowed by a factor of 2.75.
   B. It must be slowed by a factor of 1.61.
   C. It must be increased by a factor of 1.61.
   D. It must be increased by a factor of 2.75.

89. Which of these balloons has the GREATEST buoyant force in air?

   A. A 4.0-liter methane filled balloon
   B. A 3.0-liter helium filled balloon
   C. A 2.0-liter neon filled balloon
   D. A 1.0-liter nitrogen filled balloon

90. If a larger cylinder were used in Chamber 2, how must the spin rate be adjusted to keep the gas passing through the pore after half of a rotation?

   A. The rate must increase by a factor of 2.
   B. The rate must decrease by a factor of $\sqrt{2}$.
   C. The rate must increase by a factor of $\sqrt{2}$.
   D. The rate does not change.

91. Why is Chamber 2 evacuated before gas is released through Valve 2?

   A. To minimize collisions between particles within the cylinder
   B. To prevent the effusion of gas
   C. To prevent the infusion of gas
   D. To maximize the buoyancy of Chamber 2

92. How would the speed of the gas change within the system shown in Figure 1, if the temperature were increased from 25°C to 100°C?

   A. It would increase by a factor of 4.
   B. It would increase by a factor of 2.
   C. It would increase by a factor of 1.25.
   D. It would increase by a factor of 1.12.

93. How do the speeds of N_2O, CO, F_2, and Ne compare?

   A. $v_{N_2O} > v_{F_2} > v_{CO} > v_{Ne}$
   B. $v_{Ne} > v_{CO} > v_{F_2} > v_{N_2O}$
   C. $v_{N_2O} > v_{CO} > v_{F_2} > v_{Ne}$
   D. $v_{Ne} > v_{F_2} > v_{CO} > v_{N_2O}$

94. What is the partial pressure of argon in a mixture that is 32% by moles argon at STP?

- **A.** 243.2 torr
- **B.** 320.0 torr
- **C.** 500.0 torr
- **D.** 516.8 torr

95. What is the final pressure in a balloon that occupies 1.00 liter at S.T.P. after the volume is decreased to 0.75 liters at constant temperature (isothermally)?

- **A.** 1013 torr
- **B.** 833 torr
- **C.** 760 torr
- **D.** 570 torr

96. A balloon that occupies 67.2 liters at 25°C and 1.0 atm., will occupy what volume in the mountains (T = 4°C and P = 0.90 atm.)?

- **A.** 56.2 liters
- **B.** 65.1 liters
- **C.** 69.4 liters
- **D.** 80.3 liters

97. If it takes a balloon filled with argon gas 23.6 minutes to decrease its volume by 0.100 liters due to effusion at constant temperature and constant pressure, how long would it take if the balloon is filled with sulfur trioxide instead? (Ar = 39.95 g/m, SO_3 = 80.06 g/m)

- **A.** 47.2 minutes
- **B.** 33.4 minutes
- **C.** 16.7 minutes
- **D.** 11.8 minutes

98. Which of the following gases moves approximately twice as fast as water?

- **A.** He
- **B.** CO_2
- **C.** Ar
- **D.** C_5H_{12}

99. The relative rate of effusion from a balloon for methane compared to helium would be which of the following?

- **A.** 4.00 times faster than helium
- **B.** 2.00 times faster than helium
- **C.** 2.00 times slower than helium
- **D.** 4.00 times slower than helium

100. Select the sequence that corresponds to the infusion rates for the four gases indicated below, in ascending order.

- **A.** $CH_4 < CO < SO_2 < Cl_2$
- **B.** $SO_2 < Cl_2 < CO < CH_4$
- **C.** $CO < Cl_2 < CH_4 < SO_2$
- **D.** $Cl_2 < SO_2 < CO < CH_4$

1. D	2. D	3. A	4. C	5. B
6. B	7. C	8. D	9. C	10. C
11. D	12. A	13. D	14. D	15. A
16. D	17. C	18. D	19. D	20. D
21. A	22. C	23. C	24. C	25. D
26. D	27. B	28. C	29. C	30. A
31. A	32. C	33. C	34. C	35. A
36. C	37. B	38. B	39. B	40. C
41. C	42. A	43. D	44. A	45. C
46. C	47. D	48. C	49. D	50. D
51. B	52. D	53. A	54. C	55. A
56. B	57. B	58. D	59. C	60. D
61. C	62. A	63. C	64. B	65. A
66. D	67. A	68. A	69. A	70. A
71. C	72. A	73. C	74. B	75. C
76. A	77. D	78. B	79. D	80. B
81. D	82. C	83. D	84. A	85. B
86. C	87. A	88. C	89. A	90. D
91. A	92. D	93. B	94. A	95. A
96. C	97. B	98. A	99. C	100. D

YOU ARE DONE.

Gases Passage Answers

1. **Choice D is correct.** Because the particles of a real gases have a molecular volume, the volume of the container does not reflect the actual volume that the gas can occupy. This is based on the idea that in a real gas, no two particles can occupy the same point in space at the same time. As the container volume decreases, the space unoccupied by gas molecules is decreased, so the molecules collide more often. This increases the interactions between molecules, thereby increasing the deviation from ideal behavior. Choice A is eliminated. Forces between molecules (attractive or repulsive) result in deviations in the behavior of the gas. The deviations can be attributed to changes in the collision frequency of the particles with the walls. For instance, particles that experience attractive forces have a greater tendency to collide with one another, decreasing the frequency of their collisions against the walls. This eliminates choices B and C. Choices A, B, and C represent the assumptions of the ideal gas law, which under real conditions do not hold true. The gas is assumed to be uniform in the flask, so choice **D** is not a true statement. In addition, this would not necessarily account for deviations from ideal gas behavior. The collisions would simply be asymmetrically distributed against the walls. Pick **D** to be totally hip and now.

2. **Choice D is correct.** Pressure is a measure of the collisions of the gas molecules with the container walls. As the pressure of a gas increases, the gas particles strike the wall more frequently. It can be inferred from the fact that the molecules collide with the walls more frequently that they also collide with one another more frequently, eliminating choices A and C. Because they collide more frequently, their time in contact, and thus their interactions are increased, making choice **D** the best answer.

3. **Choice A is correct.** Because the question asks for the trend over a large pressure range, we need to use Table 1. As observed in Table 1, the pressure·volume product for helium gas shows a uniform increase over the period during which the pressure is increased up to 400 atm. During this same period, the pressure·volume product for oxygen gas decreases slightly before beginning to increase. This means that oxygen gas shows a change in behavior as pressure is increased, which eliminates choices B, C, and D. Although we know the answer must be choice **A** at this point, we'll analyze the trend for carbon dioxide to be certain. The pressure·volume product for carbon dioxide shows a drastic drop until some pressure around 25 atm., then the pressure·volume product rapidly increases. The best answer is choice **A**.

4. **Choice C is correct.** This is really two questions combined into one. "Is the volume larger or smaller than expected" and "Is this due to attractive or repulsive forces?" The value for the molar volume of an ideal gas at standard temperature and pressure is given in the passage as 22.41 liters. The value for the molar volume of ammonia (NH_3) at standard temperature and pressure is listed in Table 2 as 22.081 liters. This means that the molar volume for ammonia (NH_3) is smaller than it is for an ideal gas under identical conditions. This eliminates choices A and B. The smaller volume of a gas can be attributed to attractive forces. In the case of ammonia, the attractive force pulling the molecules closer together is hydrogen bonding. The best answer is choice **C**. Be a champion and choose **C**.

5. **Choice B is correct.** Table 1 lists values for the pressure·volume product. The value for the pressure·volume product at 75 atm. should be somewhere between 10.11 and 11.25. A good approximation of the value for the pressure·volume product at 75 atm. is 10.63 (an average of 1011 and 11.25). To determine the molar volume for carbon dioxide at 75 atm., the pressure·volume product (10.63 L·atm.) is divided by the pressure (75 atm.). This yields a number far less than one. Choices C and D are eliminated, because those values better approximate the product of the pressure and the volume at 75 atm., not the volume alone. The correct value is greater than 0.1333 (the value obtained when 10 is divided by 75), because 10.63 divided by 75 is greater than 10 divided by 75. Choice A should be eliminated, because it is too small (less than 0.100, which is 10 divided by 100). The best answer is choice **B**.

6. **Choice B is correct.** A gas is most ideal when there are minimal intermolecular forces between the molecules. This occurs when the gases do not contact one another as frequently. At low pressure, the gases do not collide with one another (or the walls) as often, so they have fewer intermolecular interactions. This makes low pressure more ideal than high pressure. At high temperature, gases have the necessary kinetic energy to overcome the intermolecular forces, so they do not stay in contact for as long a period of time. This makes high temperature more ideal than low temperature. The best choice is **B**, high temperature and low pressure. If you consider a phase diagram, at high temperature and low pressure, the material is in the gas phase, far from the other phases, making it most gas-like.

7.   **Choice C is correct.** In a closed system, the number of particles (moles of gas) cannot change. This means that moles are constant during the process. If the piston is motionless, then the internal gas pressure equals the external pressure. This means that overall, given that the piston starts and finishes at rest, the pressure shows no net change. Only the temperature and volume exhibit a net change. When the temperature of the system is increased, the average kinetic energy of the molecules increases. The number of molecules does not change, so choice A is eliminated. Because the average kinetic energy increases, rather than remains constant, choice B is eliminated. The concentration decreases as the container expands, so the average distance between particles increases, meaning that the mean free path increases. This makes choice **C** true. As the average kinetic energy increases, the average particle speed increases, so momentum (mv) increases. This eliminates choice D. Choice **C** is the best answer.

8.   **Choice D is correct.** Because the container is sealed, the system is closed, so the number of molecules does not change. The container is rigid, so the volume of the system does not change. Because neither the moles of particles nor the volume changes, the concentration does not change, so mean free path cannot change. Mean free path is the microscopic equivalent of concentration. The particles may collide more frequently, but that is because they cover the distance between molecules faster. The molecules on average are the same distance apart. Because mean free path does not change, choice C is eliminated. With greater average kinetic energy (and thus greater temperature), both the collision frequency (based on velocity) and the collision force (based on momentum) increase. This makes choice **D** the best answer. This question addresses both the chemist's and physicist's perspective of gases. The correlation between macroscopic measurements and microscopic ideas of gases are listed below:

Temperature correlates to Average Kinetic Energy (as T increases, KE increases)

Concentration correlates to Mean Free Path (as n/V increases, $d_{\text{mean free path}}$ decreases)

Pressure correlates to Collision Force and Collision Frequency (Pressure increases when collisions increase)

Moles correlates to Molecules (hopefully this relationship is a freebie)

Volume correlates to Container Walls (the container walls dictate the volume of the system)

9.   **Choice C is correct.** As the temperature is decreased, the speeds of the gas particles decrease, so the average speed of the particles in the gas system decreases. This eliminates choices A and B. The important thing to recall here is that the change is considered in terms of the Kelvin temperature scale, not the Celsius scale. The change is only from 293 K to 283 K, and the speed is proportional to square root of T. Because the temperature decrease is only about 3.4%, the speed decrease is even less than 3.4%, so the decrease in particle speed is only slight. Choice **C** is the best answer.

10. **Choice C is correct.** This question is asking for the effect of effusion on the absolute pressure (P) and the relative abundance (X) of component gases. Because both H_2 and D_2 are escaping from the container (due to effusion through the pore), the actual moles of each gas decrease over time. This causes the partial pressure of each gas to decrease as well, which eliminates choices B and D. However, because H_2 is lighter than D_2, H_2 escapes from the container faster than D_2, so the relative amount of D_2 in the system (X_{D_2}) actually increases. This makes choice **C** the best answer.

11. **Choice D is correct.** Under identical conditions, the gases are all at the same temperature, so they have the same average kinetic energy. The equation for kinetic energy is K.E. = $\frac{1}{2}mv^2$. This means that if two particles have different masses, they must have different average speeds. Because speed, v, is squared in the kinetic energy relationship, it varies inversely with the square root of the mass. In other words, if one particle is four times as massive as another, it has half the average speed of the lighter particle. Momentum is the product of mass and velocity, so particles with greater mass have greater momentum. This means that the gas with the greatest particle momentum is the heaviest gas. Sulfur dioxide is the heaviest gas of the choices, so choice **D** is the best answer.

12. **Choice A is correct.** Collision frequency affects the pressure. The number of molecules affects the moles. According to the ideal gas equation, PV = nRT, moles and pressure are directly proportional, if all other conditions are held constant. The relationship of pressure and moles is linear, so collision frequency with the walls as a function of the number of particles should also be linear. Twice as many particles results in twice as many collisions. The best answer is choice **A**.

13. **Choice D is correct.** According to the kinetic molecular theory of gases, particles exert no force on one another. If there are no intermolecular forces, the particles cannot be held together, so they can never form a solid or a liquid. This results in a boiling point that is extremely small, not infinitely large. Choice A is eliminated. According to the kinetic molecular theory of gases, particles have a negligible volume, whether they are atoms or molecules. This means that no matter what the particles may be on the microscopic level, they all behave the same. Choice B is eliminated. When the temperature doubles, the average kinetic energy of the particles doubles. The mass of the particles remains the same, so a change in velocity is attributable to the change in kinetic energy. However, because the equation is K.E. = $\frac{1}{2}mv^2$, the velocity doesn't double when the temperature doubles; the velocity increases by square root of two. This eliminates choice C. The pressure, according to the kinetic theory of gases, is attributed to collisions with the walls of the container. If the shape of the container changes, as long as the volume is the same, there is the same density. This results in the same number of collisions per unit area against the walls, so choice **D** is valid.

14. **Choice D is correct.** A gas has no definite volume, because its particles are in contact with one another only briefly during collisions. A liquid has a definite volume, because its particles are always in contact with one another, eliminating choices A and B. Because particles in a gas do not remain in constant contact with one another, gases are more compressible and less dense than liquids. In other words, the particles of a gas can be pushed closer together, while particles in a liquid are already touching, so they are hard to push closer together. Because gases are less dense than liquids, objects in gases are less buoyant (due to the lower density of the medium). This makes choice **D** invalid, so choice **D** is the best answer.

Passage III   (Questions 15 - 22)   Submerged Ball Experiment

15. **Choice A is correct.** From Table 1, it can be seen that the greatest change in volume takes place during the first five feet of descent. This is attributed to the inverse relationship between pressure and volume. The graph of volume as a function of pressure shown below, demonstrates that as the pressure increases in uniform increments, the volume changes by a smaller increment each time.

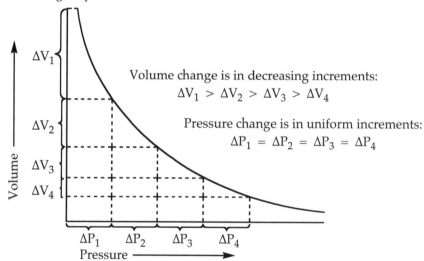

The greatest volume change is observed at relatively low pressures, because the percent change in pressure caused by an incremental increase in pressure is greatest at low pressures. This trend would be observed in data for the first seven feet of descent into water, also resulting in the greatest volume change of any increment of seven feet of the descent. The best answer is therefore choice **A**. This same phenomenon explains the pain in your ears you may have experienced, if you ever descended into the deep end of a swimming pool.

16. **Choice D is correct.** This question is asking for the point at which the ball used in the experiment experiences no net force (where the buoyant force equals the weight). At this point, the density of the ball must equal the density of the surrounding water. The ball is initially 50% submerged, so the density of the ball is initially 50% that of the surrounding water. This means that the density of the ball must double to reach a point where it is no longer buoyant. The mass of the ball is not changing as it descends, so any increase in the density of the ball must result from a decrease in the volume of the ball. The volume must decrease to half of its original value (36.0 L at the surface), in order to have a density equal to that of the surrounding water, so we are looking for the depth where the ball has a volume of 18.00 L. From Table 1, the volume of the ball equals 18.0 liters at a depth of somewhere around 32 feet. This makes choice **D** the best answer.

17. **Choice C is correct.** Fresh water is less dense than salt water, which causes the ball to be less buoyant in fresh water, although that is not the focus of this question. Because salt water is more dense than fresh water, choices A and B are eliminated. A greater volume of the ball would initially be submerged in fresh water. However, as the ball is submerged below the surface, the pressure exerted by the less massive fresh water is less than the pressure exerted by the more massive salt water. The greater the pressure, the more the volume decreases, so salt water reduces the volume of the ball more than fresh water. This means that the change in volume of the ball is greater when submerged in salt water than in fresh water, making choice C correct.

18. **Choice D is correct.** If the ball is initially only 25% submerged, then the density of the ball is 25% that of water. To cease to be buoyant in the water, the density of the ball must equal that of the surrounding water. This means that the density of the ball must increase by a factor of four. The mass of the ball is not changing, so the increase in density must result from a decreasing volume. The volume must decrease to 25% of its original value (at the surface), in order to have a density equal to that of the surrounding water. The pressure must therefore be four times its initial value (at the surface). The pressure is one atmosphere at the surface, so the ball must be submerged to a depth where the pressure is 4 atmospheres (3 atmospheres of which are due to the water). The passage says that 32.6 feet of water exerts one atmosphere of pressure, so to have 3 atmosphere of water pressure a depth of 97.8 (3×32.6) feet is required. This makes choice D correct.

19. **Choice D is correct.** Because the ball that is initially 60% submerged is denser than the ball in the experiment, it need not be submerged to as great a depth to have a density equal to that of the surrounding water. The greater density can be inferred from the greater submerged volume. This makes choice D the correct answer.

20. **Choice D is correct.** According to the ideal gas law, $PV = nRT$, the volume of the ball is directly affected by changes in the pressure (Boyle's law), the moles of gas (Avogadro's law), and the temperature of the container (Charles's law). The magnetic field strength should have no direct effect on the volume, as long as the metal ring on the ball is attached at the greatest circumference of the ball. The best (but not perfect) answer is choice D. If the magnetic ring were attached at a point other than the circumference, the ball could elongate due to the force, and thus the volume would change with the asymmetric deformation (elongation) of the ball.

21. **Choice A is correct.** If salt is added to the water, the density of the solution increases, thus making the ball more buoyant in the solution. If the ball became more buoyant, more of the ball would rise above the surface of the water, resulting in less of the volume of the ball being submerged. This eliminates both choice C and choice D. Because the ball is more buoyant, a stronger applied force is necessary to overcome the increased buoyant force, so the B field (magnetic field) must be increased. Pick A.

22. **Choice C is correct.** The compressibility of a gas is greatest when the particles are farthest apart from one another. This is true when the mean free path is largest. To maximize the mean free path, the concentration must be low, which equates to a low number of moles and a large volume. This makes choice C the best answer.

Passage IV (Questions 23 - 28)	Charles's Law

23. **Choice C is correct.** This is answered by following the trend in the data. Table 1 shows that volume increases by 5.3 every ten degrees, so at 150°C, the volume should be 15.9 greater than 208.3π cm^3, the volume at 120°C. This makes the volume approximately 224.2π cm^3, so that choice C is the best answer.

24. **Choice C is correct.** The bulb temperature increases from 7°C to 27 °C, so the bulb expands. This eliminates choice A. Three answer choices remain, making a calculation necessary. The question can be solved intuitively in the following manner. Before calculating, be sure to convert from Celsius into Kelvin. If you fail to do this, you will incorrectly choose answer choice D.

$$V_f = \frac{T_?}{T_?}V_i \text{, where } V_f > V_i \therefore V_f = \frac{300}{280} \times 7.0\,L = \frac{15}{14} \times 7.0\,L = \frac{15}{2}L = 7.50\,L$$

The key on these types of questions is to plug the numbers into the equation in such a manner that the value is reasonable (greater or less than the original value). Knowing that the volume increases with temperature implies that the final volume is greater than 7.0, so the temperature ratio must be greater than 1.0. Choice C is a terrific answer in a situation such as this.

25. **Choice D is correct.** As you drive, your car tire heats up due to friction from contact with the road surface. This eliminates choices A and B. The volume of the tire stays roughly constant, so the only significant change caused by the increasing temperature involves pressure. As the temperature of a gas at constant volume increases, the pressure must increase, according to the ideal gas law. This makes choice D the best answer.

26. **Choice D is correct.** This is a case of memorization. Charles's law equates changes in volume to changes in temperature, at constant pressure. This eliminates all of the choices except **D**. As temperature increases, the volume increases according to both Charles's law and the idea gas law. Choice **D** is the best answer.

27. **Choice B is correct.** According to the trend in the data, the volume at -15°C should be about 13.3π less than the volume at 10°C. This means that we expect the volume to be 136.7π cm^3 at -15°C. Choice A is eliminated, because there is no reason for the ideality suddenly to deviate that much. The size of the particles does not change with temperature, so choice D should be eliminated. The best explanation for the drastic drop in volume is condensation of the gas. A liquid occupies less volume than a gas. At -15°C, the compound is a liquid, so its boiling point is greater than -15°C. At 10°C it is a gas. This means that the boiling point is slightly greater than -15°C. The best answer is choice **B**.

28. **Choice C is correct.** The partial pressure due to nitrogen is found by subtracting the partial pressures of water and oxygen from the total pressure, 762 torr. The partial pressure due to oxygen is 20.9% of 762 torr. This value is just over 20% of 760, which is 152 torr (the exact value is 159.3 torr). The partial pressure of nitrogen is 762 minus the sum of 22.1 and a little more than 152. This leads to a value in the high 500s, so choice **C** is the best answer. The exact answer is found as follows:

$$P_{total} = P_{H_2O} + P_{O_2} + P_{N_2}$$

$$762 = 22.1 + 159.3 + P_{N_2}$$

$$P_{N_2} = 762 - 181.4 = 580.6 \text{ torr}$$

Passage V (Questions 29 - 35) Boyle's Law

29. **Choice C is correct.** The volume of a gas increases with temperature, so the volume of 1.000 gram of oxygen gas at room temperature is greater than the volume of 1.000 gram of oxygen gas at 0°C. The volume of 1.000 gram of oxygen gas at room temperature is less than the volume of 1.000 gram of oxygen gas at 59°C, because room temperature is less than 59°C. This means that the volume of 1.000 gram of oxygen gas at room temperature is between 1.42 liters and 1.71 liters. Pick choice **C**.

30. **Choice A is correct.** If a liquid less dense than mercury were chosen, then the mass of the liquid (and thus the force exerted by the liquid) would be less in the right side of the column as compared to the mass and force associated with mercury. This results in lower pressure being applied to the gas in the left side of the column, so the gas in the left side of the manometer would be compressed less, and the height measured would be greater than the value obtained using mercury. In layman's terms, the less dense liquid 'squishes' the gas less than mercury. Pick choice **A**.

31. **Choice A is correct.** Because molecules are larger than atoms, they are less compressible than atoms. In other words, as you compress molecules, they interact (collide and repel) more than atoms interact, so molecules cannot be compressed as easily as atoms. This means that the volume of a molecular gas does not decrease as much as it does for argon gas when a pressure of equal magnitude is applied to both systems. This means that the volume of the molecular gas is greater than the volume of the argon gas. The radius of the tube is uniform, so for the volume to be greater, the height must be greater. The heights when using a molecular gas are greater than 50 mm in the second manometer and greater than 33 mm in the third manometer. This is best described in choice **A**. Choices B and C should have been eliminated based on trend recognition. If the value is greater than 50 mm after the first addition, it must be greater than 33 mm after the second addition. Likewise, if the value is less than 50 mm after the first addition, it must be less than 33 mm after the second addition.

32. **Choice C is correct.** When the pressure of the system is increased from 0.5 atm. to 1.0 atm., the volume of the system is reduced to half of its original value. When the temperature increases from 25°C to 50°C, it has actually increased from 298 K to 323 K, so the volume of the system increases, but it won't double. This means that the overall effect is that the volume decreases, because the effect of pressure is more significant than the effect of temperature on the system. The best answer is therefore choice **C**.

33. **Choice C is correct.** According to the table, the volume of 1.000 gram of oxygen gas at 0°C and 1.00 atm. pressure is 0.7095 liters. If the mass were doubled from 1.000 gram to 2.000 grams, then the moles would also double, so the volume should likewise double. The volume would be 1.4190 liters, which is close enough to 1.42 to make choice **C** a safe choice.

34. Choice C is correct. According to both the passage and the middle of the three manometers, a difference in column heights of 76 cm is indicative of a pressure difference of 1.00 atm. This means that when 1.00 atm. of pressure is applied to an open column of mercury, it will rise 76 cm. The best answer is choice **C**.

35. Choice A is correct. The greatest change in volume is experienced when the first aliquot of mercury is added. As more and more mercury is added, the change in the total mass of mercury is less (percentage-wise), so the change in volume is less each time. This trend can be observed when comparing the difference between the first and second manometers (5.0 cm) and between the second and third manometers (1.7 cm). This change in compressibility is attributed to the fact that as the gas is compressed, the particles get closer together (more dense), so there is less room to compress them further. The best answer is choice **A**. Choices C and D should be eliminated, because the density of mercury does not change with addition of more mercury. The densities of liquids and solids are most significantly affected by temperature, not by pressure.

Passage VI (Questions 36 - 43)	Lung Function

36. Choice C is correct. The operations of the lung depends on the expansion of the thoracic cavity (defined as the region above the abdomen inside of the rib cage) and contraction of the diaphragm, which result in an increase in the volume of the lung. This reduces the internal pressure (pressure within the lung). This demonstrates Boyle's law, which states that pressure and volume are inversely proportional under isothermal conditions. Choice **C** is best. Archimedes' principle has to do with buoyancy, which plays no role in lung expansion. Bernoulli's principle deals with the flow rate of a fluid (like air), pressure differences, and the radius of a tube. While it is true that air is flowing within a lung, and Bernoulli's law may be applied to explain air flow phenomenon, the lung does not operate because of Bernoulli's principle. Charles's law states that volume and temperature are directly proportional under isobaric conditions. The lung is thermoregulated, so a temperature change cannot be responsible for the success or failure of its operation.

37. Choice B is correct. During expiration, the lung contracts, causing a decrease in volume and therefore an increase in internal pressure. This means that internal pressure is greater than external pressure (referred to as a positive pressure according to physiologists), which accounts for air flow out of the lung. This eliminates choice A and makes choice **B** the best answer. During expiration, the thoracic cavity and lung are relaxing back to their normal (smaller) size. Although they are shrinking (their volume is decreasing), they are still larger than their normal resting state, so choices C and D are eliminated.

38. Choice B is correct. At high altitudes, the gas is less concentrated (due to the lower atmospheric pressure). At low altitudes, the gas is more concentrated (due to the higher atmospheric pressure). As temperature decreases, gases become denser (and thus more concentrated). This means that at a low altitude and low temperature, there will be more of all gases, oxygen included. But each gas increases by the same proportionate amount, so as far as relative amounts are concerned, there is the same percentage of all gases. This means that oxygen has the same mole fraction, but a higher partial pressure than standard conditions. This makes choice **B** the best answer.

39. Choice B is correct. The tidal volume is the volume of air entering or leaving during a normal breath, while the total lung volume includes residual air, dead space, and tidal volume. This means that lung volume must always be greater than tidal volume. This makes Statement I invalid. Air flows out from the lung during expiration, so the pressure inside the lung must be greater than the external pressure. Air flow is from higher pressure to lower pressure. Air flow gradually lessens until it stops, once the internal pressure and external pressures are equal. This makes Statement II valid. Expiration occurs to displace carbon dioxide, so it must have a greater mole fraction of carbon dioxide than normal air (the air that is inspired). This makes Statement III invalid and makes choice **B** the best answer.

40. Choice C is correct. When the diaphragm contracts, the lung is pulled downward, which causes it to expand. The expansion of the thoracic cavity also plays a role in the expansion of the lung. Because the lung expands, its volume becomes greater than it is at rest, which makes choice C an invalid statement. The question asks for what is NOT true, so choice **C** is the best answer. Upon expansion, lung volume increases and internal pressure decreases, so the internal pressure (the pressure inside the lung) must be less than external pressure. Choice A is valid, because the internal pressure is less than the external pressure (which ultimately causes air to flow into the lung). Under these conditions, the lung is referred to as having subatmospheric pressure (which some physiologists refer to as negative pressure). Choice B is valid, because all gas concentrations, including carbon dioxide, decrease as the lung expands. This is because the moles of carbon dioxide gas remain constant while the volume increases. Choice **C** is invalid, and thus the best choice, because lung volume increases as the diaphragm contracts. Lung temperature is around 37°C and does not vary drastically as the lung expands. This means that air temperature is relatively constant, making choice D valid.

41. **Choice C is correct.** According to the laws of fluid dynamics, gas flows from a region of higher pressure to a region of lower pressure. This is true of any fluid that experiences a pressure difference across its surface. Inspiration results from internal pressure being less than external pressure, so choices A and B are eliminated. During inspiration, the volume increases from 1200 mL to 1600 mL, which results in a value that is 1.33 times greater than its original value. Because $PV = k$ at constant temperature, the pressure must decrease to 0.75 its original value, assuming that temperature and moles of gas are constant. Starting at $P_{initial}$ and finishing at 0.75 $P_{initial}$ is a 25% decrease in pressure, so choice **C** is the best answer.

42. **Choice A is correct.** A scuba diver underwater exists in an environment of high external pressure. When the thoracic cavity expands, because it is working against a much greater external pressure, more moles of air are needed to fill the lung than are needed on land. Choice **A** is valid, because the air is more concentrated, resulting in higher concentrations of all gases, including oxygen. At great enough depths, the gases are mixed with helium, to reduce the mole fraction of oxygen, helping the diver to avoid breathing excessive amounts of oxygen. Too much intake of oxygen can result in oxygen poisoning. Underwater, because of the greater external pressure, air is significantly denser (more concentrated). Consequently, the viscosity is much greater than it is at sea level and it deviates from ideal gas behavior. This eliminates choices B and C. Because all gases are more concentrated underwater, there are more moles of CO_2 throughout the lung, including the anatomical dead space, eliminating choice D.

43. **Choice D is correct.** During a normal breath, air flow is driven by pressure differences between the external environment and the internal pressure within the lung. At the very start of a breath, there is no air flow. The air does not flow until a pressure difference is created. So initially, air flow increases from zero to some value at the start of a normal breath. However, because the system is open, a large pressure difference never develops. Air flows into the lung while it is still expanding, so the pressure difference is relatively constant during the middle of the breath. This causes the flow rate to be relatively constant during the middle of a breath. At the end of a breath, once the lung stops expanding, the air flow gradually slows and comes to rest. This means that during a normal inspiration, air flow rate goes from zero, to some positive value, and then back to zero. This describes a sinusoidal function. Choice **D** is the best, albeit not a flawless, answer.

Passage VII (Questions 44 - 50)   **Isotopic Enrichment of Uranium**

44. **Choice A is correct.** The collision frequency of the gas particles depends on the concentration of the molecules in the container and the temperature of the system, not on the diameter of the molecules. This eliminates choices B and D. The greater the diameter of the molecule, the harder it is for the molecule to fit through the pore in the wall of the container. For instance, golf balls can easily pass through the circumference of a basketball rim, but basketballs cannot pass through the circumference of a golf hole. This makes choice **A** the best answer. You may recall that this is the principle behind the operation of molecular sieves.

45. **Choice C is correct.** The extra neutrons do not significantly affect the reactivity of an atom, because the orbiting electrons are responsible for the reactivity. The neutrons are in the nucleus, so they have little to no effect on reactivity. Only when the molecular velocity is involved do the isotopes make a difference. This holds true for all isotopes except hydrogen, deuterium, and tritium. There is an isotope effect that correlates to the different bond lengths associated with bonds to hydrogen, deuterium, or tritium. This is not important in this question, however. Pick choice **C**.

46. **Choice C is correct.** At the same average kinetic energy (same temperature), velocity of a particle is inversely proportional to the square root of its mass. To travel twice as fast as uranium hexafluoride, a molecule must be four times lighter than uranium hexafluoride. The mass of the uranium hexafluoride compound is roughly 350 grams per mole, so the correct answer must be a molecule with a mass just under 90 grams per mole. Sulfur dioxide has a mass of 64 grams per mole, so choice A is too light, and thus eliminated. Sulfur trioxide has a mass of 80 grams per mole, so choice B is too light, and thus eliminated. Phosphorus trifluoride has a mass of 88 grams per mole, so choice **C** is the best so far. Xenon has a mass of 131.3 grams per mole, so choice D is too heavy, and thus eliminated. The best answer is therefore choice **C**.

47. **Choice D is correct.** The size of the molecule affects its ability to escape through a pore in the wall of the container. The temperature of a gas affects the average kinetic energy of the system. The average kinetic energy of the system in turn affects the speed of the gas molecules, so the temperature affects the effusion rate of a gas. As mentioned in the passage, isotopes have different masses, and therefore different effusion rates. The concentration of a species outside of a container affects the backflow of the gas into the container, but it does not affect the effusion rate. Backflow affects the net flow of gas, which is known as diffusion, not effusion. The best choice is answer **D**.

48. **Choice C is correct.** The mass of the uranium isotope is 235 amu, and the mass of the uranium hexafluoride compound is given as 349. The mass percent is thus 235 divided by 349. This is a little less than 235 divided by 350, which is equal to 47 divided by 70. 47 divided by 70 is less than 49 divided by 70, but more than 42 divided by 70. This means that the answer is between 60 and 70 percent, making choice **C** correct.

$$\frac{235}{349} \cong \frac{235}{350} = \frac{47}{70} \Rightarrow 70\% = \frac{49}{70} > \frac{47}{70} > \frac{42}{70} = 60\%$$

49. **Choice D is correct.** Had chlorine been used instead of fluorine, then the mass of the uranium hexahalide compounds would have been greater. The greater the mass of the two isotopic compounds, the lower the ratio of the masses of the two isotopic compounds. The less the relative difference in masses, the less the difference in effusion rates, and therefore the harder it would be to separate the isotopic compounds from one another. More filtering would be required with the chlorine compounds than the fluorine compounds, making choice **D** correct.

The mass of $^{235}UF_6$ is 349 grams per mole, and the mass of $^{238}UF_6$ is 352 grams per mole. The mass of $^{235}UCl_6$ is 235 + 6(35.5) = 235 + 213 = 448 grams per mole. The mass of $^{238}UCl_6$ is 238 + 6(35.5) = 238 + 213 = 451 grams per mole. The difference in relative effusion rates is greater for the fluorine compounds than for the chlorine compounds, because $\sqrt{\frac{352}{349}} > \sqrt{\frac{451}{448}}$. In addition, chlorine has two major isotopes while fluorine has only one major isotope. The isotopic impurity associated with two majors isotopes chlorine will affect the distribution, making it harder to isolate the uranium isotopes. The UCl_6 species can have a mass anywhere in the range of 445 for $^{235}U^{35}Cl_6$ to 460 for $^{238}U^{37}Cl_6$.

50. **Choice D is correct.** It would be hardest to separate molecules with the same effusion rate. To have the same effusion rate, the molecules must have the same molecular mass. For choice A, O_2 has a mass of 32, while N_2 has a mass of 28. Choice A is thus eliminated. For choice B, H_2 has a mass of 2, while Ne has a mass of 20. Choice B is thus eliminated. For choice C, CO_2 has a mass of 44, while SO_2 has a mass of 64. Choice C is thus eliminated. For choice **D**, CO has a mass of 28 and C_2H_4 has a mass of 28, so they both have the same molecular velocity and thus the same effusion rate. They do not separate by this successive effusion technique. Choice **D** is the best answer. It should be noted that of the choices, it would be easiest to separate hydrogen gas (H_2) from neon (Ne) because of the large difference in their masses. CO could be separated from C_2H_4 by using molecular sieves, which distinguish compounds by molecular size.

Passage VIII (Questions 51 - 57)   Air Bag

51. **Choice B is correct.** In Reaction I, two liquids and three gases are formed from two solid reactants. This represents a large increase in entropy, so choices C and D are eliminated. Reaction II is employed to generate the heat that is necessary for Reaction I to proceed. The generation of heat implies that the reaction (Reaction II) must be exothermic. The best answer is therefore choice **B**.

52. **Choice D is correct.** As any gas cools (whether it be nitrogen at 350°C or any other gas), the pressure of the system and the total kinetic energy of the system and the average kinetic energy of the gas particles decrease. The temperature is a measure of the average (and therefore total) kinetic energy of the system, so a lower temperature is indicative of decreased kinetic energy for the system. The best answer is therefore choice **D**.

53. **Choice A is correct.** The key to this question is using the *Kelvin* temperature scale. Because average speed (the root mean square speed) is directly proportional to the square root of the temperature, an increase in temperature from 298 K (25°C) to 398 K (125°C) increases the average speed of the gas by a factor of roughly $\sqrt{1.33}$. This eliminates all of the answer choices except choice **A**, because 100 x $\sqrt{1.33}$ < 133 < 224 < 500. The exact mathematical solution for the problem is as follows:

$$\frac{v_{125}}{v_{25}} = \sqrt{\frac{\frac{3k(398)}{m}}{\frac{3k(298)}{m}}} = \sqrt{\frac{398}{298}} = \sqrt{1.32}$$

$$\frac{v_{125}}{100} = \sqrt{1.32} \text{ so } v_{125} = 100\sqrt{1.32} < 133$$

Because the speed is less than 133 m/s, choices B, C, and D are incorrect (too large), making choice **A** the best answer. Be sure that all of the temperature values that you use are in terms of kelvins. False answer choices on questions like this one may take advantage of the notion that you will forget to convert degrees Celsius into kelvins.

54. **Choice C is correct.** If the bag fills at a rate of 100 moles/sec and the total inflation time is 0.01 seconds (10 milliseconds), then one mole of gas has filled the bag in that period of time (100 moles/sec x 0.01 seconds = 1 mole). At 31°C, one mole of gas occupies 25 liters, as stated in the question. Had the question not stated that fact, it would have been possible to compare the volume of a gas at 0°C to the volume at 31°C. At STP (0°C and 1 atm.), one mole of gas occupies 22.4 liters. At 31°C, the temperature has increased on the Kelvin scale only slightly from 0°C (from 273 K to 304 K). The volume therefore increases only slightly above 22.4 liters. The only answer that is in the range of "slightly above 22.4" is choice **C**, your best answer.

55. **Choice A is correct.** The lighter the molecular mass of a gas, the greater the average speed of the gas at a given temperature. The greater the average speed of the gas, the faster the rate at which the gas effuses from the pores within the container's walls. The ranking of the relative effusion rates follows the trend lighter is faster than heavier. The best choice is He (4 g/mole) > N_2 (28 g/mole) > Ar (40 g/mole), making choice **A** the best choice. This assumes there are equal portions of the three gases within the container.

56. **Choice B is correct.** At STP, the total pressure of the system is 760 torr. The pressure due to carbon dioxide (CO_2) is the mole fraction of carbon dioxide (C_{CO_2}) times the total pressure of the system (P_{total}). The mole fraction of carbon dioxide can be found by dividing the moles of carbon dioxide by the total moles of the system. This is done as follows:

$$\frac{\frac{50}{44}}{\left(\frac{50}{44} + \frac{50}{28}\right)} < \frac{\frac{50}{44}}{\left(\frac{50}{44} + \frac{50}{44}\right)} = \frac{1}{2}$$

The mole fraction of CO_2 is less than one-half, which implies that less than half of the moles of gas are CO_2. This means that the partial pressure due to CO_2 is less than half of the total pressure. The partial pressure of CO_2 is less then 380 torr, which eliminates choices C and D. Choice A is considerably too small. For choice A to be true, the mole fraction of CO_2 would have to be less than 0.033. The mole fraction of CO_2 is not that small. The best answer is therefore choice **B**. You should do all of your calculations like this, zeroing in on the best answer without spending time finding an exact answer. Remember, you do not get points on the MCAT for showing your work!

57. **Choice B is correct.** Because neon is lighter than argon, neon has a greater average speed than argon. The relative average speeds of the gases are inversely proportional to the relative square roots of their masses. The mass of argon is roughly twice the mass of neon, so the average speed of neon should be roughly $\sqrt{2}$ times faster than the average speed of argon. The best answer is choice **B**, where **B** is for BEST choice on this particular question.

Passage IX   (Questions 58 - 63)   **Effusion Spheres Experiment**

58. **Choice D is correct.** Figure 2 shows the progression of the experiment as it approaches equilibrium. All of the partial pressures are equal at the start of the reaction (before the valve is opened), so the mole fraction for each gas is one-third. Once equilibrium has been established (after the valve was opened), the partial pressure of each gas in region I has dropped to about one-fourth of its original value, but all three gases have the same partial pressure once again. This means that at equilibrium, the mole fraction for each gas is still one-third. This eliminates choices A and B. The mole fraction doesn't change, but the actual moles of each gas do. The loss of moles of gas from Region I causes the drop in total pressure. All of the gases show a net movement from Region I to Region II, so the moles of gas in Region I decrease, while the moles of gas in Region II increase. But once at equilibrium, all gases have the same partial pressure, which eliminates choice C and makes choice **D** the best answer.

59. **Choice C is correct.** Helium is the lightest of the three gases in the mixture, so it travels the fastest. This means that initially, helium effuses from Region I into Region II faster than argon and nitrogen. As a result, prior to equilibrium, Region II is richest in helium and poorest in argon (the slowest gas). However, once helium has equilibrated between the two regions, argon continues to exchange, until it too reaches equilibrium. Once at equilibrium, the rate of effusion (movement from Region I to Region II) equals the rate of infusion (movement from Region II to Region I). The overall change from initial conditions to equilibrium is that the total volume of the system has increased, causing the total pressure of the system to decrease and the partial pressures of all gases to decrease equally. The mole fractions at equilibrium, however, are equal for all of the gases at any point in the system, Region I or Region II. Because the total pressure is uniform and the mole fractions are equal, the partial pressure of each gas is equal at equilibrium. Choice **C** is your answer.

60. **Choice D is correct.** Once a gas system is at equilibrium, the pressure is uniform throughout the container, so the pressure in Region II is equal to the pressure in Region I. Region II has three times the volume of Region I, but at equilibrium it also has three times the moles of gas. The result is that the mole fraction and the partial pressure of any component gases are equal in each region, once equilibrium is established. This makes statement I invalid. The system is initial charged with equal moles of all three gases, so the mole fraction of helium and the mole fraction of argon are both one-third at the start of the experiment. Once equilibrium is established, the gases are mixed evenly once again, so despite the total moles in Region I decreasing, the relative amount of each gas is the same. This also means that the relative amount of each gas is the same in Region II. Once at equilibrium, the mole fraction of helium and argon are each one-third, at any point in the system. The mole fraction of helium and the mole fraction of argon are equal, making statement II valid. When the temperature is increased, the average speed of each gas increases. This results in a greater rate of effusion and infusion, although the net flow may not be affected. At the higher temperature, the pressure of the system is greater, so each partial pressure exhibits a proportional increase. The increase is attributed to a greater frequency of collision and increased momentum for particles at higher velocity. However, the moles have not changed, so the mole fractions have not changed. This makes statement III valid. The best answer is choice **D**.

61. **Choice C is correct.** By opening the valve to a greater area, there is more space through which gases may travel from Region I into Region II. The flow rate increases, so effusion rate increases. Choice A is valid. Increasing the temperature of the system increases the average speed of each gas, so they effuse faster, infuse faster, and diffuse faster. This makes choice B valid. Increasing the volume of the system reduces the pressure (number of collisions against the walls and with the pores), which results in less gas traveling from Region I into Region II. A decrease in concentration (caused by an increase in volume) would decrease, not increase, the rate of effusion. Choice **C** is an invalid statement, and thus the best answer. Increasing the partial pressure of a component increases the number of collisions with a pore experienced by that component. An increase in mole fraction (partial pressure) increases the rate of effusion, which makes choice D a valid statement.

62. **Choice A is correct.** Hydrogen, H_2, has a molecular mass of 2 g/mole. Helium, He, has an atomic mass of 4 g/mole; nitrogen, N_2, has a molecular mass of 28 g/mole; and argon, Ar, has an atomic mass of 40.1 g/mole. Because hydrogen is lighter than all of the component gases in the system, it has a greater average speed than all of the other gases. This means that hydrogen effuses faster than the other gases, and reaches equilibrium prior to the other gases. The graph for hydrogen would have a steeper initial drop than helium, nitrogen, or argon. This makes choice **A** the best answer.

63. **Choice C is correct.** Diffusion is the net flow of gas. Initially, there is high pressure in Region I and no pressure in Region II. This means that the net flow of gas is from Region I to Region II. Over time, as pressure decreases in Region I and grows in Region II, the net flow of gas diminishes until it reaches zero once at equilibrium. This means that the rate of diffusion decreases with time until it reaches equilibrium. On a more specific level, it decreases for all three of the component gases. This makes choice **C** the best answer.

Passage X (Questions 64 - 70) **Closed-System Reactions**

64. **Choice B is correct.** The fluid in the right side of the manometer rises when the internal pressure exceeds the external pressure. This will occur when the internal pressure increases or the external pressure decreases. The likelihood of external pressure (environmental pressure) decreasing under controlled conditions is minimal, so the change in mercury height must be due to an increase in the internal pressure of the system. In order for the internal pressure to increase, the volume of gas in the reaction vessel must increase. Only Reaction II produces a gas product, so choice **B** is the correct answer.

65. **Choice A is correct.** The right column of the manometer is higher, because the left side of the manometer is "pushing" the liquid over. This means that the P_{system} is greater than the $P_{external}$. Considering that the external pressure does change during the reaction, the system pressure must have increased as the reaction went to equilibrium. The P_{system} at equilibrium is thus greater than the P_{system} initially. When the stopcock is opened, the system vents this excess pressure by allowing the net flow of gas to be outward. The best answer is choice **A**.

66. **Choice D is correct.** A small change in volume must be stretched out to be made more visible. A less dense manometer fluid increases the observed change in volume. The smaller bore radius in the atmospheric tube (assuming that the inner tube keeps the same bore size) results in the liquid climbing the atmospheric tube of the manometer (the column exposed to the atmosphere) by a greater amount (resulting in an increased height). The greater the change in column heights, the more accurately the difference between the two sides of the manometer can be measured. Pick **D** to get the tingly sensation of correctness.

67. **Choice A is correct.** This middle stopcock is the only port into and out of the system for a gas, and it must remain closed during the experiment for the system to remain closed. It is a valve, so it has no capacity for measuring pressure, meaning that choices B and C can be eliminated. The stopcock is a two-way valve, so choice D is eliminated. The best answer is therefore choice **A**. The pressure must be equal in both sides of the manometer initially to get an accurate reading of the change in pressure during the course of the reaction. Hairline differences between the two columns initially make for errors in the measurement before the reaction. Venting the system initially assures that the heights of the fluids in both sides of the manometer are equal.

68. **Choice A is correct.** Because the bore size is reduced equally in both tubes, the pressure in both tubes remains equal. Because there is no change in pressure difference between the two sides, the height of the columns is the same in each tube. The manometer measures relative pressure difference between the two sides, not absolute pressure. The question asks for the height, however, not the height difference. Because the volume depends on the radius squared, if the radius is cut in half, then the volume is reduced by a factor of four. The amount of mercury has not changed, so the total length of tube filled with mercury must increase by four. The height changes by a value close to four, so the best answer is choice **A**.

69. **Choice A is correct.** A large quantity of gas results in an increased internal pressure, causing the liquid in the left tube to descend and the liquid in the right tube to ascend. The less dense the liquid, the greater the change in heights (and thus the greater the chance for spillover of the manometer fluid). To avoid overflow, a dense liquid, such as mercury (choice **A**), should be used. Less dense manometer fluids are chosen for hairline readings of small pressure differences, where more accuracy is needed. The less dense fluid results in a greater change in height per unit difference in pressure. The greater the change in height, the easier it is to read the manometer, and thus the less significant small errors in the reading will be.

70. **Choice A is correct.** An endothermic reaction results in a cooler solution. The cooler solution contracts, creating a smaller liquid volume and thus a greater air space volume. In addition, the gas is cooled to some extent, depending on the degree of insulation provided by the glass. Either way, the internal pressure decreases. This results in the left column of manometer fluid rising initially. We eliminate choices C and D. Once at 4°C, the aqueous solution begins to expand (water is densest at 4°C). This assumes the behavior of pure water. Assuming that the gas temperature remains equilibrated with the environment, as the solution volume increases, the gas volume decreases, so the internal pressure begins to rise again. The fluid in the left side of the column begins to descend. The best answer is choice **A**.

Passage XI   (Questions 71 - 78)   **Weather-Sampling Balloon**

71. **Choice C is correct.** This question requires rearranging $PV = nRT$, to isolate R. The gas constant never changes (thus the name constant), so we can work from $\frac{P_1V_1}{n_1T_1} = \frac{P_2V_2}{n_2T_2}$, which reduces to $\frac{P_1V_1}{T_1} = \frac{P_2V_2}{T_2}$, given that no gas was added or removed ($n_1 = n_2$). From here, it is a matter of isolating V_2. We can predict that the reduced pressure increases volume and the reduced temperature decreases volume, but this doesn't help much.

$$V_2 = \frac{P_1V_1T_2}{P_2T_1} = \left(\frac{P_1}{P_2}\right)\left(\frac{T_2}{T_1}\right)V_1 = \frac{1\text{ atm.}}{0.667\text{ atm.}} \times \frac{270\text{ K}}{300\text{ K}} \times 24.63\text{ L} = \frac{3}{2} \times \frac{9}{10} \times 24.63\text{ L} = \frac{27}{20} \times 24.63\text{ L}$$

The best answer is choice **C**.

72. **Choice A is correct.** At STP (0°C, 1 atm.), 1 mole of a gas (such as helium) occupies a volume of approximately 22.4 L. The question requires you to find the density (mass per volume) of helium. The mass of 1 mole of helium is $1\text{ mole} \times 4\frac{\text{grams}}{\text{mole}} = 4$ grams He. Density $= \frac{4\text{ g}}{22.4\text{ L}} = 0.18\frac{\text{grams}}{\text{liter}}$. Select **A** for optimal satisfaction.

73. **Choice C is correct.** The center of mass for the balloon lowers as the balloon is filled with helium. This is stated in the passage. This lowering of the center of mass takes place because helium is lighter than air and thus the mass of the balloon is not as great as it is with the helium in it. In any event, the best answer places the center of mass in the basket, where the greatest portion of the mass lies. Because most of the mass is in the lower half, choice B is eliminated. Choices A and D are throwaway answers. The best answer is choice **C**.

74. **Choice B is correct.** The relative rates of effusion of two gases are given by the inverse ratio of the square roots of the masses of the gas particles (Graham's law of effusion): MW of He = 4 g/mole, MW of N_2 = 28 g/mole.

$$\frac{\text{Rate of effusion He}}{\text{Rate of effusion N}_2} = \frac{\sqrt{MW_{N_2}}}{\sqrt{MW_{He}}} = \frac{\sqrt{28}}{\sqrt{4}} = \sqrt{7} \quad \text{where } 3 = \sqrt{9} > \sqrt{7} > \sqrt{4} = 2$$

The effusion rate for helium is $\sqrt{7}$ times faster than for nitrogen, so choice **B** is the best answer.

75. **Choice C is correct.** The buoyancy of the balloon depends on the density of the surrounding air, so maximum density requires that the surrounding air be as dense as possible. This eliminates choices B and D, because they state that the surrounding air is less dense. As air is cooled (temperature decreases), the volume decreases, so the density of the air increases. This means that on a cold day, the surrounding air is densest. This is best described in choice **C**.

76. **Choice A is correct.** The easiest way to do this problem is to recall that $N_2(g)$ is 20% of the balloon. This means the partial pressure of nitrogen is 20% of the total pressure (the equation is: $P_{N_2} = (X_{N_2})(P_{total})$). Twenty percent of 507 is just slightly more than 100 torr, so choice **A** is the best answer.

77. **Choice D is correct.** It is known that molecular mass is mass per moles, which has units of grams per mole. In this problem, we are told that mass is represented by g (grams), so we need only find the reciprocal of moles. The units for n = mole, so the reciprocal of moles has units mole^{-1}, which is what we need in the best answer choice. $n = \dfrac{PV}{RT}$, so $\dfrac{1}{n} = \dfrac{RT}{PV}$, and the formula for molecular mass is $MW = \dfrac{gRT}{PV}$, choice **D**.

78. **Choice B is correct.** From the passage, we know that there is 1.0 mole of gas in the balloon at 27°C and 1 atm. The number of moles does not change with temperature or pressure, so to solve this question, you must determine only what percentage of the 1 mole of gas is due to He. He is 80% of the gas by moles, so $n_{He} = (0.80)(1 \text{ mole}) = 0.8$ moles He. Pick **B** if you crave correctness.

Passage XII (Questions 79 - 86)	Real Gas Equation

79. **Choice D is correct.** If all components start with an identical mole fraction, then after a short time, the component with the greatest molecular mass, and thus the lowest average speed, will be enriched. The correct answer is the heaviest of the molecules. Bromine is heavier than hydrogen, fluorine, and chlorine, so choice **D** is the correct answer.

80. **Choice B is correct.** The b-value for a gas describes its size (deviation from ideal volume). The molecular size of 1,1-dichloroethane is greater than the molecular size of 1,1-difluoroethane, because chlorine atoms are bigger than fluorine atoms. The non-halogen portion of each molecule is equal in size in both molecules, so 1,1-dichloroethane is only slightly greater in molecular size than 1,1-difluoroethane, so choice **B** is correct.

81. **Choice D is correct.** The a-value correlates with attractive intermolecular forces. This eliminates choice A. Nucleophilicity depends on molecular size of a gas and its ability to share electrons with an electrophile. This eliminates choice B. While boiling point depends on intermolecular forces, it also depends on molecular mass, so the a-value and boiling point do not always correlate. This eliminates choice C. As polarity increases, the strength of the intermolecular forces increases, resulting in a greater a-value. Choice **D** is the best answer.

82. **Choice C is correct.** At STP, an ideal gas has a volume of 22.4 liters per mole. At 25°C and 1.00 atm., an ideal gas has a volume of 24.5 liters per mole. While fluoromethane, CH_3F, is not an ideal gas, the correlation in volume between that of an ideal gas and that of fluoromethane is very high. This means that the volume of 1.00 moles of fluoromethane at 25°C and 1.00 atm. is close to 24.5 liters. The best answer is choice **C**. The reduced volume compared to ideal behavior can be attributed to the attractive forces of the CH_3F molecules.

83. **Choice D is correct.** As the pressure exerted on the gas within a piston increases, the volume of the gas decreases, forcing the particles closer together. The reduction in volume makes choice A a valid statement, which eliminates choice A. As the particles get closer together, they become less compressible, eliminating choice B. As the particles get closer together, the mean free path decreases, eliminating choice C. And as the particles get closer together, they become more concentrated, not less concentrated, so choice **D** is an invalid statement, making it the best answer.

84. **Choice A is correct.** Under conditions of identical temperature, concentration, volume, and total pressure, differences between CH_2F_2 and CH_2Br_2 are due to differences in their respective molecular masses. Because CH_2F_2 is lighter than CH_2Br_2, it has a greater average speed and therefore diffuses faster. This makes statement I valid. Because CH_2F_2 is lighter than CH_2Br_2, it has a lower average momentum and therefore exhibits lower collision impulse. This makes statement II invalid. At the same temperature (identical conditions), all gases have the same average kinetic energy. This makes statement III invalid, which makes choice **A** the correct answer.

85. **Choice B is correct.** The greatest a-value is found in the compound that exhibits the strongest intermolecular forces. Choices C and D are nonpolar, so they are eliminated. Fluorine is more electronegative than chlorine, so fluoromethane is more polar than chloromethane, making choice **B** the best answer.

86. **Choice C is correct.** The gas that is closest to an ideal gas has the smallest a-value and b-value. This is true of the gas with the smallest size and the fewest intermolecular forces. Fluorine gas, F_2, is the smallest and the only nonpolar gas of the answer choices. This makes F_2 the closest to ideal of the answer choices, and makes choice **C** the best answer.

Passage XIII (Questions 87 - 93)   Buoyancy and Effusion

87. **Choice A is correct.** For a balloon to float in air, its buoyant force must equal its weight. The buoyant force is proportional the volume of the balloon, so the greatest minimum volume is associated with the balloon system requiring the greatest buoyant force to float. The greatest buoyant force is required with the balloon system of greatest weight (the one filled with a gas of highest density). Ammonia is the heaviest of the choices, so choice **A** is the best answer.

88. **Choice C is correct.** Methane is lighter than nitrous oxide, so methane molecules have a greater average speed than nitrous oxide molecules. This means that the cylinder's spin rate must be increased to be in phase with the passing methane molecules. This eliminates choices A and B. The ratio of the masses of the two gases is 44 to 16, which means that nitrous oxide is 2.75 times heavier than methane. Because relative speed is inversely proportional to the square root of the relative difference in mass, the speed of methane is $\sqrt{2.75}$ times the speed of nitrous oxide. This eliminates choice D and makes choice **C** the best answer.

89. **Choice A is correct.** The buoyant force of a gas-filled object depends on the density of the surrounding medium and the volume of the object. The buoyant force does not depend on the contents of the balloon, although the weight (and thus net force) do depend on the particles in the balloon. The greatest buoyant force belongs to the object with the greatest volume, which makes choice **A** the best answer.

90. **Choice D is correct.** If a larger cylinder is used, then the diameter and circumference are both increased, albeit by the same amount. The gas must travel farther to pass through the cylinder, but the hole in the cylinder must also travel a greater distance around the circumference with each revolution. The two effects cancel out one another, so the spin rate does not need to change if the size of the cylinder increases. Choice **D** is the best answer.

91. **Choice A is correct.** Whether Chamber 2 contains gas or not, the gas from Chamber 1 can effuse into Chamber 2, and then infuse into the cylinder. This means that evacuating Chamber 2 does not limit the ability of a gas to either effuse or infuse. Choices B and C are eliminated. Buoyancy is irrelevant in this experiment, so choice D should be eliminated. In addition, upon its evacuation, the density of the gas in Chamber 2 becomes zero, so there is no buoyant force (no gas) within Chamber 2. Chamber 2 is evacuated to reduce the number of collisions, allowing the gas to travel at a greater speed through the cylinder. Choice **A** is the best answer.

92. **Choice D is correct.** If the temperature of the system increases from 25°C to 100°C, then the speeds of all gases within the system also increase. The increase in temperature is from 298 K to 373 K, so the increase is less than a factor of 2. This eliminates choices A and B. The speed of a gas depends on the square root of the temperature (as measured in kelvins), so the relative speed is equal to $\sqrt{373/298}$, which is roughly $\sqrt{1.25}$. The value of $\sqrt{1.25}$ is less than 1.25, so choice C is eliminated. The best answer is choice **D**.

93. **Choice B is correct.** The relative speeds of gases under identical conditions depend on the relative masses of the compounds. N_2O has a molecular mass of 44 grams per mole, CO has a molecular mass of 28 grams per mole, F_2 has a molecular mass of 38 grams per mole, and Ne has an atomic mass of 20 grams per mole. This means that neon has the greatest velocity, eliminating choices A and C. The next lightest gas is carbon monoxide, the velocity of CO must be second in the sequence. This makes choice **B** the best answer.

Questions 94 - 100   Not Based on a Descriptive Passage

94. **Choice A is correct.** At STP, the total pressure is 760 torr. A system with 32% argon by moles corresponds to a mole fraction of 0.32 for argon. The partial pressure of argon is 0.32(760 torr), which is roughly one third of 760. This is roughly 250 torr, which makes choice **A** the best answer. Choices C and D are all clearly too high.

95. **Choice A is correct.** Intuitively, as the volume of the balloon decreases, the pressure of the gas inside must increase, because the collisions against the walls increase. The pressure started out at 760 torr, so the final pressure should be greater than 760 torr. This eliminates choices C and D. It now becomes a question of determining how much the pressure actually changes. The equation should be set up intuitively. We are looking for the final pressure in torr, so the initial pressure must be multiplied by a ratio of the volumes to get the final pressure: $P_f = {V_?}/{V_?} \cdot P_i$, where f is final, i is initial, and '?' is yet to be determined. We know the pressure must increase, so we can insert the larger volume into the numerator and the smaller volume into the denominator. This equates to $P_f = {1.00\ L}/{0.75\ L} \cdot 760$ torr, which reduces to $4/3 \times 760$ torr, which we can split into $760 + {760}/{3}$. The value for ${760}/{3}$ is greater than 250, so the final pressure is greater than $760 + 250$ which best describes only choice **A**. This may seem like a lot of work on paper, but this should all be done in your head. **Do not write math, think math!** Every time you get a math question, try to do it in your head if possible, writing down very little and only to keep track of intermediate numbers you may need.

96. **Choice C is correct.** The pressure of the air in the balloon decreases from 1.00 atm. to 0.90 atm., and the temperature of the gas decreases from 298 K to 277 K. The decrease in pressure is accompanied by an increase in the volume. The decrease in temperature is accompanied by a decrease in the volume. The change in pressure and change in temperature have opposite effects in this question. This means that the volume should be roughly the same if the magnitudes of both changes are close to one another. Choice A is a fairly extreme drop in volume and choice D is a fairly extreme increase in volume. This allows us to eliminate choices A and D, but we'll need to do math to distinguish between choice B and choice **C**. The math, carried out as follows:

$$\text{Given: } \frac{P_1 V_1}{n_1 T_1} = \frac{P_2 V_2}{n_2 T_2} \text{ w/ } n_{constant} \Rightarrow \frac{P_1 V_1}{T_1} = \frac{P_2 V_2}{T_2}$$

$$V_2 = \left(\frac{P_1}{P_2}\right)\left(\frac{T_2}{T_1}\right) V_1 = \left(\frac{1.00}{0.90}\right)\left(\frac{277}{298}\right) \cdot 67.2\ \text{mL} = \left(\frac{277}{268.2}\right) \cdot 67.2\ \text{mL} > 67.2\ \text{mL}$$

The best answer is choice **C**.

97. **Choice B is correct.** SO_3 has a molecular mass of 80.06 grams per mole and argon has an atomic mass of 39.95 grams per mole. Sulfur trioxide is approximately twice as heavy as argon, so argon atoms should have an average speed that is roughly 1.4 (square root of 2) times greater than the average speed of the SO_3 molecules. This means it takes longer for the SO_3 molecules to effuse out of the balloon than Ar atoms. The exact amount of time is greater by a factor of 1.4. Both choices C and D are less than 23.6 minutes, which is definitely less than 23.6 minutes × 1.4, so they can be eliminated. Choice A is double that of 23.6 minutes, and the effusion time didn't double, so the value must be less than choice A. The best answer is choice **B**. This is a great example where intuition allowed us to eliminate three wrong answers without having to employ much math to find a right answer.

98. **Choice A is correct.** This can be solved without much math if you realize that lighter molecules move faster than heavier ones. Only choice **A** is lighter than water, so it must be the best answer. You can also solve this question outright if you wish. The average speed of a gas can be found by using the equation $v = \sqrt{\frac{3kT}{m}}$. For this problem, the relative rate of one gas to another is being asked for, so 3, k (Boltzmann's constant), and T all can be disregarded (canceled out in the ratio). The ratio of the speeds of the two gases is: $\frac{v_{unknown}}{v_{water}} = \frac{\sqrt{mass_{water}}}{\sqrt{mass_{unknown}}} = 2$. This can be double-checked by making sure that both ratios are greater than 1.0. The relationship can be simplified by squaring both sides of the equation: $\frac{mass_{water}}{mass_{unknown}} = 4$, so $m_{unknown} = \frac{mass_{water}}{4} = \frac{18}{4} = 4.5$ grams per mole. This is close to the molecular mass of He (4.0 grams per mole), so choice **A** is the best answer. Just by looking at the choices given, one can see the other choices have molecular weights that are well over 4.5 grams per mole.

99. **Choice C is correct.** The relative rates of effusion can be determined from the relatives masses of the two gases, according to Equation 6.12. Methane has a molecular mass of 16 grams per mole, while helium has an atomic mass of 4 grams per mole. The relative effusion rate is found as follows:

$$\frac{\text{Effusion Rate}_{Helium}}{\text{Effusion Rate}_{Methane}} = \frac{v_{He}}{v_{CH_4}} = \frac{\sqrt{m_{CH_4}}}{\sqrt{m_{He}}} = \frac{\sqrt{16}}{\sqrt{4}} = \sqrt{4} = 2$$

Because helium is lighter, the rate for helium is greater than the rate for methane (twice as fast, according to the math). Select choice **C** for optimum results in a situation such as this.

100. **Choice D is correct.** The greatest infusion rate is observed with the fastest compound, which corresponds to the lightest compound. This question is in essence asking for the relative molecular masses of the answer choices. Methane is the lightest, so choices A and C are eliminated. Chlorine gas is the heaviest, so choice **D** is correct.

Section VII

Phases
and
Phase Changes

Generic Heating Curve

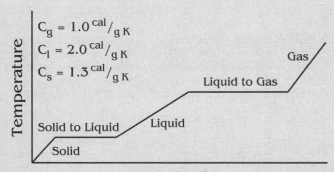

The BERKELEY
R·E·V·I·E·W®
Specializing in MCAT Preparation

Phases Section Goals

① <u>**Know the definitions for a solid and a liquid.**</u>

You must know the differences between a solid and a liquid at the microscopic and macroscopic levels. You must understand lattices, intermolecular forces, and volume. In both liquids and solids, the molecules are in contact with their neighbors, so they have a defined volume.

② <u>**Know the terms and definitions of the phase change processes.**</u>

You must know the terms and conditions for phase change processes. The phase changes include: evaporation, melting, sublimation, condensation, freezing, and deposition. You must also know the terms that describe the conditions under which these processes occur, such as isothermal, isobaric, isochoric, and adiabatic conditions. You must know the energetics associated with each phase change process in terms of free energy, enthalpy, and entropy.

③ <u>**Be able to read a heating curve.**</u>

You must be able to read a heating curve to extract information about enthalpy of fusion, enthalpy of vaporization, and heat capacities for the three phases. You should be able to identify the phase at different points on the heating curve.

④ <u>**Recognize the key points and features of the phase diagram.**</u>

You must know where the solid, liquid, and gas sections of the phase diagram are. You must also be able to identify the triple point, normal boiling point, and the critical point. Be able to identify atypical regions of the diagram, such as the area where the material exists as a supercritical fluid. Be able to recognize the phase diagram of water by focusing on the negative slope of the barrier between the solid and liquid regions of the phase diagram.

⑤ <u>**Understand vapor pressure and boiling point.**</u>

The conversion between liquid and gas occurs over a wide range of temperatures. At the boiling point, the vapor pressure is equal to the atmospheric pressure. At temperatures lower than the boiling point, vapor pressure still exists, but at a value that is lower than atmospheric pressure. The easier it is to vaporize a compound (in terms of lower enthalpy), the greater its vapor pressure.

⑥ <u>**Understand the principle behind Raoult's law.**</u>

Raoult's law describes vapor pressure above a mixture of two or more liquids. According to Raoult's law, in an ideal mixture, the vapor pressure of any given component depends on the mole fraction of that component in the solution and its normal vapor pressure under the system conditions. Vapor pressure increases with temperature and mole fraction.

⑦ <u>**Understand the theory behind distillation.**</u>

Distillation is a purification method you normally consider to be an organic chemistry laboratory technique. On the theoretical level, it is based on the relative vapor pressures of the components and on Raoult's law. The vapor above a solution is richer in the more volatile component than the solution. This difference in relative mole fraction can be exploited by repeatedly evaporating and condensing the mixture. With each cycle, it gets becomes richer in the less volatile component.

⑧ <u>**Understand the colligative properties of matter.**</u>

Colligative properties are properties of a solution that depend on the number of solute particles in the solution, not on the nature of the solute particles. Examples include: freezing point depression, boiling point elevation, osmotic pressure, and conductance. The colligative properties can be exploited to convert salt water into a more ion-free state.

Phases and Phase Changes

The three common phases of matter are solid, liquid, and gas. The fundamental difference between the three phases is how the molecules (or atoms) interact with one another as they move. Solids have the least kinetic energy of the three common phases. Their kinetic energy is in the vibrational and rotational forms. The molecules of a solid do not change their positions. Liquids are more energetic than solids, yet not as energetic as gases. Their kinetic energy is in the translational, vibrational, and rotational forms, although the amount of their kinetic energy is less than that of a gas. The molecules of a liquid do change their positions. Gases have the most kinetic energy of the three common phases, and it exists in the translational, vibrational, and rotational forms. The molecules of a gas rapidly change their positions.

Of more interest than the phases themselves are the phase change processes. Going from a less energetic phase to a more energetic phase is an endothermic process. Changing phases requires changing the environmental conditions acting on a system. Each material has a unique phase diagram that summarizes this information. We shall look at several phase diagrams in this section, noting key points and features of generic and specific phase diagrams. We shall focus on the atypical aspects of phase diagrams. Terminology for both conditions and phase changes will make up much of the phase change portion of this section.

Great amounts of energy can be stored and released via phase change processes. The liquid-gas phase change process converts the energy that drives engines and makes refrigeration possible. It is important to understand that phase changes occur with changes in temperature *or* pressure, not just changes in temperature. The idea of vapor pressure is not a complicated one, but it certainly has complicated applications. The study of vapor pressure includes Raoult's law, the Clausius-Clapyeron equation, and the theoretical perspective on distillation. The largest portion of this section shall address the nuances of the liquid-gas equilibrium.

We shall also address the behavior of solute particles in solution. The addition of solute affects certain physical properties of a solution, including boiling point, freezing point, osmotic pressure, and electrical conductivity (when dealing with aqueous solutions.) These are known as *colligative properties*, and they vary with the concentration of solutes in the solution. Increasing the amount of a soluble material (solute) increases the interactions between molecules in the liquid phase only, not in the gas or solid phase. Ice that is frozen from a solution of salt water is relatively pure, with the occasional trapped ion in its lattice structure. Equally, steam formed from evaporation from a saltwater solution consists of pure water vapor. Purification processes are affected by colligative properties.

The most important features of the phase change section are applications of phase changes. Applications and experiments often make up the bulk of the material from this section that appears on the MCAT. Understanding water as both a pure material and as a solvent is critical. Water has many unique features, due to its extensive hydrogen bonding. Water has the highest density of hydrogen bonding per molecule of any material, which drastically affects its physical properties, such as boiling point, melting point, and solubility.

Phases

Definitions of Solids and Liquids

Solids and liquids are two of the three common phases in which we observe matter. In both cases, molecules are in contact at the microscopic level with one another, which accounts for solids and liquids having a definite volume. The difference between the two phases lies in the ability of their molecules to move. In solids, molecules are in a lattice structure, and they experience vibrational and rotational motion only. The atoms are not displaced, so there is no translational motion. This results in solids having definite shapes on the macroscopic level. In liquids, molecules are free to move, so they experience translational motion, although there is no net motion of the system. The molecules also experience vibrational and rotational motion. The result of translational motion of its component molecules is that liquids have no definite shape on the macroscopic level. Definitions for both a solid and a liquid are listed below:

Solid: A state of matter having both a definite shape and a definite volume. The molecules do not change position, resulting in a fixed structure, whose molecules are in contact with neighboring molecules at all times.

Liquid: A state of matter having a definite volume, but no definite shape. The molecules change position, resulting in continuous random motion, and molecules that remain in contact with neighboring molecules at all times.

Properties of a Solid

Because solids are defined as having both a definite shape and a definite volume, they have dimensions on the macroscopic level. The molecules of a solid are arranged in a fixed lattice structure, on the microscopic level, so they have repeating structural subunits referred to as *unit cells*. The macroscopic shape of a solid object can vary, but the microscopic arrangement (lattice structure) is constant. This is often referred to as the *crystal structure* (or *lattice structure*) of the solid. Lattice structures exist for both elements and compounds. Figure 7-1 shows two lattice structures and unit cells for atomic solids.

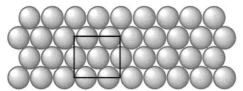
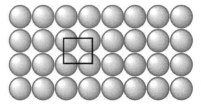

Unit cell is a face centered cubic with four atoms per cell.

Unit cell is a simple cubic with one atom per cell.

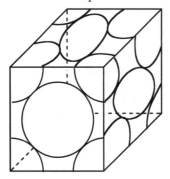
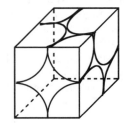

Figure 7-1

The three most common unit cells are the simple cubic with one atom per repeating unit cell, the body-centered cubic with two atoms per repeating unit cell, and the face-centered cubic (which forms the *cubic closest packed* structure) with four atoms per repeating unit cell. Alkali metals often pack to form the simple cubic. Gold and silver pack to form a face-centered cubic.

Solids have density (which is often used as a physical measurement in the identification of an unknown solid). A common procedure for determining the density of a solid is to place the solid into a volumetric container filled with a known liquid. The solid's volume is determined by measuring the displacement volume of the liquid. It is assumed that the displaced volume is due strictly to the volume of the solid. The mass is measured separately, and from this, the density of the solid may be calculated. This technique should not be mistaken for displacement weight, as in buoyancy. If the solid is buoyant in the liquid, then the density of the solid is less than the density of the liquid, and the relative density ratio of the two materials is equal to the percent of the solid that is submerged. It should be intuitive that in an immiscible mixture of a solid and liquid, the less dense material rises to the top. When the solid is less dense than the liquid, the mass of the floating solid is equal to the mass of the liquid occupying the same volume as the submerged portion of the floating solid. These topics are traditionally studied in physics, but the MCAT incorporates physics into general chemistry, so subjects that overlap between the two sciences make for great passage topics.

Example 7.1
Which of the following statements about solids is (are) NOT true?

   I: Solids change molecular structure constantly.

  II: Solids have less kinetic energy than gases and liquids.

 III: Solids have more entropy than gases or liquids.

A. I only
B. III only
C. I and II only
D. I and III only

Solution
Solids have organized lattice structures, so they do not change molecular structure, making statement I an invalid statement. The question is asking for invalid statements, so the correct answer choice must contain I. This eliminates choice B. Because atoms in solids exhibit no translational motion, solids have the least kinetic energy of the three common phases. This makes statement II valid, and eliminates choice C. Because solids form lattice structures, their atoms maintain position, resulting in lower entropy than liquids and gases (where the molecules are free to move and thus change position). This makes statement III invalid. From this, it can be concluded that choice **D** is the best answer.

Properties of a Liquid
Liquids have no definite shape, but they do have a definite volume. Understanding liquids is important in both chemistry and physics. Liquids are classified as fluids, so they are fundamental to all discussions of hydraulics, buoyancy, and the Bernoulli effect. From a chemistry point of view, however, it is more important to know the molecular structure and the solvent properties of liquids. You must consider intermolecular forces such as hydrogen bonding, polar interactions, dipole moments, and van der Waals forces. The strength of these forces is in the same order as just listed in the preceding sentence.

These forces become less significant above the boiling point, because molecules are no longer in contact with one another. Some intermolecular forces affect solubility properties. Figure 7-2 is a schematic representation of a liquid.

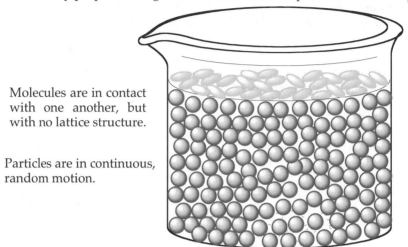

Molecules are in contact with one another, but with no lattice structure.

Particles are in continuous, random motion.

Figure 7-2

Because their molecules are in motion, liquids can flow, which defines them as a fluid. Incidental facts about liquids that you should know are that liquids typically have the highest heat capacity of the three common phases, and liquids are compressible. A liquid's density decreases as the temperature increases (because the volume increases), with the exception of water from 0°C to 4°C. A compound is a liquid at room temperature, if its melting point is less than room temperature and its boiling point is greater than room temperature. A liquid also has physical properties such as *surface tension* and *viscosity*, as defined below.

Surface tension: The resistance of a liquid to an increase in its surface area. It generally increases as the intermolecular forces or molecular mass increase.

Viscosity: The resistance of a liquid to flow. It can also be observed as the resistance to flow by an object through the liquid.

Example 7.2
If a solid object floats on the surface of a liquid in such a manner that sixty percent of the object is submerged, which of the following sets of density values accurately describes the liquid and solid?

A. Liquid: 0.90 grams per mL; solid: 1.50 grams per mL
B. Liquid: 1.25 grams per mL; solid: 0.75 grams per mL
C. Liquid: 1.00 grams per mL; solid: 1.67 grams per mL
D. Liquid: 1.50 grams per mL; solid: 1.00 grams per mL

Solution
For a solid that floats on the liquid, the buoyant force upward offsets the weight (gravitational force) downward. This is because the volume of liquid displaced by the solid is less than the total volume of the solid, so the solid must be less dense than the liquid in which it is immersed. This eliminates choices A and C. According to Archimedes' principle, **for a solid floating in a liquid, the percent of the solid submerged is equal to the density of the solid divided by the density of the liquid**. This means that choice D is eliminated, because the ratio of the solid density to the liquid density is 2/3, which equals 0.67, not 0.60. This would make the solid 67% submerged. The best answer (and only choice remaining) is choice **B**. The ratio of 0.75 to 1.25 is equal to 0.60.

Phase Change Processes

Terminology and Energetics

A phase change process is a physical process, not a chemical process, by which the state of matter changes. In a phase change, the molecules themselves do not change, but the interactions between molecules do change. A phase change process is reversible. For instance, if a solid is converted into a liquid by changing the external conditions, then the liquid can be converted back into a solid upon reestablishing the original conditions. All phase changes involve a change in the enthalpy (heat energy of the system) and entropy (organizational potential energy of the system, considered as randomness of the molecules). Phase changes are either endothermic or exothermic processes, depending on whether the final state is of higher or lower energy than the original state. If a particular phase change is an exothermic process, then the reverse process must be an endothermic process. On the macroscopic level, phase changes result in changes in volume and changes in shape. The six typical phase change processes are listed in Table 7.1 below.

Phase Change	Term	Enthalpy and Entropy	Heat Energetics
Liquid → gas	Vaporization	$\Delta H_{vap} > 0$ and $\Delta S_{vap} > 0$	Endothermic
Gas → liquid	Condensation	$\Delta H_{vap} < 0$ and $\Delta S_{vap} < 0$	Exothermic
Solid → liquid	Melting	$\Delta H_{fus} > 0$ and $\Delta S_{fus} > 0$	Endothermic
Liquid → solid	Freezing	$\Delta H_{fus} < 0$ and $\Delta S_{fus} < 0$	Exothermic
Solid → gas	Sublimation	$\Delta H_{sub} > 0$ and $\Delta S_{sub} > 0$	Endothermic
Gas → solid	Deposition	$\Delta H_{sub} < 0$ and $\Delta S_{sub} < 0$	Exothermic

Table 7.1

As a point of interest, you should know that the relative energetics for the three phase change processes are: $\Delta H_{sublimation} > \Delta H_{vaporization} > \Delta H_{fusion}$ and $\Delta S_{sublimation} > \Delta S_{vaporization} > \Delta S_{fusion}$

Example 7.3

The conversion from a solid to a gas represents what kind of phase change and has what kind of energy change is associated with it?

A. It is known as sublimation, and it is exothermic.
B. It is known as deposition, and it is exothermic.
C. It is known as vaporization, and it is endothermic.
D. It is known as sublimation, and it is endothermic.

Solution

This question focuses on either memorization or your ability to move your eyes up this page slightly to read Table 7.1. (For your exam, you may prefer the memorization route, because if you have Table 7.1 in sight, you are probably cheating.) According to Table 7.1, conversion from solid to gas is sublimation, and the process is endothermic (i.e., because the particles finish at a higher energy level, then energy must have been added to the system.) Choice **D** is the best answer.

Example 7.4

Which of the following statements is NOT true with regard to phase changes starting from the solid phase?

A. Sublimation results in a system with increased entropy.
B. During melting, the lattice structure of solid matter is broken down.
C. Following sublimation, the space between molecules is increased.
D. Following melting, atoms lose their ability to migrate freely.

Solution

Sublimation changes a material from the solid phase into the gas phase. In the solid phase, molecules are held in a rigid lattice structure and are not free to move. Once in the gas phase, the molecules are free to move in any direction until a collision occurs. Because of the increased mobility associated with the gas phase, there is more entropy in the gas phase than the solid phase. This makes choice A a valid statement. During melting, the material transforms from the solid phase into the liquid phase. Any lattice structure that may exist in the solid phase is lost in the liquid phase, as the molecules are free to migrate. This makes choice B a valid statement. Because a gas is less dense than a solid, more free space must exist between the molecules of a gas than the molecules of a solid. In the gas phase, the molecules are independent and exhibit no intermolecular forces, so they are far apart. In the solid phase, the molecules exhibit intermolecular forces, and they are touching one another. This makes choice C a valid statement. In the liquid phase, molecules have the ability to migrate freely through a solution, so when the phase changes from a solid (with no free migration of molecules) to a liquid (which has free migration of molecules), molecules are able to go in any direction through solution. This makes choice **D** an invalid statement, and thus the best answer.

In addition to the phase change terminology, you should know the terms that describe the conditions of a system. There are four terms that describe static system conditions with which you should be familiar. They are listed below:

Isothermal   Conditions where the temperature of the system does not change (sometimes referred to as $T_{constant}$).

Isobaric   Conditions where the pressure of the system does not change (sometimes referred to as $P_{constant}$).

Isochoric   Conditions where the volume of the system does not change (sometimes referred to as $V_{constant}$).

Adiabatic   Conditions where the system is perfectly insulated, so that heat neither enters nor exits the system (referred to as $q_{constant}$).

Isochoric is least likely to be seen, but nonetheless it is a relevant concept. You can often distinguish whether a term is important or not by its familiarity. If it was never mentioned during your course lectures on campus (e.g., words like isochoric and deposition), it is less likely that you will need it memorized for the MCAT. They will likely define it for you. That said, a perfect example is a *supercritical fluid*, which has appeared on several different versions of the MCAT. This is a great example of how the MCAT presents an unfamiliar term to describe an interesting concept, which can be deciphered from its name. Beyond the critical point exists a supercritical fluid. It is supercritical because it exists beyond the critical point, and it is a fluid because it is part gas and part liquid, both of which flow (are amorphous).

Typical Phase Diagrams

A phase diagram is a graph that summarizes the different states of matter for a given compound or element with respect to temperature and pressure. From a phase diagram, you can determine the phase that is most favorable or the interface of phases for a material under a given set of conditions. Reading phase diagrams accurately requires drawing lines from a given point on the diagram to the x-axis and the y-axis. The point where the lines intersect is in the region of the graph for the most favorable phase. Figure 7-3 is a generic phase diagram.

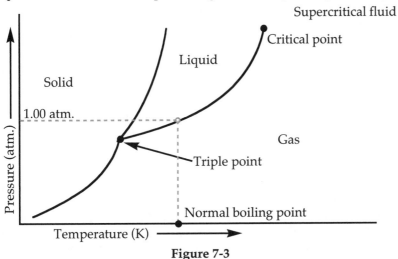

Figure 7-3

The *triple point*, *critical point*, and *normal boiling point* are shown in Figure 7-3. The triple point is where all three phase can coexist simultaneously The critical point is the highest temperature and pressure at which a liquid may be observed. Beyond the critical point, it is impossible to distinguish between a gas and a liquid, so it is referred to as a *supercritical fluid*. The normal boiling point is the temperature at which a material boils when the pressure is 1.00 atm.

Example 7.5

In what phase (or phases) does the material exist at point **e** on the graph below?

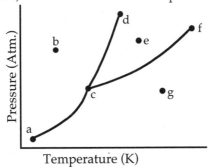

A. Liquid only
B. Liquid with a small amount of solid
C. Liquid with a small amount of gas
D. Liquid with a small amount of vapor

Solution

The middle region of a phase diagram is where the compound exists as a liquid. Evaporation and condensation exist in equilibrium, so liquids exhibit vapor pressure. Choice **D** is the best answer. Choice C looks tempting (because a vapor is a gas), but vapor is the better word. The term *vapor* describes a gas that exists in equilibrium with a liquid at a temperature below the boiling point.

It should be noted that the phase diagram does not show the only phase that is observed under specific conditions, but the most abundant (and stable) phase under those conditions. The most challenging part of phase diagrams is working through the terminology.

Example 7.6

If a compound that exists primarily as a liquid at 39°C and 1.12 atm. is heated at constant pressure, it converts into a gas. Upon cooling the compound back to 39°C and 1.12 atm., the compound remains a gas. Which of the following explanations BEST explains this observation?

A. The boiling point for the compound at 1.12 atm. must be 39°C.
B. The molecules rearranged so that the bonds are different from those in the original compound.
C. The compound must have two liquid phases.
D. The compound was heated beyond its critical temperature and thus cannot become a liquid again.

Solution

A compound can exist in either of two phases when it is at its boiling point (liquid/gas), melting point (solid/liquid), or sublimation point (solid/gas). For the compound to exist as either a liquid or gas at a given temperature and pressure, that temperature must be the boiling point at that pressure. There is no indication that a chemical reaction took place, so choice B is not the best choice. Having two unique liquid phases would not explain the observation, so choice C is eliminated. Even after a compound is heated beyond its critical temperature, it is capable of changing back to its original phase once cooled, so choice D is eliminated. The best answer is choice **A**.

Example 7.7

Which arrow is INCORRECTLY identified below?

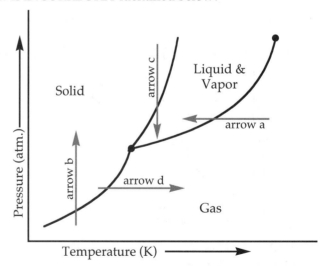

A. Arrow a is isobaric condensation.
B. Arrow b is isothermal deposition.
C. Arrow c is isothermal freezing.
D. Arrow d is isobaric sublimation.

Solution

Isobaric condensation is where the material is cooled at constant pressure from a gas into a liquid. Because pressure is constant, the arrow must be horizontal, which it is. Because it is condensation, the arrow must start in the gas region and finish in the liquid region, which it does. Arrow a is correctly identified, so choice A is eliminated. Isothermal deposition is where the material is compressed at constant temperature from a gas into a solid. Because temperature is constant, the arrow must be vertical, which it is. Because it is deposition, the arrow must start in the gas region and finish in the solid region, which it does. Arrow b is correctly identified, so choice B is eliminated. Isothermal freezing is where the material is compressed at constant temperature from a liquid into a solid. Because temperature is constant, the arrow must be vertical, which it is. Because it is freezing, the arrow must start in the liquid region and finish in the solid region, which it does not. Arrow c is *incorrectly* identified, so choice **C** is the best answer. Isobaric sublimation is where the material is heated at constant pressure from a solid into a gas. Because pressure is constant, the arrow must be horizontal, which it is. Because it is sublimation, the arrow must start in the solid region and finish in the gas region, which it does. Arrow d is correctly identified, so choice D is eliminated.

Atypical Phase Diagrams

The phase diagram for water is different from typical phase diagrams. The difference between the two phase diagrams is the negative slope associated with the line separating liquid from solid. Most compounds can be compressed from a liquid into a solid at constant temperature. The unusual thing about water is that an isothermal increase in pressure compresses the solid (ice) into a liquid (water), resulting in the liquid being denser than the solid. As such, the properties of water are *weird*! Figure 7-4 shows the phase diagram for water and a typical compound.

Phase Diagram for Typical Compound

Phase Diagram for Water (H_2O)

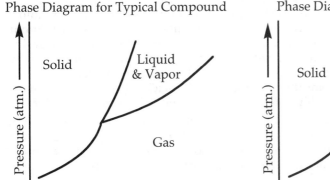
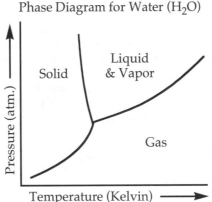

Figure 7-4

Example 7.8
Point **a** on the phase diagram below is which of the following?

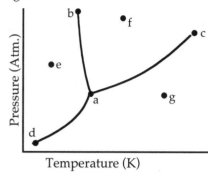

A. The critical point for carbon dioxide
B. The triple point for water
C. The triphasic point for carbon dioxide
D. The plasma point for water

Solution
Point a is where all three phase lines intersect, so it is the triple point. The triple point is defined as the temperature and pressure at which a compound may exist in any or all of the three phases simultaneously. The negative slope of the liquid-solid interface line confirms that the compound is water. The correct answer is choice **B**.

Water Trivia
Random, unrelated facts about water have been tested on the MCAT on more than one occasion. Two key facts about water are that its liquid form is denser than its solid form, and it is densest at 4°C. The solid can be compressed into a liquid under relatively mild conditions. The ramifications of this include our ability to ice skate upon frozen water. The fact that water is densest at 4°C results in the presence of the warmest water being at the bottom of a partially frozen lake (useful information on your next ice fishing trip). Water also has an extremely high boiling point for a compound with such a low molecular mass. Ammonia (NH_3) is of roughly comparable mass, and it has a boiling point of -33.4°C. Methane (CH_4) is also of roughly comparable mass, and it has a boiling point of -162.6°C. This means that for water, hydrogen bonding has a substantially more significant effect on the boiling point than mass or other intermolecular forces. Water has the densest hydrogen bonding per molecule of any compound.

Supercritical Fluids
A supercritical fluid exists when the conditions exceed the critical point. Super-critical fluids take on properties that are a compromise between gases and liquids. Molecules are in free-moving clumps, where the density is greatest at the bottom of the container (like a liquid), but the material fills the entire container (like a gas). Supercritical fluids have a density between that of a liquid and gas. Specific examples of supercritical fluids that are used industrially are carbon dioxide and oxygen. Supercritical fluid carbon dioxide is used as a decaffeinating solvent for coffee. It is a safe solvent for dry cleaning, which makes it a great alternative to the more toxic organic solvents like methylene chloride. Supercritical fluid oxygen chambers are used to completely oxidize materials that do not burn cleanly under standard conditions with oxygen gas.

Heating Curves

To generate a heating curve, a material is heated or cooled at a constant rate under isobaric conditions over a broad temperature range, and the temperature is recorded as a function of the heat added (or removed). A heating curve shows the same features as a horizontal line in a standard phase diagram, but in significantly more detail than a phase diagram. Figure 7-5 shows a typical heating curve, drawn according to convention. As a good practice, redraw graphs with the axes interchanged, so that you recognize non-conventional views.

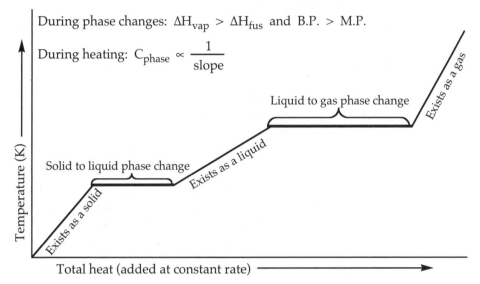

During phase changes: $\Delta H_{vap} > \Delta H_{fus}$ and B.P. > M.P.

During heating: $C_{phase} \propto \dfrac{1}{slope}$

Figure 7-5

Figure 7-5 depicts the overall view of the phase change process at constant pressure from an energy perspective for a generic material. The graph of temperature as a function of heat added shows the phases, the phase changes, and heat capacity of each phase. As labeled, plateaus in the graph represent phase change processes. As a material changes phase, the temperature remains constant, because the energy added to the system is being used to break intermolecular forces, rather than to increase the average kinetic energy of the molecules. The enthalpy of vaporization (represented by the second plateau) is greater in magnitude than the enthalpy of fusion (represented by the first plateau). This is because more energy is necessary to break the intermolecular forces (as observed with the conversion from a liquid into a gas) than is necessary to weaken the intermolecular forces (as observed with the conversion from a solid into a liquid). Perhaps it is more obvious that the boiling point is greater than the melting point, than it is that $\Delta H_{vaporization}$ is greater than ΔH_{fusion}, but both concepts are rooted in the same supporting idea.

Non-horizontal lines represent where the material is being heated without any phase change transpiring. In these regions, the temperature of the material is increasing. This means that the slope of each line correlates with the ratio of temperature change to the heat input. The heat capacity of a material is the heat required to raise one gram of the material by one degree Celsius, so the units of heat capacity (C) are calories per gram·kelvins. The slope of the line in the temperature change regions of a heating curve is temperature change per heat added, which has units of kelvins per calories. The slope of the line is inversely proportional to the heat capacity of the material in that particular phase. This is to say that the flatter the line, the greater the heat capacity.

In Figure 7-5, the slopes for each of the three phases are different, implying that the heat capacities for each of the three phases are different. The heat capacity of the liquid is the greatest of the three phases. This is not unusual, given that liquids can absorb intermolecular vibration energy as well as translational kinetic energy. Solids can only vibrate, and gases can essentially only translate (move in such a way where each molecule's the center of mass is displaced). This is the reasoning behind choosing a liquid as the medium to absorb heat in a heat-exchange system, such as an automobile radiator. Heat-exchange systems are always set so that heat is transferred in a counter-current fashion. This is also seen with ion exchange (a good example is the kidney).

Example 7.9

If melting a solid requires exactly 20 kJ per mole, then which of the following statements is true?

A. Sublimation requires less than 20 kJ per mole.
B. Vaporization requires less than 20 kJ per mole.
C. Freezing releases more than 20 kJ per mole.
D. Condensing releases more than 20 kJ per mole.

Solution

Given that $\Delta H_{sublimation}$ is roughly equal to $\Delta H_{fusion} + \Delta H_{vaporization}$, and that $\Delta H_{vaporization}$ is greater than ΔH_{fusion}, then $\Delta H_{sublimation}$ must be greater than ΔH_{fusion} (which equals 20 kJ per mole). This eliminates choices A and B. Freezing *releases* the same amount of heat that melting absorbs, so choice C is eliminated. Because vaporizing absorbs more heat than melting, condensation releases more heat than freezing. The correct answer is choice **D**.

Liquid-Gas Equilibrium

Vapor Pressure

Above every liquid and solid (although we mostly consider liquids), there is a finite amount of vapor formed when molecules at the surface layer escape. A vapor is composed of gas particles that are in equilibrium with the liquid phase, so they temporarily exist a gas, until they condense back into their more favorable phase. For example, we refer to oxygen as "oxygen gas" at room temperature, because it exists as a gas in its most stable form. On the other hand, we refer to water in the gas phase as "water vapor," because the most favorable form of water at room temperature is a liquid. We refer to steam as "water gas" only when it exists at a temperature above the boiling point of water (100°C). Gaseous water molecules at temperatures lower than 100°C are in a state of equilibrium between evaporation and condensation. The formal definition of vapor pressure above a liquid is:

Force per unit area above the surface of a liquid exerted by molecules formed upon evaporation of the liquid.

The vapor pressure of a liquid is simply the partial pressure exerted by the gas molecules formed by evaporation from the surface of the liquid, when it is in equilibrium with the gas molecules condensing back into the liquid. The vapor pressure above a pure liquid depends on the temperature of the liquid and the $\Delta H_{vaporization}$ of the liquid. Figure 7-6 shows the surface of a liquid and the most favorable points from which molecules can evaporate.

Molecules can evaporate only from the surface, and tend to evaporate from the corners.

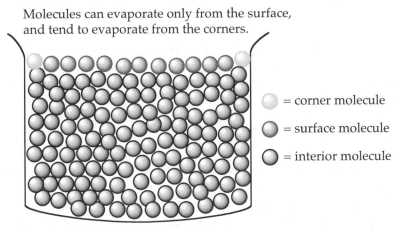

Figure 7-6

In the liquid phase, molecules are not packed in the same orderly fashion as they are in a solid, as shown in Figure 7-6. Corner molecules have the fewest neighbors, so they have the fewest intermolecular forces. Because of the minimal forces, molecules evaporate most readily from the corners and next most readily from the surface.

Vapor pressure can be measured in either an open or closed system. In a closed system, a partial pressure of vapor exists, because the rate of vaporization equals the rate of condensation. This is most typically how vapor pressure is determined. However, the definition of vapor pressure does not apply only to a closed system. In an open system, the vapor can escape, so it does not necessarily reach a state of equilibrium between the rate of vaporization and the rate of condensation. The vapor pressure is a measure of the pressure just above the surface of the liquid. It is difficult to measure, so we generally consider vapor pressure in an open system from a theoretical perspective, and apply values that have been determined previously in a closed system at known temperature.

Vapor pressure is independent of the shape and volume of a container. The vapor pressure above a dish of ethanol is the same as the vapor pressure above a test tube of ethanol. Despite the fact that the dish has substantially more liquid surface area, vapor pressure is still measured as force per unit area. The same amount of ethanol is vaporizing from each system per unit area of its surface, as long as the temperature of both systems is the same. The rate of vaporization is greater with the greater surface area in Container 2, but the vapor pressure is the same in both containers. Figure 7-7 compares two containers that share the same vapor pressure, when they contain the same liquid at the same temperature.

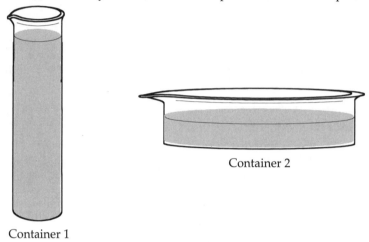

Container 1

Container 2

Figure 7-7

Because vapor pressure depends primarily on solution temperature (energy of the molecules) and $\Delta H_{vaporization}$ (the energy necessary to overcome intermolecular forces), the atmospheric pressure does not significantly affect the vapor pressure. Boiling point depends on the atmospheric pressure, but do not confuse boiling point and vapor pressure. The following relationships hold true with regard to the vapor pressure of a system:

P_{vapor} increases as temp increases; P_{vapor} decreases as $\Delta H_{vaporization}$ increases

Example 7.10
Which of the following statements is TRUE about vapor pressure?
A. The vapor pressure of a liquid decreases with increasing temperature.
B. The vapor pressure of a liquid is always lower at higher elevations.
C. The vapor pressure of a liquid is always higher at higher elevations.
D. The vapor pressure of Liquid X is greater than the vapor pressure of Liquid Z, if the normal boiling point of X is lower than the normal boiling point of Z.

Solution
Vapor pressure correlates with temperature, so vapor pressure increases with temperature. This makes choice A incorrect. Elevation has no (or a negligible) effect on the vapor pressure, because the atmospheric pressure does not affect the vapor pressure (or rate of vaporization) to any appreciable extent. The temperature and $\Delta H_{vaporization}$ have the greatest effect on the vapor pressure. A lower atmospheric pressure lowers the boiling point, but it has no effect on the vapor pressure. This eliminates choices B and C. As the boiling point increases, the ability for a compound to vaporize decreases. This means that as the boiling point increases, less of the vapor is formed and consequently the vapor pressure decreases. This makes choice **D** correct.

Vapor Pressure Graphs

Vapor pressure increases as the temperature of the solution increases, but not in a linear fashion. The graph in Figure 7-8 shows the relationship between vapor pressure and temperature. The graph cannot intersect the y-axis if the units of temperature are kelvins and the axis originates at zero.

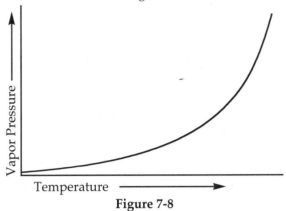

Figure 7-8

The relationship between vapor pressure and temperature is exponential. It is highly unlikely that you have the Clausius-Clapeyron relationship memorized, so the only way to know this is using intuition. If you have ever boiled water for any reason, then you have observed the process that generates the graph in Figure 7-8. It takes a while for the bubbles to form in water as it nears its boiling point. Once bubbles form, it is only a short period of time before the water actually starts to boil. The graph shows a small increase in vapor pressure at lower temperatures (which fits with the lengthy duration before bubbles form), but a rapid ascent at higher temperatures (which fits with the short period of time between bubble formation and boiling).

Equation 7.1, the Clausius-Clapeyron equation, can be used to explain the relationship between vapor pressure and temperature.

$$\ln P_1 - \ln P_2 = \frac{\Delta H_{vaporization}}{R}\left(\frac{1}{T_2} - \frac{1}{T_1}\right) \qquad (7.1)$$

Vaporization is always an endothermic process, so $\Delta H_{vaporization}$ is always a positive value and R is a positive number. If T_2 is greater than T_1, then the value of $\frac{\Delta H_{vap}}{R}\left(\frac{1}{T_2} - \frac{1}{T_1}\right)$ is negative, so the value of $\ln\frac{P_1}{P_2}$ is negative. When $\ln\frac{P_1}{P_2}$ is negative, P_2 is greater than P_1. The conclusion from this is that *as the temperature of a liquid increases, the pressure of its vapor increases*, but in an exponential manner.

Equation 7.1 can be used to calculate the vapor pressure of a liquid at any given temperature, as long as the vapor pressure of the same liquid a different temperature is known. The vapor pressure at the normal boiling point is 760 torr so the normal boiling point is generally one temperatures used in the calculation. In addition to determining the vapor pressure of a liquid at a given temperature using its boiling point, the boiling point for a compound can be calculated at any given atmospheric pressure if any other vapor pressure for it is known. Detailed calculations involving Equation 7.1 are unlikely, but it should still be understood conceptually and graphically. It is a natural log function of pressure and temperature, but it is tricky to use because of the minus sign.

Of more use than doing calculations is a conceptual understanding of the relationship between boiling point, enthalpy of vaporization, volatility, and vapor pressure. Figure 7-9 demonstrates the relationship of these measurements.

As $\Delta H_{vaporization} \uparrow$; Volatility $\downarrow$; Boiling point $\uparrow$; Vapor pressure $\downarrow$

Figure 7-9

The reason the graph in Figure 7-8 reaches an endpoint is because the solution reaches its boiling point, the highest temperature at which liquid may still exist. The boiling point is dependent on the atmospheric pressure, because the highest vapor pressure that the solution can reach is equal to atmospheric pressure. **The boiling point is defined as the temperature at which the vapor pressure is equal to the atmospheric pressure.** The limits of the graph in Figure 7-8 are shown below in Figure 7-10.

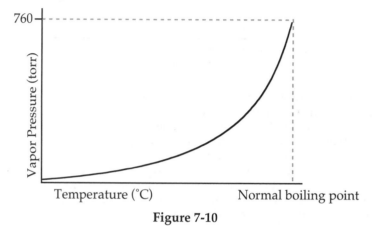

Figure 7-10

Example 7.11
If Compound X evaporates more readily than Compound Y, then which of the following statements must be FALSE?

A. Compound X has a greater vapor pressure than Compound Y at room temperature.
B. Compound X has a greater boiling point than Compound Y.
C. Compound X has greater volatility than Compound Y.
D. Compound X has a lower enthalpy of vaporization than Compound Y.

Solution
Because Compound X is evaporating more readily than Compound Y, Compound X must be more volatile than Compound Y, making choice C a valid statement. A more volatile compound has a greater vapor pressure (more evaporated molecules) at a given temperature, so choice A is also a valid statement. With greater volatility, Compound X must have weaker intermolecular forces, and thus a lower $\Delta H_{vaporization}$ than Compound Y, making choice D a valid statement. The easier it is to vaporize a compound, the less energy that is required to vaporize it, so it has a lower boiling point. This means that Compound X has a lower boiling point than Compound Y. Choice **B** is an invalid statement, making it the best answer.

Boiling Point

The boiling point of a compound is defined in two ways: one based on phases and the other based on vapor pressure:

The boiling point is the temperature above which a substance may not exist as a liquid.

> *The temperature at which the vapor pressure of a liquid is equal to the atmospheric pressure.*

This means that at reduced atmospheric pressure (for example, in the mountains) the boiling point of a liquid is lower than normal. Under cases of increased pressure (such as the typical pressure in a pressure cooker), the boiling point of a liquid is higher than normal. The normal boiling point of a compound is measured at 1.00 atmospheres of pressure. The boiling process involves vaporization of a compound in its liquid phase, which converts it to its gas phase.

Figure 7-11 compares the boiling points for the hydrogen-based compounds of sixteen different elements. Notice that compounds containing elements aligned in the same column of the periodic table are connected in groups of four by solid or broken lines.

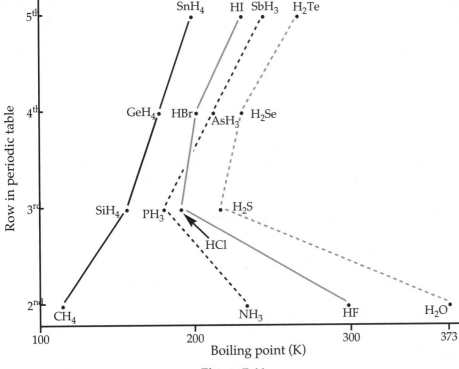

Figure 7-11

This graph shows the effects of hydrogen bonding, molecular mass, and polarity on the boiling point. The effect of hydrogen bonding on the boiling point of a compound is seen with the deviation of H_2O, HF, and NH_3 from linear behavior. The effect of molecular mass on the boiling point is seen in the gradual increase in boiling point as a periodic group is descended. The effect of polarity on the boiling point is demonstrated by the higher boiling points associated with the compounds having two lone pairs, rather than with the compounds of roughly equal mass having either one or three lone pairs. The molecules with two lone pairs are the most polar of any compounds having comparable molecular masses.

This graph (Figure 7-11) presents a large package of data, from which you must be able to extract useful information and understand it in terms of the definitions and background knowledge that you already possess. For instance, the boiling points of HCl, HBr, and HI vary because of the increasing molecular mass of each compound. The greater the molecular mass of the compound, the more energy you need to vaporize the compound. A greater energy to vaporize the compound manifests itself as a higher boiling point for that compound. This accounts for the increase in boiling point with increased mass for the haloacids. The same trend is observed with the other compounds in their periodic column (family).

Much can be observed when the boiling points of H_2S and HCl are compared, because their molecular masses are roughly equivalent, and neither forms hydrogen bonds (the hydrogen must be bonded to an N, O, or F for hydrogen bonding). The boiling point of H_2S is greater than that of HCl, because the H_2S molecule is more polar than HCl, due to its bent geometry. To see this, the compounds must be viewed in three dimensions. The slight deviation from linear behavior within the family that is observed with H_2S and HCl is used by some chemists to argue that the two compounds form very weak hydrogen bonds. This deviation is small compared to the ones observed in NH_3, H_2O, and HF, so any hydrogen bonding is minimal in HCl and H_2S (if not negligible).

The boiling point of water is the greatest of the sixteen compounds listed in Figure 7-11, because the oxygen has two lone pairs and two hydrogens that are capable of forming hydrogen bonds. Therefore, all of the lone pairs and hydrogens have partners with which to form hydrogen bonds. In the case of HF, there are three lone pairs but only one hydrogen on fluorine, so only one H bond can exist bond per HF molecule. This means that there are lone pairs on fluorine that have no hydrogen with which to form a hydrogen bond. The lesser degree of hydrogen bonding accounts for the lower boiling point of HF relative to H_2O. The same holds true for the relative boiling point of ammonia (which has three hydrogens but only one lone pair present on the central nitrogen) relative to water.

Example 7.12
Which of the following compounds has the highest boiling point?

A. H_3CNH_2
B. $H_3CCH_2NH_2$
C. H_3COH
D. H_3CCH_2OH

Solution
The highest boiling point is associated with the compound with the greatest intermolecular forces and greatest molecular mass. Each compound can form hydrogen bonds, but the alcohols are more polar and form stronger hydrogen bonds than their amine equivalents. This eliminates choices A and B. Ethanol (H_3CCH_2OH) is heavier than methanol (H_3COH), so the higher boiling point is found with ethanol, choice **D**.

Boiling Point Variations

The boiling point of a compound can be altered either by varying the atmospheric pressure or by varying the intermolecular forces (which in turn alters $\Delta H_{vaporization}$). Boiling point decreases as the atmospheric pressure above a liquid decreases (this is evident when you boil water in mountainous regions and in vacuum distillation). Boiling point increases as the atmospheric pressure above a liquid increases. Boiling point increases as soluble impurities are added to solution (this is evident when you add salt to boiling water).

Increasing Atmospheric Pressure (Example: A Pressure Cooker)

As mentioned, the boiling point of a liquid increases as the atmospheric pressure above the liquid increases. This can be accomplished by vaporizing the liquid in a closed system. You should never heat a closed system, for it will eventually explode. This is why experiments that attempt to raise the boiling point of a compound often use a partially closed system, one with some means of venting gas when the pressure gets too high. A pressure cooker is an example of a partially closed system. As the water in the system is heated, it vaporizes. This increases the atmospheric pressure, and thus increases the boiling point. Eventually, when the pressure is great enough, it forces the pressure valve open (or lifts the lid) to vent the atmospheric gases, thus reducing the pressure inside. This occurs in cycles, which is why the lid (or valve) of a pressure cooker flutters as its contents heat up. By increasing the mass of the lid or the tension in the pressure valve, the boiling point of the water can be raised. In essence, a pressure valve serves as a primitive kind of thermostat. More sophisticated thermostats are usually a coiled bimetallic strip that expands or contracts as it is heated or cooled. A mercury trip-switch is connected to the coil so that a bead of mercury balances at a certain point. When the temperature being maintained gets too high, the metal loop uncoils slightly, tilting the glass tube with the mercury in it. This causes the mercury liquid to fall to one side thereby connecting the open ends of a wire hooked to a cooling fan, which turns it on.

Decreasing Atmospheric Pressure (Example: Vacuum Distillation)

Decreasing the atmospheric pressure above the liquid decreases the boiling point of a liquid. Reducing the atmospheric pressure makes it easier for a compound to boil. This is why all liquids boil in a vacuum, despite the extremely low temperature. A neat experiment to conduct is to fill a syringe partially with a volatile organic liquid (acetone works well), making sure that no air is in the syringe. Plug the tip with your thumb, then pull up on the plunger. A vacuum is generated in the syringe, so the organic liquid should begin to boil (small bubbles can usually be seen). As it boils, the walls of the syringe actually get very cold. This experiment confirms that reducing atmospheric pressure reduces the boiling point. The same principle is observed in vacuum distillation, where a mixture is distilled under reduced pressure, so that the boiling points are reduced. Vacuum distillation is employed when a compound has an extremely high boiling point or when it has a decomposition temperature lower than its normal boiling point.

Raoult's Law

According to Raoult's law, the vapor pressure above a solution of two or more miscible liquids depends on the mole fraction of each compound in solution. The concept behind this theory is that the mole fraction of a compound corresponds to the percentage of the surface of the liquid mixture due to that compound. If any component makes up only half of the surface, then only half as much as what normally evaporates from the pure liquid, vaporizes from the mixture. Raoult's law is shown below as Equation 7.2.

$$P_{vapor} = X_i P_{vapor \, (pure)} \qquad (7.2)$$

The X_i in Raoult's equation is the mole fraction of the component *in solution*, not in the vapor state. The mole fraction in vapor for the more volatile component is always greater than the mole fraction in solution for the more volatile component. As the mole fraction of a compound in solution decreases, the vapor pressure of that component above the solution decreases. This is attributed to the reduced surface area of that component, and consequently less of that component evaporating away from the surface. $P_{vapor \, (pure)}$ is the vapor pressure of a pure sample of the component under those conditions, and P_{vapor} is the measured vapor pressure of the component. Raoult's law is used to calculate the vapor pressure of one component, which can be thought of as a partial vapor pressure.

Example 7.13

0.10 moles of NH_3, PH_3, and AsH_3 are placed into a beaker at -100°C, where all three exist in liquid phase. What can be said about their relative vapor pressures?

A. $P_{AsH_3} < P_{PH_3} < P_{NH_3}$
B. $P_{PH_3} < P_{AsH_3} < P_{NH_3}$
C. $P_{AsH_3} < P_{NH_3} < P_{PH_3}$
D. $P_{NH_3} < P_{AsH_3} < P_{PH_3}$

Solution

According to Raoult's law, the vapor pressure depends on the mole fraction and the pure vapor pressure of the component. The solution contains equal molar quantities of the three components, so the mole fraction is identical for all three components. Consequently, the highest vapor pressure results from the compound with the lowest boiling point (highest pure vapor pressure). Ammonia (NH_3) has the highest boiling point, because it forms hydrogen bonds, so it has the lowest vapor pressure. Only choice **D** shows ammonia with the lowest vapor pressure, so choice **D** is the best answer. To verify the order in choice **D**, the relative boiling points of PH_3 and AsH_3 should be determined. Both compounds are equally polar, so the most significant factor in determining their relative boiling points is molecular mass, not intermolecular forces. Lighter molecules are easier to vaporize, resulting in greater vapor pressure for the compound. PH_3 is lighter than AsH_3, so the vapor pressure of PH_3 is greater than the vapor pressure of AsH_3. This relationship is listed in choice **D**, confirming that it is a valid answer.

Example 7.14
Given a solution that is made by mixing 8.0 grams of methanol (CH_3OH) with 23.0 grams ethanol (C_2H_5OH) at a temperature where the vapor pressure of pure methanol is 150 torr and the vapor pressure of pure ethanol is 120 torr, what are the vapor pressures of methanol and ethanol?

A. Methanol = 37.5 torr; ethanol = 50 torr
B. Methanol = 37.5 torr; ethanol = 60 torr
C. Methanol = 50.0 torr; ethanol = 60 torr
D. Methanol = 50.0 torr; ethanol = 80 torr

Solution
Equation 7.2 can be used to determine the vapor pressure of methanol and ethanol, as shown below:

$$P_{vapor\ (CH_3OH)} = \frac{n_{CH_3OH}}{n_{total}} \times P^{\circ}_{vapor\ (pure\ CH_3OH)}$$

$$P_{vapor\ (CH_3CH_2OH)} = \frac{n_{CH_3CH_2OH}}{n_{total}} \times P^{\circ}_{vapor\ (pure\ CH_3CH_2OH)}$$

The first task at hand is to solve for the mole fraction of the two components in the mixture. The molecular mass of CH_3OH is 32 grams per mole, so 8 grams results in 0.25 moles CH_3OH. The molecular mass of CH_3CH_2OH is 46 grams per mole, so 23 grams results in 0.50 moles CH_3CH_2OH. It is important that you remember to use the mole fraction, and not inadvertently use the moles of each component. The mole fraction is found by dividing the moles of the component by the total moles in solution. There are 0.75 moles total, so the mole fraction of CH_3OH is one-third, which is 0.33. The mole fraction of CH_3CH_2OH is two-thirds, which is 0.67.

$$P_{vapor\ (CH_3OH)} = \frac{1}{3} \times 150\ torr = 50\ torr$$

$$P_{vapor\ (CH_3CH_2OH)} = \frac{2}{3} \times 120\ torr = 80\ torr$$

The best answer is choice **D**. As a point of interest, the total vapor pressure of the system is 130 torr. The total vapor pressure of a solution must fall between the pure vapor pressure of the least volatile component (120 torr) and the pure vapor pressure of the most volatile component (150 torr). This is a good double-check to use, as this would have eliminated choice A ($P_{vapor\ total}$ = 87.5 torr), choice B ($P_{vapor\ total}$ = 97.5 torr), and choice C ($P_{vapor\ total}$ = 110 torr).

The total vapor pressure above a solution consisting of a mixture of two or more liquids is the sum of the individual vapor pressures of each component liquid. This is listed as Equation 7.3.

$$P_{vapor\ total} = P_{vapor\ A} + P_{vapor\ B} + P_{vapor\ C}\ \cdots \qquad (7.3)$$

At the boiling point of the solution, the total vapor pressure of the components equals the atmospheric pressure. However, because the cumulative vapor pressure contains a mixture of compounds, there is not a single pure compound in the vapor. This is a problem during distillation, because it is not possible to generate an absolutely pure product. Because a mixture of vapors can generate enough vapor pressure to reach the boiling point, the addition of volatile components to a mixture of liquids lowers the boiling point of a solution. This idea is derived from the concept that all of the liquids in solution exert some vapor pressure of their own, independently of the other components.

Figure 7-12 represents an ideal mixture with a linear relationship between the mole fraction of a component and the vapor pressure of that component.

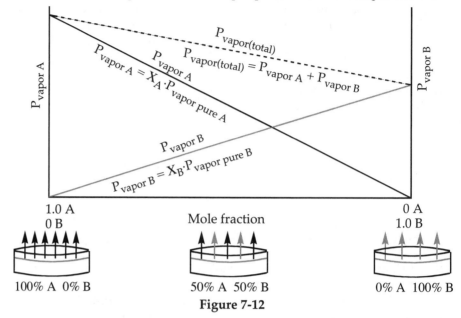

Figure 7-12

Figure 7-12 shows that as the mole fraction of a compound in solution decreases, its vapor pressure above the solution decreases proportionally. As the mole fraction of Component A is reduced, the mole fraction of Component B increases, because the mole fractions add to 1.0. The graph shows that the total vapor pressure is a weighted average of the vapor pressures of Components A and B.

With real compounds, because of intermolecular forces within liquids, there are other factors that come into play. The molecules interact in both the liquid and gas phases, so the vapor pressure relationship is not linear as Raoult's equation approximates it to be. Intermolecular forces are greater in the solution than the gas phase. If there is an overall increase in attractive forces in solution when the components are mixed, then vaporization, and thus vapor pressure, decreases. This is a negative deviation from linearity. If there is an overall decrease in attractive forces in solution when the components are mixed, then vaporization, and thus vapor pressure, increases. This is a positive deviation from linearity. These deviations are empirical and used to explain deviations from Raoult's law.

Distillation

Distillation can be used to remove a liquid from a solution. To do so, the liquid is first converted into vapor, and then the vapor is allowed to flow up a distilling column. Once at the top of the column, it can either return to solution, or take a new pathway where it will be cooled and condensed back into liquid form.

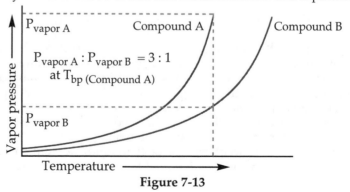

Figure 7-13

Figure 7-13 shows the vapor pressure as a function of temperature for two hypothetical compounds, Compound A and Compound B. From Figure 7-13, the relative vapor pressures of any two compounds for any temperature at which they are both liquids may be determined. The graph shows the values for vapor pressure at the boiling point of Compound A. The ratio of vapor pressures is 3 : 1 in favor of Compound A. This means that for a solution where the mole fraction is one-half for each component in solution, the mole fraction in the vapor phase is three-fourths for Compound A and one-fourth for Compound B. When the vapor is condensed, the solution becomes richer in Compound A, but it is not pure Compound A. After each evaporation and condensation cycle, it gets richer, but never perfectly pure. Figure 7-14 shows the numbers following a series of evaporation and condensation cycles.

A : B ratio (In vapor)

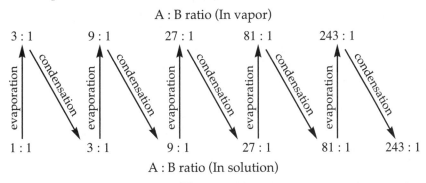

A : B ratio (In solution)

Figure 7-14

Figure 7-14 shows that the effectiveness of distillation does not become evident until a series of evaporation and condensation cycles have transpired. This is the principle behind *fractional distillation*. In fractional distillation, the distilling column has additional surface area, either from packing the column with an inert material, such as glass beads, or by increasing the length of the distilling column. Providing additional surface area results in more evaporation and condensation cycles, and thus results in a more purified product.

Over time, two things occur that reduce the effectiveness of distillation. The distillation pot becomes richer in the less volatile component, so the initial ratio is less than 1 : 1 in favor of Compound A. The second, and more significant, factor is that the glassware heats up, so condensation does not occur as readily. With less condensation, there are fewer evaporation and condensation cycles, so the vapor becomes less rich in the more volatile component.

Example 7.15
Which of the following distillations results in the purest product?

A. Methanol (b.p. = 56°C) from ethanol (b.p. = 78°C)
B. Hexane (b.p. = 69°C) from heptane (b.p. = 98°C)
C. Diethyl ether (b.p. = 35°C) from tetrahydrofuran (b.p. = 67°C)
D. 2,3-dimethylbutane (b.p. = 58°C) from benzene (b.p. = 80°C)

Solution
The distillation that generates the purest product is the one with the greatest vapor pressure ratio of more volatile component to less volatile component. The greatest ratio is found in the pair of compounds that has the biggest difference in boiling points. The difference in boiling points in choice A is 22°C, in choice B is 29°C, in choice **C** is 32°C, and in choice D is 22°C. The best answer is choice **C**.

Colligative Properties

Concentration Effects

Colligative properties are properties of a solution that are affected by the concentration of a soluble impurity. Colligative properties include boiling point elevation (the same as vapor pressure reduction), freezing point depression, and osmotic pressure. The electrical conductivity of a solution, although it is not formally a colligative property, shows a dependence on ion concentration. Changes in the colligative properties occur when solutes in solution bind the solvent molecules. The greater the number of impurities in solution, the greater the magnitude of the effect. Figures 7-15 and 7-16 show the relative boiling point, freezing point, osmotic pressure, and conductivity of an aqueous salt solution as the concentration of salt is gradually increased.

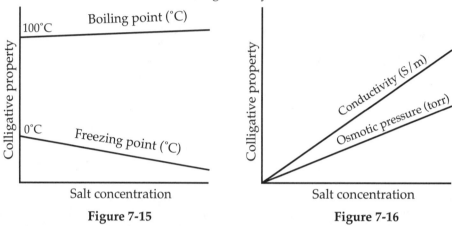

Figure 7-15   **Figure 7-16**

Figure 7-15 shows that as impurities are added to solution, the solvent has a greater tendency to remain as a liquid. This is attributed to increased intermolecular forces in the solution phase. Solute particles interact only with a liquid. For instance, water tends to stay in the liquid phase with the increased solvation energy of impurities, rather than changing to another phase. This is why the boiling point of an aqueous salt solution increases and the freezing point of an aqueous salt solution decreases. The magnitude of the effect is not the same for boiling point as for the freezing point, as shown by the slope of the lines in Figure 7-15. There are different values for the boiling point elevation constant and the freezing point depression constant for a given liquid. Both constants are symbolized by the term k, but each has a different subscript character to identify its purpose. The boiling point elevation constant is k_b, while the freezing point depression constant is k_f.

Figure 7-17 presents the heating curve for a 1.0 M aqueous salt solution overlapped against the heating curve for pure water (for comparison). Heating curves are generated by adding heat uniformly at a constant rate to the solution of salt water and monitoring the temperature of the solution. The freezing point of the saltwater solution is lower than the normal freezing point of water, and the freezing point of the saltwater solution is decreasing as more water freezes out from the solution. The reason that the freezing point of the salt solution continues to decrease as water freezes away from solution is that the molality of the impurity in the solution is increasing as water is removed. As the molality of the solute in solution increases, the freezing point decreases, due to the greater relative number of impurities in the solution. The same is true for the boiling point elevation of a solution. This is the explanation of why the last portion of water to boil away from saltwater solution is so difficult to remove.

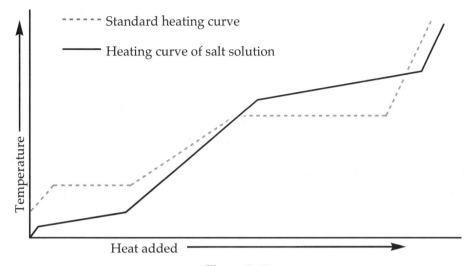

Figure 7-17

Boiling Point Elevation

As stated before, the boiling point of a solution increases with the addition of impurities. This is why it is referred to as the *boiling point elevation*. The increase in boiling point (and decrease in vapor pressure) is attributed to both a decreased surface area from which the liquid can evaporate and an increase in the intermolecular forces binding the liquid in solution. In the case of a saltwater solution, water has stronger attraction to the ionic impurities than it does to other water molecules. The intermolecular forces of water with water, and of water with an ion are presented in Figure 7-18. The difference in strength is attributed to the larger positive charge on a cation than the partial positive charge present on a protic hydrogen.

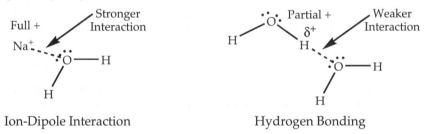

Ion-Dipole Interaction   Hydrogen Bonding

Figure 7-18

Because it requires more energy to break the ion-dipole interaction than the hydrogen bond between water molecules, more heat energy is required to remove a water molecule from a solution with ions present than from pure water. This is the molecular level explanation for the elevation of the boiling point for an aqueous solution containing ions. This idea can be applied to any solute added to water, based on the notion that a solute is soluble in water when the attractive force between the water molecule and the solute particle is greater than the attractive force between two water molecules. This is very similar to a principle of solubility, that the most soluble species has the greatest solvation energy associated with it. Organic species do not readily dissolve into water, because there are no charged interactions (Coulombic attraction). Calculating boiling point elevation is generally simple. Although calculations are few on the MCAT, it is still essential that you understand the setup of the equation, and the influence of variables on the boiling point of the solution.

Equation 7.4 is used to calculate the increase in boiling point when solute is added to a solution.

$$\Delta T_b = k_b \cdot i \cdot m \tag{7.4}$$

The k_b term is a constant for the solvent, i is the Van't Hoff factor (ionizability constant--essentially the number of ions that form upon dissolving), and m is molality. The k_b value for water is 0.51 $^\circ C \cdot kg/mole$. On the MCAT years ago, they introduced a fourth term called gamma. The gamma term described the solute, based on the idea that not all solutes interact with the solvent in the same manner. This term may be referred to as an *activity coefficient*.

Example 7.16
Which solution has the HIGHEST boiling point?
A. 0.10 moles magnesium chloride in 100 mL water
B. 0.15 moles lithium bromide in 150 mL water
C. 0.20 moles sodium iodide in 100 mL water
D. 0.25 moles potassium fluoride in 150 mL water

Solution
The highest boiling point is associated with the solution that has the highest concentration of impurities. The tricky part to this question is determining the i value. Magnesium chloride ($MgCl_2$) has an i value of 3.0, while the other salts all have i values of 2.0. Choice A has 0.3 moles of impurities (3×0.1) in 100 mL water, choice B has 0.3 moles of impurities (2×0.15) in 150 mL water, choice **C** has 0.4 moles of impurities (2×0.2) in 100 mL water, and choice D has 0.5 moles of impurities (2×0.25) in 150 mL water. The highest concentration of impurities is present in choice **C**. When looking at questions like this, you should realize that there are several ways to test your understanding. The question could have asked for "GREATEST vapor pressure", in which case you would be hunting for the lowest boiling point.

Keep in mind that addition of a solute not only increases the boiling point of a compound, but it also changes other colligative properties. For instance, by adding salt to a pot of water when you cook pasta, you increase the boiling point of the water slightly. However, contrary to what people think about adding salt to the water when cooking pasta, it is not actually done for the purpose of increasing the boiling point. For a 4.0 liter pot of water (roughly a gallon), about 234 grams of sodium chloride are required to raise the boiling point by 1°C to 101°C. This is roughly half a pound of salt. The amount of salt needed to effectively increase the boiling point is so great that the health risks are not worth it. The reason salt is added to water when cooking noodles is based on another colligative property, osmotic pressure. As the salt concentration increases, so does the osmotic pressure of the solution, preventing the noodles from getting too soggy (water-logged). There are other interesting observations that can be explained through colligative properties. When salt is added to hot water, it suddenly froths (boils) for a moment, and then returns to a state of not boiling. This is because the dissociation of salt into water is exothermic, and the energy released causes localized pockets of boiling water. Once the salt is dissociated, however, the boiling point rises, so the solution is no longer at its boiling point.

Freezing Point Depression

The freezing point of a solution can be altered by varying the intermolecular forces (which in essence varies ΔH_{fusion}). Freezing point decreases as soluble impurities are added to solution. The reasoning behind the change in melting point is that impurities are found dissolved in a substance in its liquid phase, not the solid phase. When salt is added to the surface of an ice cube, the water molecules on the surface of the lattice are attracted to the salt, and thus can be removed from the lattice (which is melting the ice). This is an exothermic process, so additional energy is released to melt the ice further. The melting process is made easier by lowering the melting point. This is why salt is used to help melt ice on roads and prevent future freezing by lowering the freezing point. Water molecules experience stronger interactions in salt water than freshwater, so they do not freeze out from a saltwater solution as readily as they do from pure water. Solute particles exhibit attractive forces in solution. The effect that this has on melting is that solvent molecules tends to stay in solution, so they freeze at a lower temperature.

Calculating the freezing point depression for a solution is just like calculating boiling point elevation, except that k_f replaces k_b. The other terms are the same as in Equation 7.4. Equation 7.5 is used to calculate the decrease in freezing point when solute is added to a solution.

$$\Delta T_f = k_f \cdot i \cdot m \qquad (7.5)$$

To find the freezing temperature, subtract the change in temperature (ΔT) from the regular freezing point (under ambient conditions). This new value is the freezing point of the solution at that given concentration. Equation 7.6 shows how this is done.

$$T_f = T_{nfp} - \Delta T, \text{ where } T_{nfp} = \text{normal freezing point.} \qquad (7.6)$$

If you are careless, it is easy to forget to use the i on these problems when the solute is a salt. The i value for sugar is 1, because when sugar dissolves into water, it does not form any ions; it remains an intact sugar molecule.

Example 7.17
What is the freezing point of a solution made by mixing 5.84 grams of sodium chloride into 200 grams of water? ($k_f = 1.86$ °C kg/mole for water)

A. -0.42°C
B. -0.93°C
C. -1.86°C
D. -3.72°C

Solution
The molecular mass of NaCl is 58.4 g/mole, so there are 0.10 moles of NaCl. There are 200 grams of water, which is 0.2 kg water. The molality is found by dividing the moles of solute (NaCl) by the kilograms of solvent (H_2O). The solution concentration in molality is 0.50 m NaCl. Each molecule of NaCl results in 2 molecules of impurities, because NaCl fully dissociates into Na^+ cations and Cl^- anions when added to water. The total impurity concentration is 1.0 molal, which lowers the freezing point by 1.86 °C from the normal freezing point of 0°C. The freezing point of the solution -1.86°C, so choice **C** is the best answer.

$$\Delta T_f = k_f \cdot i \cdot m = -1.86 \times 2 \times \frac{0.10 \text{ moles NaCl}}{0.20 \text{ kg } H_2O} = -1.86 \times 2 \times 0.5 = -1.86°C$$

Osmotic Pressure

Water has a natural tendency to flow from solutions of higher water concentration (lower solute concentration) to solutions of lower water concentration (higher solute concentration) to reach equal concentrations. Pressure differences cause fluids to flow, and the driving force causing water to flow is known as *osmotic pressure*. Osmotic pressure is the force per unit area exerted by a solution through osmosis across a semipermeable membrane. Osmotic pressure is calculated using Equation 7.7.

$$\pi = MiRT \tag{7.7}$$

where π is osmotic pressure, M = molarity, i is the ionizability constant (number of ions upon dissociation), R is the energy constant, and T is temperature in kelvins. Osmotic pressure experiments in a U-tube apparatus are used to measure the mass of polymers, including natural polymers like proteins. The two sides of the U-tube are separated by a semipermeable membrane, which segregates molecules according to size. Water molecules can pass through the membrane, because they are small. However, proteins cannot pass through the membrane. A known mass of protein is added to one side of the U-tube, creating a difference in osmotic pressure between the two sides. Water flows from the side without protein to the side with protein, so the water levels become uneven. The protein cannot migrate across the barrier, so the concentration is always greater on one side than the other. Water stops flowing when the osmotic pressure equals the hydrostatic pressure. Equation 7.8 is used to calculate the hydrostatic pressure.

$$P_{hydrostatic} = \rho g \Delta h \tag{7.8}$$

where ρ is the density, g is the gravitational force constant, and Δh is the height difference between the solution in the left side of the U-tube and the solution in the right side of the U-tube. The experiment is shown in Figure 7-19.

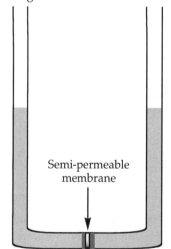
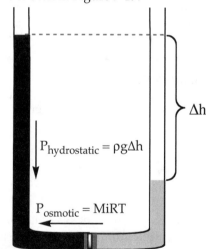

Before solute has been added, each side of the U-tube contains the same amount of H_2O at 25°C.

A height difference exists after solute has been added to the left side of the U-tube.

Figure 7-19

As shown in Figure 7-19, the osmotic pressure and hydrostatic pressure oppose one another. Once the water levels reach a fixed height, then Equation 7.7 is set equal to Equation 7.8. From that, molarity can be determined, which can be converted to moles. A given mass of protein was used, so the molecular mass is found by dividing this number by moles.

Example 7.18
How many grams of a 12,000 $gram/mole$ polymer must be added to water to make a 10-mL solution with an osmotic pressure of 0.0246 atm. at 27°C? (R = 0.082 $L \cdot atm./mole \cdot K$)

A. 0.012 grams polymer
B. 0.120 grams polymer
C. 1.200 grams polymer
D. 12.00 grams polymer

Solution
Using Equation 7.7, $\pi = MiRT$, we can determine how many grams are required. The polymer does not dissociate, so for a polymer (or protein-- a biological polymer) the value of i is 1. Substituting into the equation yields:

$$0.0246 \text{ atm} = \frac{z\,g/12,000 \text{ g} \cdot mole^{-1}}{0.01 \text{ L}} \times 1 \times 0.082 \text{ L} \cdot atm \cdot mole^{-1} \cdot K^{-1} \times 300 \text{ K}$$

$$0.0246 = \frac{z}{120} \times 1 \times 8.2 \times 3 \Rightarrow z = \frac{0.0246 \times 120}{1 \times 8.2 \times 3} = \frac{24.6 \times 0.12}{24.6} = 0.12 \text{ g}$$

0.12 grams of polymer are needed, so the best answer is choice **B**. Not very much polymer is necessary to generate enough pressure difference to be measurable. The units are tricky, because Equation 7.8 expresses pressure in terms of pascals, while Equation 7.7 is in terms of atm. To do a problem where osmotic pressure is equated with hydrostatic pressure, a conversion between pascals and atm. is necessary. The likelihood of seeing such a calculation on the MCAT is minimal, although it can be estimated closely by dividing the pressure in atm. by 10^5.

Example 7.19
The GREATEST osmotic pressure is associated with which of the following solutions?

A. 10 grams polymer with molecular mass 10,000 g/mole in 10 mL water.
B. 100 grams polymer with molecular mass 10,000 g/mole in 100 mL water.
C. 10 grams polymer with molecular mass 10,000 g/mole in 100 mL water.
D. 100 grams polymer with molecular mass 10,000 g/mole in 10 mL water.

Solution
The greatest osmotic pressure results from the solution with the greatest polymer concentration. The polymer is the same in each answer choice, so they each have the same molecular mass. This question reduces to a hunt for the most grams of polymer in the least amount of solvent (which is the highest concentrated solution). The greatest mass of polymer in the least water is found in choice **D**.

Conductance
Pure water does not conduct an electrical current, because there are no ions present in solution to transfer electrons. In order for water to conduct electricity, there must be ions present in solution. The specific conductance of an aqueous salt solution is directly proportional to the concentration of salt in solution. Electrical conductance is observed only with ionic solutes. Specific conductance is measured relative to aqueous sodium chloride solutions.

There is also a term for electrical conductance in an aqueous salt solution known as *condosity*. The condosity of a solution is defined as the molar concentration of an aqueous sodium chloride solution that has the same specific conductance as the aqueous salt solution. Salts that form aqueous solutions capable of conducting electricity better than sodium chloride solutions have a condosity greater than their molarity. The greater the ratio of condosity to molarity, the better the salt at conducting electricity in an aqueous environment. For instance, if a salt were twice as good as NaCl at conducting current in an aqueous solution, then 2.0 M NaCl(*aq*) solution would have the same conductivity as a 1.0 M salt(*aq*) solution. In that case, the 1.0 M salt(*aq*) solution has a condosity of 2.0.

Example 7.20
As salt is dissolved into a glass of water, all of the following observations could be made EXCEPT that:
A. objects will float higher in the new solution.
B. electricity will conduct better through the new solution.
C. the heat capacity will be greater in the new solution.
D. the freezing point of the new solution will be increased.

Solution
As salt is dissolved into water, the impurity concentration increases and the density of the solution increases. Because the density is greater, objects in the solution will experience an increase in the buoyant force. The result is that floating objects will float higher after salt has been added to the solution, making choice A a valid observation. This eliminates choice A. Electricity conducts through water because of the ions in solution, so the addition of salt to water will in fact increase the electrical conductivity. This eliminates choice B. The addition of a soluble salt to water will increase the intermolecular forces in solution, which in turn will cause the solution to need additional heat energy to have the particles increase their average speed in solution. The result is that the solution has a greater heat capacity, so choice C is a valid observation. This eliminates choice C. Addition of impurities to water lowers the freezing point of the solution (recall that it's known as freezing point depression), so choice **D** is an invalid observation. Choice **D** is the best answer.

Example 7.21
If an ice cube floats in a glass of water in such a way that the surface of the water is flush with the brim, and the ice cube sticks out above the level of the water, what will occur as the ice cube melts?
A. The water level will drop below the top of the glass.
B. The water will overflow the top of the glass.
C. The water level will remain flush with the top of the glass.
D. The water level will rise above the top of the glass, but will not overflow it.

Solution
For this question, it is important to remember that when ice melts, it becomes water. The mass of the water displaced by the floating ice cube is equal to the mass of the water generated by melting the ice cube. When the ice cube melts, the water that is formed has exactly the same mass and density as the water displaced. This means that it also has the same volume, so it fills the volume occupied by the submerged portion of the ice cube. The net result is that the level of the water remains constant at the top of the glass. As more and more ice melts, the exposed portion of the ice cube drops lower, but the top of the water remains at the same height. Choice **C** is the best answer.

Phases
and
Phase Changes
Passages

13 Passages

100 Questions

Suggested Phases Passage Schedule:

I: After reading this section and attending lecture: Passages I, IV, V, & IX
Grade passages immediately after completion and log your mistakes.

II: Following Task I: Passages II, III, VI, VII, & X (36 questions in 47 minutes)
Time yourself accurately, grade your answers, and review mistakes.

III: Review: Passages VIII, XI - XIII & Questions 93 - 100
Focus on reviewing the concepts. Do not worry about timing.

The BERKELEY
R·E·V·I·E·W®
Specializing in MCAT Preparation

Phases and Phase Change Study Passages

Phases and Phase Changes Scoring Scale

Raw Score	MCAT Score
85 - 100	13 - 15
68 - 84	10 - 12
48 - 67	7 - 9
35 - 47	4 - 6
1 - 34	1 - 3

Passage I (Questions 1 - 7)

The changing of phases for matter has a commercial use in everyday heating and cooling. Phase changes are either endothermic (heat absorbing) or exothermic (heat releasing). The phase changes that are endothermic are *sublimation* (solid to gas), *melting* (solid to liquid), and *evaporation* (liquid to gas). The phase changes that are exothermic are *condensation* (gas to liquid), *deposition* (gas to solid), and *freezing* (liquid to solid). Artificial snow-making involves the deposition of water vapor.

Commercial freeze-drying processes employed to make many of the coffees marketed today, involve exactly what the name implies. A batch of freshly brewed coffee is first frozen, and then water is removed. In the first step of the process, the coffee is cooled until it has frozen (which occurs at a temperature around -1.7°C, because impurities in the water lower the freezing point). In the second step, the atmospheric pressure is reduced, which allows the ice to escape to form the dehydrated coffee. As the water molecules leave, the temperature of the frozen coffee slurry lowers (because sublimation is endothermic). This results in the formation of freeze-dried coffee. The process is shown in Reaction 1 below.

$$H_2O(s) + heat \rightarrow H_2O(g)$$

Reaction 1

The condensation process occurs naturally when rain clouds form. To enhance the chances of rainfall in draught-stricken areas, techniques for cloud-seeding have been developed over the years. Clouds are masses of condensed water vapor. Rain is formed when the droplets of this vapor aggregate into rain drops as the water mist in the clouds collects on the surface of fine ice crystals, which one might expect to form at 0°C. In actuality, however, the cloud must be supercooled to roughly -6.4°C in order for the ice crystals to form.

To induce the formation of ice crystals, tiny dry ice pellets of solid carbon dioxide can be dropped from an airplane. These pellets freeze the water mist in the clouds. The solid CO_2 is maintained at its sublimation point (approximately -78°C). Once some ice crystals have begun to form in a cloud, the water mist can quickly aggregate on the surface, to form many raindrops.

1. The drying procedure involved in freeze-drying of coffee is an example of what physical process?

   A. Melting
   B. Boiling
   C. Sublimation
   D. Condensation

2. The optimum conditions for freeze-drying coffee are which of the following?

   A. 25°C and 1.0 atm.
   B. 25°C and 1.0 torr
   C. -10°C and 1.0 atm.
   D. -10°C and 1.0 torr

3. Which of the following is an alternative way to dehydrate coffee than the freeze-drying procedure?

   A. Recrystallization using a water-ether mixed solvent
   B. Distillation of the water to collect the residue
   C. Distillation and collection of the solvent
   D. Filtration of the solute with sieves

4. To lower the temperature of a cloud, what can be dropped into its core?

   A. Ice crystals at 0°C
   B. Water at its freezing point
   C. Dry ice at its sublimation point
   D. Sodium chloride at standard temperature

5. Supercooled water would be which of the following?

   A. Water at 0°C
   B. Ice at 10°C
   C. Ice at 0°C
   D. Water at -10°C

6. Cloud-seeding to form rain exemplifies which kind of phase change involving H_2O?

   A. Vaporization
   B. Melting
   C. Fusion
   D. Sublimation

7. Each locale in the following answer choices has a different standard boiling point for water. Which sequence of places reflects the correct relationship of these boiling points in DESCENDING order?

   A. A seaport > the mountains > a Midwestern town
   B. The mountains > a Midwestern town > a seaport
   C. A Midwestern town > the mountains > a seaport
   D. A seaport > a Midwestern town > the mountains

Passage II (Questions 8 - 14)

Standard phase diagrams graph the phase of a material or compound against ambient pressure (abscissa) and temperature (ordinate). The lines of the graph represent phase changes for the compound. The two phase diagrams drawn in Figure 1 and Figure 2 below show that at low pressure and temperature, it is possible to convert directly from the solid phase to the gas phase (referred to as *sublimation*). Phase diagrams do not intersect with either axis, because it is physically impossible to reach conditions of 0 kelvins and 0 torr pressure. The two phase diagrams drawn below for standard compounds are typical. The phase diagram in Figure 1 is for an unknown substance, Compound A, while the phase diagram in Figure 2 is for Compound B. The dashed lines are drawn to aid your seeing the point on the graph where the indicated temperatures and pressures intersect.

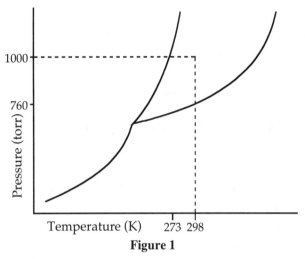

Figure 1

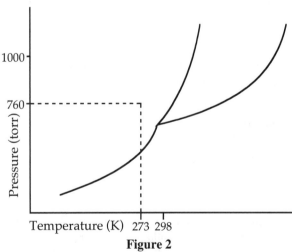

Figure 2

Both phase diagrams show a similar slope and have only three phases associated with them. There are some phase diagrams that show more than three phases. For instance, sulfur can assume two different crystalline structures, so it has two unique solid phases. As a consequence, the phase diagram for sulfur shows four phases.

8. Which labeled point in the phase diagram below is the critical point?

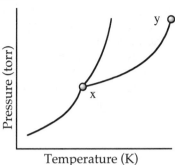

A. Point x, where all three phases coexist
B. Point x, above which gas and liquid do not exist
C. Point y, where all three phases coexist
D. Point y, above which gas and liquid do not exist

9. If you were to reduce the pressure on Compound A at 298 K from 1.3 atm. to 0.9 atm., the compound would:

A. undergo melting (from solid to liquid).
B. undergo vaporization (from liquid to gas).
C. undergo condensation (from gas to liquid).
D. undergo deposition (from solid to gas).

10. At which of the following temperatures is sublimation NOT possible for Compound B?

A. 273 K
B. 10°C
C. 283 K
D. 100°C

11. Which of the compounds would be a gas at 1.0 atm. and 10°C?

A. Compound A only
B. Compound B only
C. Both compounds A and B
D. Neither compound A nor B

12. In what phase does Compound B exist at standard temperature and pressure?

A. Solid
B. Liquid
C. Gas
D. Lambda

13. Which arrow represents an isothermal evaporation?

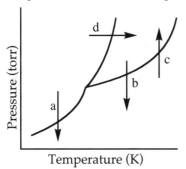

A. Arrow a

B. Arrow b

C. Arrow c

D. Arrow d

14. Which of the following conclusions is INVALID for Compound A?

A. Compound A does not sublime at 25°C.

B. Compound A is solid at 250 K, 760 torr.

C. Compound A has a triple point of slightly lower T and P than water.

D. For Compound A there exists a solid that is less dense than its liquid phase.

Passage III (Questions 15 - 21)

A researcher synthesized an unknown material referred to as Compound C. After purifying the material and verifying its purity by spectroscopic methods, the researcher recorded the physical properties of the material. Included in the inventory of physical properties are: normal melting point, molecular mass, and the specific heats for all three phases. The researcher then investigated the enthalpy values associated with the phase changes (fusion and vaporization). Figure 1 is a heating curve for Compound C, showing the temperature of the material as it is heated at a constant rate.

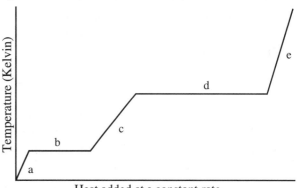

Heat added at a constant rate

Figure 1

Table 1 lists the physical properties for Compound C, as determined by the researcher. The molecular weight of compound C is 100, and its normal boiling point is 64.5°C.

Physical constants for Compound C	
C_{liquid}	$1.0 \dfrac{cal}{g \cdot °C}$
C_{gas}	$0.5 \dfrac{cal}{g \cdot °C}$
$\Delta H_{vaporization}$	$30 \dfrac{kcal}{mole}$

Table 1

The physical constants were determined by observing the effects of temperature change over a range of temperatures. The data listed were recorded at standard pressure. The enthalpy of vaporization was determined by measuring the vapor pressure of Compound C at various temperatures, and then using those data in the following equation to determine the enthalpy of vaporization:

$$\ln \frac{P_1}{P_2} = \frac{\Delta H_{vaporization}}{R} \left(\frac{1}{T_2} - \frac{1}{T_1} \right)$$

Equation 1

By measuring the vapor pressure at many temperatures, $\Delta H_{vaporization}$ can be determined with great accuracy. The heat capacities were found by repeated calorimetry experiments in a closed, insulated vessel.

15. According to Figure 1, the heat capacity of Compound C in the solid phase is:

    A. equal to the heat capacity in the liquid phase.
    B. greater than the heat capacity in the liquid phase.
    C. less than the heat capacity in the liquid phase.
    D. exactly twice the heat capacity in the liquid phase.

16. According to Figure 1, the enthalpy of fusion is:

    A. equal to the enthalpy of vaporization.
    B. greater than the enthalpy of vaporization.
    C. less than the enthalpy of vaporization.
    D. equal to the enthalpy of formation.

17. If 10.0 grams of an unknown substance, Compound Q(l) heats up to a higher temperature than 10.0 grams of Compound C(l) when exposed to the same amount of heat, which of the following conclusions is valid?

    A. Compound Q has a larger heat capacity than Compound C.
    B. Compound Q has a larger enthalpy of fusion than Compound C.
    C. Compound Q has a smaller heat capacity than Compound C.
    D. Compound Q has a smaller enthalpy of fusion than Compound C.

18. How much heat would be required for 10.0 grams of Compound C to go from a liquid at ten degrees below the boiling point to a gas at ten degrees above the boiling point?

    A. 3,015 calories
    B. 3,150 calories
    C. 30,015 calories
    D. 30,150 calories

19. Which of the following conclusions can be made about Compound C relative to water?

    A. Compound C has a lower vapor pressure than water at room temperature.
    B. Compound C has a lower ΔH_{fusion} than water.
    C. Compound C has a lower $\Delta H_{vaporization}$ than water.
    D. Compound C has a lower heat capacity in the liquid phase than water.

20. Which of the following statements about phase change in Compound C is NOT true?

    A. During phase changes, temperature remains constant.
    B. The process of going from the solid phase to the liquid phase is an endothermic process.
    C. The process of sublimation is exothermic.
    D. The heat capacity for the compound varies for each phase.

21. Which statement accurately relates the heat capacity of Compound C and the slope of the ascending line in its heating curve?

    A. The slope is directly proportional to heat capacity.
    B. The slope is inversely proportional to heat capacity.
    C. The slope is independent of heat capacity.
    D. The slope and heat capacity differ by a constant amount.

Passage IV (Questions 22 - 28)

Phase diagrams relate ambient temperature and pressure to the most abundant phase for a material to exist in under those conditions. Under conditions where the phase diagram shows that a liquid is present, a small amount of vapor may also be present, but not in a high concentration. For instance, water at 0°C and 1.00 atm. is present in all three phases, although the phase diagram shows that only the solid and liquid may coexist. The amount of water vapor is minimal. The triple point of water, where any of the three phases may be present in abundance, is 0.01°C and 4.57 torr.

Complications arise in materials that have more than three phases. In the phase diagrams shown in Figure 1 and Figure 2, each material has two solid phases, both of which have different lattice structures and physical properties.

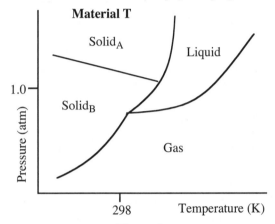

Figure 1

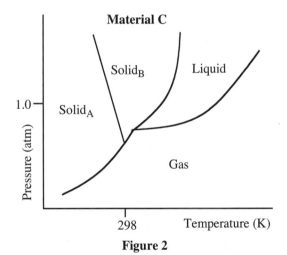

Figure 2

At 1.0 atm and 25°C, both materials exist as Solid$_B$.

22. For which material can both solids exist simultaneously with the liquid phase?

   A. Both Material T and Material C

   B. Only Material T

   C. Only Material C

   D. Neither Material T nor Material C

23. Which of the following statements is NOT true?

   A. It is possible to sublime the solid$_A$ form of Material C at temperatures below the first triple point by changing the pressure.

   B. It is possible for gas of Material C to undergo deposition to solid$_B$ at temperatures between the first and second triple points.

   C. Both Material T and Material C have two triple points each.

   D. At standard temperature and pressure (0°C and 1.00 atm.), Material T exists as solid$_A$.

24. Which direct conversion is NOT possible?

   A. Material T: Solid$_B$ into liquid.

   B. Material C: Liquid into solid$_B$.

   C. Material C: Gas into solid$_A$.

   D. Material T: Solid$_A$ into gas.

25. For both Material T and Material C, which phase can coexist with the other three at some point?

   A. Solid$_A$

   B. Solid$_B$

   C. Liquid

   D. Gas

26. How can the two different solids be explained for both of the compounds?

   A. The two solids have different lattice structures.

   B. The two solids have different connectivity of atoms.

   C. The two solids have different molecular masses.

   D. The two solids have different chiral centers.

27. At a temperature of 25°C, which of these statements must be true?

   I. For Material T, solid$_A$ is less dense than solid$_B$.

   II. For Material C, conversion from solid$_A$ into solid$_B$ is an endothermic process.

   III. For Material T, it is possible to undergo deposition only to form solid$_B$, but not solid$_A$.

   A. I only

   B. II only

   C. I and II only

   D. II and III only

28. Which solid deforms upon heating at atmospheric pressure?

A. Both Material T and Material C
B. Only Material T
C. Only Material C
D. Neither Material T or Material C

Passage V (Questions 29 - 35)

Three beakers were prepared with a mixture of methanol and ethanol. In Beaker I 50 grams of methanol and 50 grams of ethanol were mixed. In Beaker II 50 milliliters of methanol and 50 milliliters of ethanol were mixed. In Beaker III 1.00 moles of methanol and 1.00 mole of ethanol were mixed. The three beakers were separated and placed into individual 10-liter sealed containers. The total vapor pressure and vapor pressure due to methanol were recorded for the three separate beakers. This was done by analyzing the gas above each beaker in the closed system. Listed in Table 1 below are data for both methanol and ethanol:

Compound	Formula	ρ at 20°C	MW	b.p.
Methanol	CH_3OH	0.7914 g/mL	32.04	56°C
Ethanol	C_2H_5OH	0.7893 g/mL	46.07	79°C

Table 1

According to Raoult's law, the vapor pressure of any component of a mixture can be determined by multiplying the mole fraction of that component in solution by the pure vapor pressure of that component at the same temperature. The mole fraction is defined as the moles of a component divided by the total moles of the solution. Raoult's law is for an ideal mixture and holds true as long as the components of the solution do not interact.

If there are attractive forces between the components in the solution mixture, then the vapor pressure is lower than would be calculated by Raoult's law. If there are repulsive forces between the components in the solution mixture, then the vapor pressure is higher than would be calculated by Raoult's law. These are referred to as negative and positive deviations from Raoult's law, respectively.

29. Above which beaker is the vapor pressure of methanol the GREATEST?

A. Beaker I
B. Beaker II
C. Beaker III
D. The vapor pressure of methanol is the same above all three beakers.

30. As the temperature of the solution in Beaker I increases, what is observed for the vapor pressure of methanol, and the total vapor pressure above the beaker?

A. $P_{total\ vapor}$ increases; $P_{methanol}$ increases.
B. $P_{total\ vapor}$ increases; $P_{methanol}$ decreases.
C. $P_{total\ vapor}$ decreases; $P_{methanol}$ increases.
D. $P_{total\ vapor}$ decreases; $P_{methanol}$ decreases.

31. During the first minute of evaporation, before equilibrium is established and the temperature changes to any significant degree, what is observed for the solution in Beaker III?

A. The ratio of moles methanol to moles ethanol increases, and the rate of vaporization from the beaker also increases.

B. The ratio of moles methanol to moles ethanol increases, while the rate of vaporization from the beaker decreases.

C. The ratio of moles methanol to moles ethanol decreases, while the rate of vaporization from the beaker increases.

D. The ratio of moles methanol to moles ethanol decreases, and the rate of vaporization from the beaker also decreases.

32. The same experiment is carried out with propanol and methanol in one case, and with ethanol and propanol in another case, and the following data are collected:

Mixture	Pvapor at 35°C
10 mL methanol w/ 10 mL propanol	42.7 torr
10 mL methanol w/ 20 mL propanol	37.1 torr
10 mL ethanol w/ 10 mL propanol	38.4 torr
10 mL ethanol w/ 20 mL propanol	33.5 torr

What can be said about the vapor pressure of pure propanol compared to both ethanol and methanol?

A. $P_{methanol} > P_{propanol}$; $P_{ethanol} > P_{propanol}$

B. $P_{propanol} > P_{methanol}$; $P_{ethanol} > P_{propanol}$

C. $P_{methanol} > P_{propanol}$; $P_{propanol} > P_{ethanol}$

D. $P_{propanol} > P_{methanol}$; $P_{propanol} > P_{ethanol}$

33. What is the total pressure above Beaker I at 27°C, if the vapor pressure of pure methanol is 40.0 torr and the vapor pressure of pure ethanol is 30.0 torr at that temperature?

A. Greater than 40.0 torr

B. Greater than 35.0 torr, but less than 40.0 torr

C. Greater than 30.0 torr, but less than 35.0 torr

D. Less than 30.0 torr

34. If the vapor pressure of pure methanol is greater than the vapor pressure of pure ethanol, then what must be true about the relative temperatures of each solution in order to have equal total vapor pressures above all three beakers?

A. $T_I > T_{II} > T_{III}$

B. $T_{III} > T_I > T_{II}$

C. $T_I > T_{III} > T_{II}$

D. $T_{II} > T_I > T_{III}$

35. If the vapor above Beaker I were collected and condensed into another beaker, what would be true about the vapor pressures of ethanol, methanol, and the total vapor pressure above the new beaker, relative to what was originally observed above Beaker I?

A. The total vapor pressure and the vapor pressures of methanol and ethanol would all be greater above the new beaker.

B. The total vapor pressure and the vapor pressure of methanol would be greater above the new beaker. The vapor pressure of ethanol would be less.

C. The total vapor pressure and the vapor pressure of methanol would be less above the new beaker. The vapor pressure of ethanol would be greater.

D. The total vapor pressure would be the same, while the vapor pressure of methanol would be greater and the vapor pressure of ethanol would be less.

GO ON TO THE NEXT PAGE

To reduce the temperature necessary to distill a liquid, distillation can be conducted under vacuum conditions. Appropriately enough, this procedure is referred to as *vacuum distillation*. In vacuum distillation, the solution is heated in a closed container with reduced atmospheric pressure. The system is not closed, but one-way valves hinder the flow of gas into the system. By definition, the boiling point of a liquid is the point (temperature) at which the vapor pressure equals the atmospheric pressure. By reducing the atmospheric pressure, the vapor pressure required for boiling is lowered and thus the energy needed to boil the liquid is reduced.

A student performs vacuum distillation on 120 grams of a mixture that is 50% by mass 2-propanol with 50% by mass acetophenone. This solution is made by adding 60.0 grams of 2-propanol to 60.0 grams acetophenone in a 250-mL flask. The boiling points, molecular masses, and room temperature vapor pressures of the two compounds are listed below:

Compound	Boiling Point	MW	P°_{vapor}
Acetophenone	203°C	120.15	12 torr
2-Propanol	82°C	60.10	48 torr

Table 1

Table 1 lists the normal boiling point, molecular weight, and room temperature vapor pressure. The structures of acetophenone and 2-propanol are shown in Figure 1.

Acetophenone   2-Propanol

Figure 1

The researcher reduces the pressure above the mixture and collects the vapor in successive aliquots of 5.0 mL. A total of twenty-five 5.0-mL aliquots are collected before the amount of solution remaining in the flask becomes too small to measure. The twenty-five samples are labeled 1 through 25, in the order in which they were collected.

36. At room temperature, what is TRUE about the vapor pressure of 2-propanol above the mixture?

A. The vapor pressure of 2-propanol equals the vapor pressure due to acetophenone.

B. The vapor pressure of 2-propanol is double the vapor pressure due to acetophenone.

C. The vapor pressure of 2-propanol is eight times the vapor pressure due to acetophenone.

D. The vapor pressure of 2-propanol is equal to the total vapor pressure.

37. How many moles of acetophenone ($C_6H_5COCH_3$) are contained in the mixture?

A. 0.25 moles

B. 0.50 moles

C. 1.00 moles

D. 2.00 moles

38. What is TRUE for the boiling point for pure acetophenone at 500 torr?

A. It is greater than 203°C, because decreasing the atmospheric pressure makes it easier to boil.

B. It is less than 203°C, because decreasing the atmospheric pressure makes it easier to boil.

C. It is greater than 203°C, because decreasing the atmospheric pressure makes it harder to boil.

D. It is less than 203°C, because decreasing the atmospheric pressure makes it harder to boil.

39. The mole fraction of acetophenone in the original solution is which of the following values?

A. 0.25

B. 0.33

C. 0.50

D. 0.67

40. What is observed when comparing Aliquot 5 with Aliquot 10?

A. Aliquot 10 has a greater total vapor pressure and larger mole fraction of acetophenone than Aliquot 5.

B. Aliquot 10 has a smaller total vapor pressure and lower mole fraction of acetophenone than Aliquot 5.

C. The total vapor pressure is greater above Aliquot 10 than Aliquot 5, while the mole fraction of acetophenone is greater above Aliquot 5.

D. The total vapor pressure is greater above Aliquot 5 than Aliquot 10, while the mole fraction of acetophenone is greater above Aliquot 10.

41. After time, the mole fraction due to acetophenone should do which of the following?

A. It should increase, due to evaporation.

B. It should decrease, due to evaporation.

C. It should stay constant, due to evaporation.

D. It should stay constant, regardless of evaporation.

42. Addition of another 60.0 grams of 2-propanol to the original mixture would affect the vapor pressure of acetophenone in what way?

A. It would reduce the vapor pressure of acetophenone.

B. It would have no effect on the vapor pressure of acetophenone.

C. It would increase the vapor pressure of acetophenone.

D. It would increase by exactly one-half the vapor pressure of acetophenone.

43. Aliquot 1 from the mixture has which of the following mole distribution percentages?

A. 50.0% acetophenone and 50.0% 2-propanol

B. 33.3% acetophenone and 66.7% 2-propanol

C. 20.0% acetophenone and 80.0% 2-propanol

D. 11.1% acetophenone and 88.9% 2-propanol

Passage VII (Questions 44 - 50)

According to Raoult's law, the vapor pressure above a solution consisting of more than one liquid is equal to the sum of the individual vapor pressures. The individual vapor pressures for each component can therefore be calculated by multiplying the mole fraction (χ_A) of a given component by the vapor pressure (P_A°) of a pure sample of that same component. The equation for the total vapor pressure due to all of the components is expressed in Equation 1.

$$P_{total} = \chi_A P_A^\circ + \chi_B P_B^\circ + \chi_C P_C^\circ + \cdots$$

Equation 1

This equation is based on ideal behavior for solutions. If the attractive force between the component liquids in solution is strong, a decrease in the vapor pressure above the mixture is observed. This decrease in vapor pressure is referred to as *negative deviation* from Raoult's law. The strong attractive forces are associated with a large negative heat of dilution. The opposite holds true for *positive deviations* from ideal behavior. Drawn in Figure 1 are graphs showing positive and negative deviations for hypothetical solution mixtures.

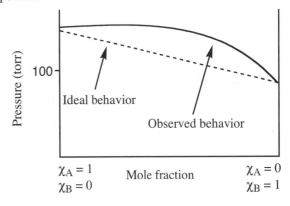

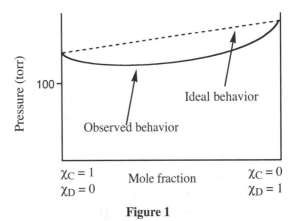

Figure 1

The first graph shows a positive deviation from ideal behavior, because the observed vapor pressure is greater than the ideal vapor pressure. The second graph shows a negative deviation from ideal behavior, because the observed vapor pressure is less than the ideal vapor pressure.

GO ON TO THE NEXT PAGE

44. What is TRUE about the dilution energies for a mixture with positive deviation from Raoult's ideal behavior?

A. $\Delta G > 0$; $\Delta H > 0$

B. $\Delta G < 0$; $\Delta H > 0$

C. $\Delta G > 0$; $\Delta H < 0$

D. $\Delta G < 0$; $\Delta H < 0$

45. Which of the following pairs of solvents would be expected to have the LARGEST negative deviation from ideal behavior?

A. Ethanol and carbon tetrachloride

B. Ethanol and acetone

C. Ethanol and hexane

D. Ethanol and cyclohexene

46. If the vapor above a 50% mixture of methanol with butanol at 22°C were collected and placed into a flask where it condenses, what is the mole percent of methanol in vapor above the new (second) flask? [Pure methanol has a vapor pressure of 87 torr and pure butanol has a vapor pressure of 29 torr at 22°C.]

A. Less than 25%

B. Between 25% and 50%

C. Between 50% and 75%

D. Greater than 75%

47. Positive deviations from ideal behavior in the vapor pressure above a mixed solution can be attributed to which of the following?

A. Attraction between liquids, $\Delta H > 0$

B. Attraction between liquids, $\Delta H < 0$

C. Repulsion between liquids, $\Delta H > 0$

D. Repulsion between liquids, $\Delta H < 0$

48. Using the information in Figure 1, what is the vapor pressure due to Substance B (l) in a 40% (by mole) mixture of Substance B in Substance A, if the pure vapor pressures of A and B are 150 torr and 75 torr respectively?

A. 27 torr

B. 33 torr

C. 70 torr

D. 80 torr

49. Referring to the liquids in the lower graph in Figure 1, what can be said about the *mole fractions* of each liquid solution over time, if the flask is open to the environment and the mixture is allowed to evaporate?

A. C and D both increase.

B. C and D both decrease.

C. C increases and D decreases.

D. C decreases and D increases.

50. Two liquids exhibiting a drastic negative deviation from ideal behavior can attribute the behavior to which of the following?

A. A bond-forming reaction between the two compounds in solution

B. A bond-breaking reaction between the two compounds in solution

C. An increase in one compound's polarity

D. A decrease in one compound's polarity

GO ON TO THE NEXT PAGE

Reverse osmosis can be employed to extract fresh water from salt water. The process involves applying a force to the salt water that is greater than the osmotic pressure of aqueous salt solution, consequently forcing the flow of fresh water out from the aqueous salt solution. The apparatus used to accomplished this consists of a container for the salt water solution and a cellophane filter through which no ions can pass, so that only water may flow through it. The cellophane filter is referred to as a semipermeable membrane. It distinguishes and segregates molecules by charge. There are other semipermeable membranes, which segregate according to particle size. The apparatus is shown below in Figure 1.

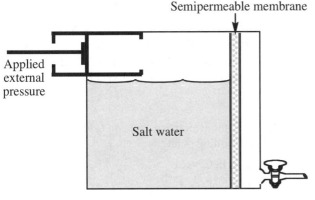

Figure 1

To convert sea water to water that is suitable for consumption, an applied pressure of 1100 p.s.i. (~70 atm.) is employed. This process of water purification is referred to as desalination. The osmotic pressure (π) of the solution can be calculated using the following formula:

$$\pi = MiRT$$
(where M = molarity and i = ionizability)

Equation 1

A solution with 5.84 grams NaCl dissolved into 100 grams water (with a final volume that is just over 100 mL) is placed into a desalination tube. The desalination tube is then connected to a plunger used to vary the applied pressure. The *desalination* tube employs a cellophane membrane for segregation of the impurities from the water.

51. An external pressure of 4.61 atm has what effect on an aqueous solution of $MgCl_2$ with an osmotic pressure of 1.19 atm?

   A. External pressure forces water out from the salt solution, which increases $[MgCl_2]$ over time.

   B. External pressure forces water out from the salt solution, which decreases $[MgCl_2]$ over time.

   C. External pressure forces water into the salt solution, which increases $[MgCl_2]$ over time.

   D. External pressure forces water into the salt solution, which decreases $[MgCl_2]$ over time.

52. Which of the following solutions has the GREATEST osmotic pressure at 20°C?

   A. 0.20 moles NaCl(s) with one liter water (where K_{sp} for NaCl is greater than 1)

   B. 0.30 moles KCl(s) with one liter water (where K_{sp} for KCl is greater than 1)

   C. 0.25 moles $MgCl_2$(s) with one liter water (where K_{sp} for $MgCl_2$ is greater than 1)

   D. 0.30 moles $PbCl_2$(s) with one liter water (where K_{sp} for $PbCl_2$ is equal to 1.6×10^{-5} M^3)

53. In order to reduce the osmotic pressure of a 100-mL sample of brine solution from 25 atm. to 10 atm., what amount of pure water must be added?

   A. 100 mL

   B. 125 mL

   C. 150 mL

   D. 250 mL

54. What is the external pressure necessary to stop osmosis of a 1.0 M NaCl(aq) solution at 31°C where, R = .0821 L atm. mole^{-1} K^{-1}?

   A. Between 2.5 and 5 atm.

   B. Between 5 and 10 atm.

   C. Between 10 and 35 atm.

   D. Between 35 and 70 atm.

55. In desalination, once an external pressure source is removed, the flow of water:

   A. continues from higher salt concentration to lower salt concentration.

   B. from higher to lower salt concentration reverses to lower to higher salt concentration.

   C. continues from lower salt concentration to higher salt concentration.

   D. from lower to higher salt concentration reverses to higher to lower salt concentration.

56. Which of the following methods could also be used for purifying salt water?

   A. Filtering through glass beads to remove the salt

   B. Freezing the solution and removing the relatively pure ice that forms

   C. Centrifuging the solution into cotton

   D. Increasing the pressure to force the salt to precipitate out of solution

 GO ON TO THE NEXT PAGE

A researcher wanted to study the effects of salt concentration on the physical properties of a solution. To do this, she set up six flasks that varied in content and concentration (see Table 1 for contents). She used distilled water that had been recently heated to remove any dissolved carbon dioxide. Each solution was made by first adding the solid to the flask, followed by adding the water to the flask. In each of the flasks, the salt fully dissolved into the water at ambient temperature. The researcher concluded that the solutes are fully soluble in water at room temperature.

Flask	Grams salt	Grams water added
# 1	2.0 grams NaCl	100 grams H_2O
# 2	2.0 grams NaCl	200 grams H_2O
# 3	4.0 grams NaCl	100 grams H_2O
# 4	2.0 grams KCl	100 grams H_2O
# 5	2.0 grams KCl	200 grams H_2O
# 6	4.0 grams KCl	100 grams H_2O

MW (NaCl) = 58.4 grams/mole

MW (KCl) = 74.5 grams/mole

Table 1

Properties of the solution that are affected by the concentration of solute are referred to as *colligative properties*. The colligative properties include the freezing point, the boiling point, osmotic pressure, and conductance. As more non-volatile soluble impurities are added to a solution, the freezing point decreases and the boiling point and osmotic pressure increase. Conductance increases, if the solute is ionic. For covalently bound solutes, conductance is not detectably affected.

As an aqueous salt solution boils, the kilograms of water (solvent) decrease, so that the molality of the solution increases. This means that as the solution boils away, the boiling point is increasing. A similar effect is observed with freezing point depression. An interesting observation involves ice cubes. Ice cubes freeze from the outside inward, so as they freeze, the exterior is pure, but solute impurities get trapped in the core. This explains why the insides of ice cubes are cloudy. If it is a gas particle that is trapped in the ice cube, it makes a loud noise as it escapes, once the ice cube is broken open.

57. When considering only solutions in Table 1, what can be said about the melting of the solution in Flask #3?

   A. The freezing point is the greatest of all the solutions, and it increases as the solution freezes.

   B. The freezing point is the lowest of all solutions, and it increases as the solution freezes.

   C. The freezing point is the greatest of all solutions, and it decreases as the solution freezes.

   D. The freezing point is the lowest of all solutions, and it decreases as the solution freezes.

58. The HIGHEST boiling point would be associated with which of these solutions in Table 1?

   A. Solution B (Flask # 2)

   B. Solution C (Flask # 3)

   C. Solution E (Flask # 5)

   D. Solution F (Flask # 6)

59. Upon comparing solutions in Table 1, which of the following is NOT true?

   A. The solution in Flask # 1 has a higher electrical conductivity than the solution in Flask # 4.

   B. The solution in Flask # 2 has a higher vapor pressure than the solution in Flask # 5.

   C. The solution in Flask # 3 has a higher osmotic pressure than the solution in Flask # 6.

   D. The solution in Flask # 4 has a higher freezing point than the solution in Flask # 6.

60. Which of the following aqueous solutions has the LOWEST boiling point?

   A. 0.20 m $BeCl_2(aq)$

   B. 0.20 m $NaCl(aq)$

   C. 0.30 m $KCl(aq)$

   D. 0.30 m $MgCl_2(aq)$

61. If K_f for water is 1.86 °C/molal, then the freezing point of Solution C (Flask # 3) is which of the following?

   A. -0.12 °C

   B. -0.24 °C

   C. -1.20 °C

   D. -2.40 °C

62. As more solute is added to solution, which of the following does NOT increase?

   A. The freezing point

   B. The boiling point

   C. The osmotic pressure

   D. The density

63. The LOWEST freezing point for the solutions is associated with which of the following solutions?

   A. Solution A (Flask # 1)

   B. Solution B (Flask # 2)

   C. Solution D (Flask # 4)

   D. Solution E (Flask # 5)

 GO ON TO THE NEXT PAGE

A student set out to determine k_f, the freezing point depression constant, for cyclohexanol. The freezing point depression constant is a property of a solvent, and solutes are added to a solvent to study it. In separate experiments, the student added known quantities of menthol and camphor to separate test tubes containing 10.000 grams of cyclohexanol liquid at 27°C. The solutions were thoroughly mixed and then immersed in an ice bath until they were frozen. Then the test tubes were removed from the ice bath and placed into a water bath held constant at 35°C. The temperature of the mixture in the test tube was recorded every twenty seconds, until the solution was completely liquefied again. The time and temperature data for Experiment 1, using camphor as the solute, are listed in Table 1 below:

Camphor	
Mass = 1.0102 grams MW = 152.25	
Time (seconds)	Temperature (°C)
0	13.9
20	14.3
40	14.7
60	15.1
80	15.6
100	16.0
120	16.4
140	16.7
160	17.1
180	17.8
200	18.7
220	19.6
240	20.5
260	21.4
280	22.4
300	23.3
320	24.2
340	25.1
360	26.1

Table 1

For Experiment 2, using menthol as the solute, the procedure was carried out in exactly the same manner as in Experiment 1. The formula for camphor is $C_{10}H_{16}O$, and the formula for menthol is $C_{10}H_{20}O$. The data from Experiment 2 for temperature over uniform increments of time was graphed (rather than listed in a table). The graph for the menthol experiment is shown in Figure 1. The freezing point of the solution is determined by finding the inflection point. A horizontal line is extrapolated back from the inflection point to the temperature axis to determine the freezing point of the solution. The horizontal line used to determine the freezing point is also shown in Figure 1.

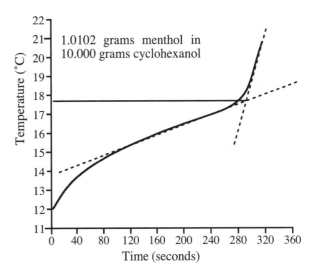

Figure 1

The normal freezing point of cyclohexanol is found to be 22.6°C, according to the thermometer used in Experiment 2.

64. Why must the normal freezing point be determined using the thermometer, rather than using the standard value from the literature?

A. The standard value may not hold during the experimental conditions.

B. The thermometer may not be calibrated, so the normal freezing point must be determined to determine the ΔT accurately.

C. The normal freezing point is not the same for all samples of cyclohexanol.

D. The freezing point varies with the shape of the container.

65. Menthol and camphor do not dissociate once in solution. If an impurity were chosen that can dissociate into two particles in solution, how would the freezing point be affected?

A. The freezing point would decrease by twice as much as expected, if the impurity did not dissociate.

B. The freezing point would decrease by as much as expected, if the impurity did not dissociate.

C. The freezing point would decrease by half as much as expected, if the impurity did not dissociate.

D. The freezing point would remain constant.

66. The freezing point for the camphor-cyclohexanol solution in Experiment 1 was reached:

A. during the first minute of observation.

B. during the second minute of observation.

C. during the third minute of observation.

D. during the sixth minute of observation.

         GO ON TO THE NEXT PAGE

67. For an experiment in which the compound chosen was a solid at room temperature rather than a liquid, the mixture must be heated from room temperature to its melting point instead of being cooled from room temperature to its freezing point. This would be the case with naphthalene. Which of the following graphs represents what should be observed, if a naphthalene-camphor mixture were heated to its liquid state and then observed while it was allowed to cool to its solid form?

A.

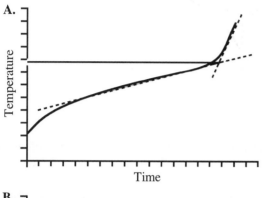

B.

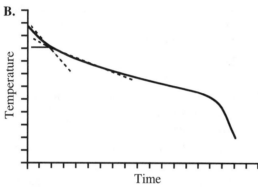

C.

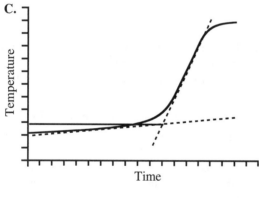

D.

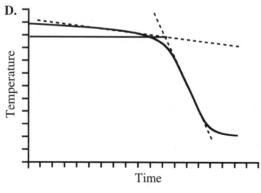

68. The freezing point for which solution is lower, the one used in Experiment 1 or the one used in Experiment 2?

A. The camphor solution has a lower freezing point, because the camphor solution has a higher molality than the menthol solution.

B. The camphor solution has a lower freezing point, because the camphor solution has a lower molality than the menthol solution.

C. The menthol solution has a lower freezing point, because the menthol solution has a higher molality than the camphor solution.

D. The menthol solution has a lower freezing point, because the menthol solution has a lower molality than the camphor solution.

69. What would be expected for the freezing point of a solution made by mixing 20.000 grams of cyclohexanol with 1.0102 grams of menthol?

A. The freezing point would be 22.6°C.

B. The freezing point would be 20.2°C.

C. The freezing point would be 17.8°C.

D. The freezing point would be 13.0°C.

70. Which of the following statements BEST explains the reason for the observed depression in the freezing point as an impurity is added to the solution?

A. The molecules can form a lattice structure more easily with impurities present, because the impurities repel the solvent molecules to form a lattice-like structure. The solution thus freezes more easily, which results in an increase in the freezing point.

B. The molecules can form a lattice structure more easily with impurities present, because the impurities repel the solvent molecules to form a lattice-like structure. The solution thus freezes less easily, which results in a decrease in the freezing point.

C. The molecules cannot form a lattice structure as easily with impurities present, because the impurities attract the solvent molecules and keep them in solution. The solution thus freezes more easily, which results in an increase in the freezing point.

D. The molecules cannot form a lattice structure as easily with impurities present, because the impurities attract the solvent molecules and keep them in solution. The solution thus freezes less easily, which results in a decrease in the freezing point.

Passage XI (Questions 71 - 76)

The Dumas experiment involves filling a flask of known mass and volume with an organic liquid. The organic liquid is heated, so that it begins to vaporize. Assuming that the air in the flask is lighter than these organic vapors, the air is displaced out of the flask by the organic vapors through a small hole at the top of the flask. The ideal flask is a spherical flask with a stopcock attached, but a good substitute would be any flask with a foil cap that has a small pinhole in the foil cap. Foil is chosen in lieu of plastic or rubber, because organic solvents will dissolve both plastic and rubber. The solution is heated by flame until the last trace of liquid residue has evaporated.

Once the liquid has completely evaporated, it is assumed that the flask is filled entirely with organic vapors. As the flask cools, the vapors condense back into a liquid, and air flows back into the flask through the pinhole. Once the flask is back to its initial temperature (ambient temperature), the combined mass of the flask and condensed organic liquid is measured. The increase in mass over the initial weighing of the empty flask can be attributed to the organic liquid in the flask. The small amount of air displaced by the organic liquid is assumed to be negligible.

An example of the flask is drawn in Figure 1 below:

Pinhole

Organic liquid

Figure 1

The mass of the organic liquid can be used to determine the molecular mass of the unknown organic liquid. Because the pressure, temperature, and volume of the gas in the flask are known at the boiling point of the liquid, the moles of the liquid in the flask can be determined using $PV = nRT$.

71. Why should this experiment NOT be carried out with a plastic cap on the flask?

A. The plastic cap can expand during the experiment.

B. The pore size in the plastic cap would be too small.

C. The plastic cap does not allow air to flow back into the flask as it cools.

D. The plastic cap can dissolve in the organic vapors.

72. Which of these equations provides the correct way to calculate the molecular weight of the liquid in the flask? Note: $m_{condensed\ vapor}$ = mass of the organic liquid condensed in the flask.

A. $MW = m_{condensed\ vapor} \times \dfrac{RT}{PV}$

B. $MW = m_{condensed\ vapor} \times \dfrac{PV}{RT}$

C. $MW = \dfrac{1}{m_{condensed\ vapor}} \times \dfrac{RT}{PV}$

D. $MW = \dfrac{1}{m_{condensed\ vapor}} \times \dfrac{PV}{RT}$

73. What would be the result if the heating source were removed before all of the organic liquid had completely vaporized?

A. The mass measured at the end of the experiment would be too high, and the molecular mass calculated from the experiment would be too high.

B. The mass measured at the end of the experiment would be too high, and the molecular mass calculated from the experiment would be too low.

C. The mass measured at the end of the experiment would be too low, and the molecular mass calculated from the experiment would be too high.

D. The mass measured at the end of the experiment would be too low, and the molecular mass calculated from the experiment would be too low.

74. Which of the following changes to the flask would NOT increase the accuracy of the experiment?

A. Rather than using a foil cap, use a permanent attachment with a small valve that can be opened and shut manually.

B. Use an electric heating mantle to encompass the flask, rather than a flame from a gas burner.

C. Increase the size of the pore in the aluminum foil cap.

D. Use a spherical flask with less internal surface area.

75. Which type of organic liquid could be measured MOST accurately using the Dumas technique?

A. A less volatile organic liquid with a high molecular mass.

B. A highly volatile organic liquid with a high molecular mass.

C. A less volatile organic liquid with a low molecular mass.

D. A highly volatile organic liquid with a low molecular mass.

GO ON TO THE NEXT PAGE

76. Which of the following liquids would form the DENSEST vapor upon heating?

　A. $CH_3CH_2CH_2OH$

　B. $CH_3(CH_2)_3CH_2Cl$

　C. $CH_3(CH_2)_4CH_2Br$

　D. $(CH_3)_3CCH_2OH$

Passage XII (Questions 77 - 84)

Liquids have certain properties that provide an indirect measure of their intermolecular forces. These properties are viscosity, surface tension, and vapor pressure. Table 1 lists the values for these properties for various selected solvents.

	Viscosity	Surface Tension	P_{vapor} (@ 20°C)
$CHBr_3$	$2.0 \times 10^{-3} \frac{kg}{m \cdot s}$	$4.2 \times 10^{-2} \frac{J}{m^2}$	3.9 torr
$CHCl_3$	$5.8 \times 10^{-4} \frac{kg}{m \cdot s}$	$2.5 \times 10^{-2} \frac{J}{m^2}$	173 torr
CCl_4	$9.7 \times 10^{-4} \frac{kg}{m \cdot s}$	$2.5 \times 10^{-2} \frac{J}{m^2}$	86.8 torr
$C_3H_8O_3$	$1.57 \frac{kg}{m \cdot s}$	$6.3 \times 10^{-3} \frac{J}{m^2}$	.00018 torr
H_2O	$1.0 \times 10^{-3} \frac{kg}{m \cdot s}$	$7.3 \times 10^{-2} \frac{J}{m^2}$	18.2 torr
C_6H_{14}	$2.6 \times 10^{-4} \frac{kg}{m \cdot s}$	$1.6 \times 10^{-2} \frac{J}{m^2}$	44 torr

Table 1

The definition of each physical property is listed below. The SI units for each value are indicated in Table 1 above.

Viscosity: A resistance to flow exhibited by all liquids.

Surface tension: The amount of energy required to increase the surface area of a liquid by a specified unit amount.

Vapor pressure: The pressure exerted by a gas formed through evaporation above the surface of the liquid.

77. Which of the following does NOT affect the vapor pressure above a liquid?

　A. Hydrogen bonding

　B. Polarity

　C. Molecular mass

　D. Surface area

78. For non-hydrogen-bonding liquids, as the viscosity increases, what is observed with the vapor pressure and surface tension?

　A. The vapor pressure increases, while the surface tension shows no distinct trend.

　B. The surface tension increases, while the vapor pressure shows no distinct trend.

　C. Both the surface tension and vapor pressure show increases.

　D. Neither the surface tension nor the vapor pressure shows a distinct trend.

GO ON TO THE NEXT PAGE

79. Through a column of which solution would a metal ball fall the fastest, if the only external force exerted on the falling ball were gravity?

A. Bromoform
B. Carbon tetrachloride
C. Glycerol
D. Water

80. A dense piece of paper when laid flat atop a liquid to maximize its surface area would remain atop the surface of which solvent for the longest time?

A. Carbon tetrachloride
B. Chloroform
C. Hexane
D. Water

81. Which compound is MOST likely to form beads on the surface of the indicated solid?

A. A polar liquid with low surface tension on the surface of a polar solid
B. A polar liquid with high surface tension on the surface of a polar solid
C. A polar liquid with low surface tension on the surface of a nonpolar solid
D. A polar liquid with high surface tension on the surface of a nonpolar solid

82. What explains the higher vapor pressure for chloroform than for carbon tetrachloride?

A. Carbon tetrachloride is more polar than chloroform.
B. Carbon tetrachloride has more hydrogen bonding than chloroform.
C. Carbon tetrachloride has greater surface tension than chloroform.
D. Carbon tetrachloride has a greater molecular mass than chloroform.

83. What is the more critical factor when determining the P_{vapor} and viscosity of CCl_4 compared to $CHCl_3$?

A. For both P_{vapor} and viscosity: the molecular mass
B. For both P_{vapor} and viscosity: the polarity
C. For P_{vapor}: polarity; and for viscosity: the molecular mass
D. For P_{vapor}: the molecular mass; and for viscosity: polarity

84. Which set of values is the BEST estimate for the surface tension, vapor pressure at 20°C, and viscosity of CH_2Cl_2?

A. Surface tension $= 2.5 \times 10^{-2} \frac{J}{m^2}$

   Vapor pressure $= 223$ torr

   Viscosity $= 4.7 \times 10^{-4} \frac{kg}{m \cdot s}$

B. Surface tension $= 4.9 \times 10^{-2} \frac{J}{m^2}$

   Vapor pressure $= 67.4$ torr

   Viscosity $= 4.7 \times 10^{-4} \frac{kg}{m \cdot s}$

C. Surface tension $= 4.9 \times 10^{-2} \frac{J}{m^2}$

   Vapor pressure $= 223$ torr

   Viscosity $= 4.7 \times 10^{-2} \frac{kg}{m \cdot s}$

D. Surface tension $= 2.5 \times 10^{-2} \frac{J}{m^2}$

   Vapor pressure $= 67.4$ torr

   Viscosity $= 4.7 \times 10^{-2} \frac{kg}{m \cdot s}$

GO ON TO THE NEXT PAGE

Allotropes are made of the same element, but have different physical properties. The difference in physical properties can be attributed to the type of molecular bonding, as is seen with diamond and graphite, both of which are made of carbon. In diamond, all carbons have sp^3-hybridization and the lattice is held together completely by sigma bonds. In graphite, all carbons have sp^2-hybridization and their are sheets of conjugated carbon atoms in a network of six-membered rings. The structure of a sheet of graphite is shown in Figure 1.

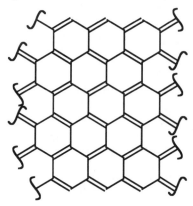

Figure 1

Buckminster fullerene, *buckyball*, is also an allotrope of carbon. One example is C_{60}, which is a spheroidal structure made entirely of carbon atoms. Buckyball can be separated from other allotropes, such as C_{70} and C_{72}, by sublimation. These allotropes have different physical properties than C_{60} due to different packing in their respective lattice structures. Because the molecules are spheroidal in nature, it can function like microscopic ball bearings, so buckyball is often used as a lubricant. The molecular mass is the most significant factor in the energy required to undergo a phase change.

85. How can it be explained that diamond is more dense than graphite?

    A. Double bonds are longer than single bonds.

    B. Layering in graphite allows atoms to get closer, because they are in direct contact.

    C. Carbon atoms in diamond are smaller than carbon atoms in graphite.

    D. Packing is closer in diamond's tetrahedral lattice than graphite sheets.

86. How can the difference in melting point between two allotropes BEST be explained?

    A. The two have different polarities.

    B. The two have different lattice packing.

    C. The two have different interatomic bonding.

    D. The two have different electronegativities.

87. How can the black color associated with graphite be explained in terms of structure?

    A. Graphite has conjugation, so it absorbs all light.

    B. Graphite has conjugation, so it reflects all light.

    C. Graphite has no conjugation, so it absorbs all light.

    D. Graphite has no conjugation, so it reflects all light.

88. Which of the following materials is the best electrical conductor?

    A. C_{60} Buckminster fullerene

    B. C_{72} Buckminster fullerene

    C. Diamond

    D. Graphite

89. What are the bond angles found in graphite?

    A. 90°

    B. 109.5°

    C. 120°

    D. 144°

90. Which of the following materials is LEAST likely to form an allotrope?

    A. Argon

    B. Carbon

    C. Phosphorus

    D. Sulfur

91. Which of the following three dimensional structures MOST accurately depicts P_4?

    A.   **B.**

    C.   **D.**

92. Which of the following allotropes of carbon has the GREATEST sublimation point at 0.010 atm.?

    A. C_{60}

    B. C_{64}

    C. C_{70}

    D. C_{72}

93. If a solution made by adding 0.10 moles KCl(*s*) to 1.00 liters of water conducts electricity better than a solution made by adding 0.10 moles AgCl(*s*) to 1.00 liters of water, then:

    A. 0.10 M KCl(*aq*) has a greater osmotic pressure than 0.10 M AgCl(*aq*).

    B. 0.10 M KCl(*aq*) has the same osmotic pressure as 0.10 M AgCl(*aq*).

    C. 0.10 M KCl(*aq*) has a lower osmotic pressure than 0.10 M AgCl(*aq*).

    D. 0.12 M KCl(*aq*) has a lower osmotic pressure than 0.10 M AgCl(*aq*).

94. Which of the following phase change processes *absorbs* the GREATEST amount of energy?

    A. Evaporation

    B. Condensation

    C. Sublimation

    D. Deposition

95. Given that the normal boiling point for Compound A is 127.0°C, and the enthalpy of vaporization is 33.26 kJ/mole, what would the boiling point of Compound A be in Running Springs, California (elevation 9,870 ft. and P_{atm} = 603 torr)?

    A. 115.0°C

    B. 133.3°C

    C. 137.4°C

    D. 151.0°C

96. CH_4 has a lower boiling point than SiH_4, due to:

    A. its lower molecular mass.

    B. its stronger ionic interactions.

    C. its lower affinity entropy.

    D. its increased hydrogen bonding.

97. Which of the following is a property of a solid, under isobaric and isothermal conditions?

    A. The ability to flow

    B. An amorphous structure

    C. Molecules that undergo displacement

    D. Static dimensions

98. A liquid is defined as:

    A. having a definite shape and definite volume.

    B. having a definite shape and indefinite volume.

    C. having an indefinite shape and definite volume.

    D. having an indefinite shape and indefinite volume.

99. Water has a vapor pressure of 149.4 torr at 60°C. An unknown liquid is found to have a vapor pressure of 130.6 torr at 60°C. If the vapor pressure of water at room temperature is 22.65 torr, then at room temperature, the vapor pressure of the unknown is:

    A. 7.61 torr.

    B. 20.00 torr.

    C. 22.65 torr.

    D. 45.35 torr.

GO ON TO THE NEXT PAGE

100. Chloroform is a liquid at room temperature (roughly 20°C). Which set of physical constants is possible for $HCCl_3$?

A. Boiling point: 88°C; melting point: 31°C

B. Boiling point: 18°C; melting point: -31°C

C. Boiling point: 61°C; melting point: -64°C

D. Boiling point: 32°C; melting point: 31°C

1. C	2. D	3. B	4. C	5. D
6. C	7. D	8. D	9. B	10. D
11. D	12. A	13. B	14. D	15. C
16. C	17. C	18. B	19. C	20. C
21. B	22. B	23. D	24. D	25. B
26. A	27. D	28. C	29. B	30. A
31. D	32. A	33. B	34. B	35. B
36. C	37. B	38. B	39. B	40. D
41. A	42. A	43. D	44. B	45. B
46. D	47. C	48. B	49. C	50. A
51. A	52. C	53. C	54. D	55. B
56. B	57. D	58. B	59. B	60. B
61. D	62. A	63. A	64. B	65. A
66. C	67. B	68. A	69. B	70. D
71. D	72. A	73. A	74. C	75. A
76. C	77. D	78. B	79. B	80. D
81. D	82. D	83. A	84. A	85. D
86. B	87. A	88. D	89. C	90. A
91. B	92. D	93. A	94. C	95. A
96. A	97. D	98. C	99. B	100. C

YOU ARE DONE.

Phases Passages Answers

1. **Choice C is correct.** In freeze-drying, the ice in the frozen coffee is exposed to a reduced pressure environment where the water molecules in the ice sublime directly into a gas. The process of converting from a solid directly into a gas is known as sublimation, making choice **C** the best answer.

2. **Choice D is correct.** Because water is in the form the ice when it sublimes away from its frozen state, the temperature must be set so that the ice does not melt (into liquid). This means that the temperature must be less than 0°C. This eliminates choice A and B. The atmospheric pressure must be low enough to allow for sublimation, so 1 torr is better than 1 atm. The best answer is thus choice **D**, a temperature well below the normal freezing point of water and a pressure well below atmospheric pressure.

3. **Choice B is correct.** The goal of freeze-drying is to remove the water from the coffee solution. Any alternative to freeze-drying would also remove water from the coffee solution. Recrystallization won't work, because coffee solutes are soluble in water. Choice A can be eliminated. When water is distilled (as opposed to sublimed) away from the solution, so the residue left behind should be similar. Collecting the residue, rather than the distilled water, gets the same result as freeze-drying, so choice **B** is a better answer than choice C. The high temperatures required for distillation would destroy the flavor of the coffee, however, which makes the technique impractical. So although distillation works well for dehydrating coffee in theory, freeze-drying works better in practice. Filtering away solute particles through sieves won't work, so choice D is eliminated. The best answer is choice **B**.

4. **Choice C is correct.** The temperature of a cloud can range from 0 to -10°C, according to the passage. To cool the cloud to a lower temperature, a substance must be introduced into it that is either cooler than that temperature or that reacts in an endothermic fashion. The only choice that meets either of these requirements is choice **C**. It is stated in paragraph four of the passage that the sublimation point of CO_2 is -78°C.

5. **Choice D is correct.** Supercooled water is water that is cooled below its normal freezing point, but it remains a liquid. Water normally freezes at 0°C, so pure water at any temperature below this value is considered to be supercooled. Water at -10°C meets this description, making choice **D** the best choice. Choices B and C should have been eliminated, because they are in the wrong phase.

6. **Choice C is correct.** Cloud-seeding involves turning pockets of water moisture in the air into ice crystals. The conversion of a liquid to a solid is referred to as fusion, making choice **C** the best answer. This answer can be determined by elimination of the wrong answers. The dry ice is sublimed in the process, but dry ice is carbon dioxide, not water.

7. **Choice D is correct.** The boiling point of a substance is defined as the temperature at which the vapor pressure is equal to the atmospheric pressure. This means that the boiling point of a solution is the greatest where the atmospheric pressure is the greatest. The greatest atmospheric pressure of these at the three locations is at sea level (an ocean port), which eliminates choices B and C. The mountains have the lowest atmospheric pressure of the three locations, so the boiling point is lowest in the mountains, making choice **D** the correct answer.

8. **Choice D is correct.** The critical point is point y, where the liquid-gas interface line terminates. Above this temperature and pressure, the material may not exist as a true liquid or true gas, and it is referred to as a *supercritical fluid*. It is no longer possible to distinguish between a liquid and a gas above the critical point. A supercritical fluid exhibits properties of both a liquid and a gas, including the ability to flow and an amorphous nature. This makes choice **D** the best choice. Point x is referred to as the *triple point*, the point at which all three phases may coexist.

9. **Choice B is correct.** The phase diagram in Figure 1 represents compound A. Figure 1 shows that at 298 K and 1.3 atm. (just over 1000 torr), Compound A exists as a liquid. After reducing the pressure from 1.3 atm. to 0.9 atm. (just less than 700 torr), Compound A crosses into the gas phase (following the vertical line downward for the decrease in pressure). Therefore, the correct answer is **B**. Even if you are not certain from drawing lines on the diagram that it actually crosses into the gas phase, there is no answer choice saying that it undergoes no phase change and remains as a liquid. When reading graphs, it is often a good idea to use your answer sheet for fold the pages of the test to generate a reliable straight edge.

10. **Choice D is correct.** Sublimation is the process by which a substance converts from the solid phase directly into the gaseous phase without passing through the liquid phase. At an appropriate pressure, any temperature below the triple point (in this case, about 290 K = 17°C) is adequate for sublimation of Compound B to occur, since under these conditions the compound has an interface between solid phase and the gas phase on the phase diagram. From the choices given, the only temperature above 290 K (17°C) is 100°C (373 K), which is choice **D**. At this temperature sublimation cannot occur, since the compound cannot exist in the solid state for any of the possible pressures. Choices B and C could have been eliminated, because they are the same temperature. Choice **D** is the highest temperature, so it was the most likely answer.

11. **Choice D is correct.** At 1.0 atm. (760 torr) and 10°C (283 K), Compound A (Diagram I) is in the liquid phase. Looking at Figure 2 under the same conditions places Compound B in the solid phase. The question asks which of the compounds is a gas (under the given conditions); and neither one is, so choice **D** is the best answer.

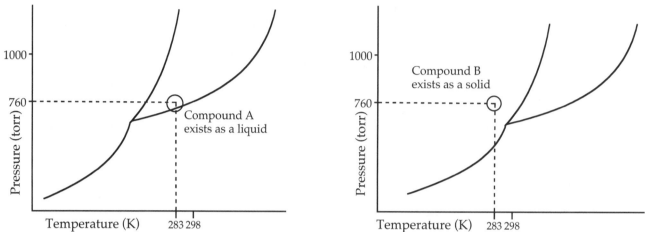

12. **Choice A is correct.** STP is 0°C and 1 atm. (273 K and 760 torr). Looking at Figure 2, at a temperature of 273 K and a pressure of 760 torr (the perpendicular lines are already drawn in the passage), Compound B definitely exists as a solid, so choice **A** is the best answer.

13. **Choice B is correct.** The key to answering this question is to know that the lower right quadrant of the graph (at low pressure and high temperature) indicates the conditions under which the material exists as a gas. Evaporation is defined as the conversion from a liquid to a gas, so a vertical arrow down from the liquid region to the gas region represents the isothermal liquid-to-gas phase change (evaporation). The correct Arrow is arrow b, so the answer is choice **B**.

14. **Choice D is correct.** Compound A does sublime at 25°C (298 K), if at a pressure below 760 torr; Compound A is a solid at 250 K and 760 torr; and Compound A does have a triple point roughly equal to water (the triple point of water is at 0°C). The only uncertainty is the relative densities of the solid and liquid phases. There is no point at which an increase in pressure at constant temperature converts the solid to a liquid. An increase in the pressure increases the density of the material. This makes choice **D** the best choice.

15. **Choice C is correct.** The graph plots temperature as a function of heat, while heat capacity describes heat per temperature change. This means that the relative heat capacities for the three phases can be determined from the graph. From Figure 1, we know that the solid phase heat capacity is proportional to 1 divided by the slope of line a. The liquid phase heat capacity is proportional to 1 divided by the slope of line c. The graph shows that slope a > slope c, so the heat capacity of the solid phase is less than the heat capacity of the liquid phase. Choice **C** is the best answer. It is given numerically in Table 1 that the heat capacity of the liquid phase is twice the heat capacity of the gas phase. For the heat capacity of the liquid phase to be twice the heat capacity of the solid phase, the slopes of lines a and e would have to be equal. The slopes of lines a and e are not equal.

16. **Choice C is correct.** Enthalpy is a measure of energy in the form of heat, so the heat added to the system is the increase in enthalpy. The enthalpy of fusion is represented by line segment b in Figure 1, and the enthalpy of vaporization is represented by line segment d. The length of segment b is less than the length of segment d, so choice **C**, which states that the ΔH_{fusion} is less than the $\Delta H_{vaporization}$, is correct.

17. **Choice C is correct.** Heat capacity is the amount of energy required to raise the temperature of a substance by 1°C (or 1 K). It is observed that Compound Q heats to a higher temperature than Compound C when both are exposed to the same amount of heat; this means that Compound Q requires a smaller input of heat energy to reach the same increased temperature that Compound C reaches. Because less heat energy is required to raise the temperature of Compound Q by one increment, the heat capacity of Compound Q is smaller than the heat capacity of Compound C, so choose **C**. Because no phase change transpired for either Compound Q or Compound C, no conclusion can be drawn about their enthalpies of fusion. For this reason, choices B and D are not necessarily wrong, but they are not valid for the question.

18. **Choice B is correct.** The heat required for this transformation is the sum of the heats for the three steps:

$$\Sigma\,\Delta H_{steps}\;=\;\underset{\text{(from 10°C below the bp to the bp)}}{\Delta H_{\text{liquid heating}}}\;+\;\Delta H_{\text{vaporization}}\;+\;\underset{\text{(from the bp to 10°C above the bp)}}{\Delta H_{\text{gas heating}}}$$

The MW of Compound C is given in the passage as 100 grams per mole, so 10 grams of Compound C is equal to 0.1 mole of Compound C. The heat capacities are given as $C_{liquid} = 1.0\ ^{cal}/_{g\cdot °C}$ and $C_{gas} = 0.5\ ^{cal}/_{g\cdot °C}$.

$$\Delta H_{liquid} = m\cdot C_{liquid}\cdot\Delta T = (10\ g)(1.0\ ^{cal}/_{g\cdot °C})(10°C) = 100\text{ calories.}$$

$$\Delta H_{vaporization} = 30\ ^{kcal}/_{mole}\,(0.1\text{ mole}) = 3\text{ kcal} = 3000\text{ calories.}$$

$$\Delta H_{gas} = m\cdot C_{gas}\cdot\Delta T = (10\ g)(0.5\ ^{cal}/_{g\cdot °C})(10°C) = 50\text{ calories}$$

$\Delta H_{total} = 100 + 3000 + 50 = 3150$ calories, so choice **B** is the best answer.

19. **Choice C is correct.** Compound C has a lower boiling point than water (64°C for Compound C versus 100 °C for water), so it has a higher vapor pressure than water at all temperatures at which both compounds are liquids (temperatures lower than 64°C). This eliminates choice A. There is nothing mentioned about the melting point of Compound C or its heat of fusion, so choice B can be eliminated. Compound C has a lower boiling point than water, so it must be easier to vaporize than water, resulting in a lower heat of vaporization for Compound C than for water. Choice **C** is the best answer. Both Compound C and water have a liquid phase heat capacity of 1.0. Choice D is therefore eliminated.

20. **Choice C is correct.** From the graph in Figure 1 of the passage, we see that the phase changes are represented by segments b and d. It can be seen that the temperature remains constant during the phase changes, so A is true. Melting (the process of going from solid phase to liquid phase) requires the addition of heat, which makes it endothermic, so B is true also. After looking at the data given in the passage for the heat capacities at different phases, we find that D is true. When going from the solid phase to the gas phase, heat is added at a constant rate, so the process must be endothermic, not exothermic. The false statement is choice **C**.

21. **Choice B is correct.** The slope of the line is defined as the change in temperature over the heat added. The heat capacity of a material is the heat added per unit change in temperature for a given mass. The slope of the line and the heat capacity are inversely proportional to one another, which can verified by comparing their units. This makes choice **B** the best answer.

Passage IV (Questions 22 - 28)   Bizarre Phase Diagrams

22. **Choice B is correct.** The two solid phases can coexist with the liquid phase for Material T at the upper triple point (roughly 1.0 atm. and greater than 298 K). The two solid phases cannot coexist with the liquid phase for Material C at either triple point. The lower triple point is the intersection of the two solid phases and the gas phase, while the upper triple point is the intersection of $solid_B$, liquid, and gas. Only Material T can have the two solid phases coexisting with the liquid phase, so choice **B** is the best answer.

23. **Choice D is correct.** For Material C, the first triple point is the intersection of the gas, $solid_A$, and $solid_B$ phases. This means that at temperatures below this point, the only possible forms in which Material C can exist are either the $solid_A$ or gas form. It is a true statement that $solid_A$ may be sublimed into gas, so choice A is valid. Between the two triple points of Material C, the line segment is the interface of $solid_B$ and gas. This means that at temperatures in this range, it is possible to convert gas into $solid_B$, which is referred to as *deposition*. This makes statement B valid. Both of the phase diagrams shown have two triple points each, so statement C is valid. At the intersection of 1.0 atm. and 273 K on the upper phase diagram (the phase diagram of Compound T), the phase present is $solid_B$, not $solid_A$. This makes choice **D** an untrue statement.

24.   **Choice D is correct.** Direct conversion refers to the direct interfacing of the two phases, so that the phases may interconvert without first passing through an intermediate phase. For Material T, solid$_B$ may be converted directly into the liquid form at temperatures between the two triple points. This makes choice A valid. For Material C, liquid may be converted directly into solid$_B$ at temperatures above the second triple point, and solid$_A$ may be converted directly into the gas form at temperatures below the lower triple point. This makes choices B and C valid. To convert solid$_A$ into gas for Compound T, the conversion must pass through either liquid or solid$_B$. Direct conversion is *not* possible; choice **D** is the best answer.

25.   **Choice B is correct.** For Material T, solid$_A$ and gas cannot coexist; and for Material C, solid$_A$ and liquid cannot coexist. The only phase that can coexist with the other three phases in both Material T and Material C is solid$_B$. Pick choice **B** for optimal satisfaction.

26.   **Choice A is correct.** The two solids, in order to belong to the same compound, must have the same atomic composition. Therefore, they must both have the same molecular mass. This eliminates choice C. Different connectivity implies different sigma bonds, which describes structural isomers, and not the same compound. Different chiral centers describes stereoisomers, not different solid phases. The best way to explain different forms of solids for the same compound is to say that they crystallize into different lattice structures. Examples are calcium carbonate and sulfur, where each has different solid form that is stable under different conditions. The best answer is choice **A**.

27.   **Choice D is correct.** For Material T, when the pressure is increased at 298 K, the phase converts from solid$_B$ into solid$_A$. The increase in pressure compacts the solid, so the denser solid phase is solid$_A$. Statement I is therefore invalid. For Material C, heating solid$_A$ converts it into solid$_B$, so the conversion from solid$_A$ into solid$_B$ must be endothermic (heat-consuming). Statement II is therefore valid. For Material T, there is no interconversion between solid$_A$ and the gas phase, so deposition of gas into solid$_A$ is not possible. This makes statement III valid. Only statements II and III are valid, making choice **D** the best answer.

28.   **Choice C is correct.** The deformation of a solid can be associated with the change of the solid phase from solid$_A$ into solid$_B$. At 1.0 atm., the solid$_A$ and solid$_B$ forms of Material T do not intersect, while they do for Material C. Only Material C shows deformation of the solid phase with temperature change at 1.0 atm. This makes choice **C** the best answer.

Passage V (Questions 29 - 35)   **Methanol-Ethanol Vapor Pressure**

29.   **Choice B is correct.** The solution with the greatest mole fraction of methanol has the highest vapor pressure of methanol. Methanol has the lower molecular mass between ethanol and methanol, so Beaker I have more moles of methanol than ethanol. This means that Beaker I will exhibit a higher vapor pressure due to methanol than Beaker III. Because the density of methanol is greater than the density of ethanol, Beaker II with equal volume quantities of methanol and ethanol has more methanol by mass than ethanol by mass. The mole fraction of methanol in Beaker II is even greater than the mole fraction of ethanol in Beaker I. The highest vapor pressure of methanol is therefore above Beaker II. Pick choice **B**.

30.   **Choice A is correct.** As the temperature of the solution increases, the energy of the system increases, so that the amount of evaporating liquid increases. This means that both the vapor pressure of ethanol and of methanol increase, resulting in an increase in the total vapor pressure as well. The best answer is choice **A**.

31.   **Choice D is correct.** Over time, both ethanol and methanol evaporate from the solution. Because methanol has a higher pure vapor pressure than ethanol (this can be concluded from the lower boiling point associated with methanol), it is evaporating faster than ethanol. This means that the solution is losing methanol faster than it is losing ethanol. The remaining solution is thus growing rich in ethanol. This eliminates choice A and B. Because ethanol has a lower vapor pressure than methanol, the rate of vaporization decreases as the mole fraction of methanol decreases. Choice **D** is the best answer.

32.   **Choice A is correct.** As more propanol is added to the mixtures of both methanol and propanol, and of ethanol and propanol, the vapor pressure decreases, as seen with the reduced vapor pressure associated with the addition of 20 mL propanol. The reduced mixed vapor pressure shows that propanol has a lower pure vapor pressure than both methanol and ethanol. This makes choice **A** the best answer. The relative vapor pressures of pure samples of the three alcohols is $P_{methanol} > P_{ethanol} > P_{propanol}$, which can be deduced from the passage and the information in this question.

33. **Choice B is correct.** Beaker I has equal amounts of methanol and ethanol by mass. Because methanol has a lower molecular mass than ethanol, the number of moles of methanol is greater than the number of moles of ethanol. If the moles of ethanol were equal to the moles of methanol, then the total vapor pressure would be an average of the two pure vapor pressures (30.0 torr and 40.0 torr), which is 35.0 torr. Due to the excess methanol in the mixture, the vapor pressure is greater than 35.0 torr. It can be no higher than pure methanol, with a vapor pressure of 40.0 torr. This means that the vapor pressure above Beaker I is between 35.0 and 40.0 torr. The best answer is choice **B**.

34. **Choice B is correct.** The solution richest in methanol has the greatest vapor pressure. The greatest mole fraction of methanol is found in Beaker II, so at equal temperatures, the vapor pressure above Beaker II is the greatest. The mole fraction of methanol is greater in Beaker I than in Beaker III, so at equal temperatures, the vapor pressure is given by: $P_{vapor\ Beaker\ II} > P_{vapor\ Beaker\ I} > P_{vapor\ Beaker\ III}$. To increase the vapor pressure above the solution, the temperature must be increased, so for the Beaker III solution to exert the same vapor pressure as the Beaker II solution, the temperature of the solution in Beaker III must be increased. This means that the temperature of the solution in Beaker III must be greatest, if the vapor pressures above all three beakers were equal. This eliminates all of the choices except **B**.

35. **Choice B is correct.** Because the methanol has a higher vapor pressure than ethanol, the vapor above Beaker I must be richer in methanol than the solution in Beaker I. If this vapor were collected, condensed, and added to a new beaker, then the solution in the new beaker would have a higher mole fraction of methanol than the Beaker I solution. This means that the vapor pressure of methanol above the new beaker would be even greater than it is above Beaker I, while the vapor pressure of ethanol above the new beaker would less than it is above Beaker I. The total vapor pressure above the new beaker would be greater than the total vapor pressure above Beaker I, because the solution in the new beaker is richer in methanol, which vaporizes more easily than ethanol. The best answer is choice **B**.

Passage VI (Questions 36 - 43)   Mixed Vapor of Methanol and Acetophenone

36. **Choice C is correct.** The molecular mass of 2-propanol is 60 g/mole. The molecular mass of acetophenone is 120 g/mole. The mixture is made with equal parts of the two components by mass, but we need to know its composition in terms of moles. Because the mass of acetophenone is twice that of 2-propanol, there are twice as many moles of 2-propanol as acetophenone in the solution. The pure vapor pressure of 2-propanol is normally four times that of pure acetophenone (as given in the chart), so the solution should show the effect of both greater volatility for 2-propanol as well as the effect of being richer in 2-propanol. This results in a vapor pressure of 2-propanol is eight times that of acetophenone. The best answer is therefore choice **C**. To solve for the vapor pressure precisely, you need to first solve for the mole fraction of 2-propanol, because the vapor pressure of 2-propanol depends on it. $P_{CH_3CH(OH)CH_3} = (X_{CH_3CH(OH)CH_3})(P_{pure\ CH_3CH(OH)CH_3})$. The mole fraction of 2-propanol is:

$$\frac{1\ mole\ 2\text{-}propanol}{1\ mole\ 2\text{-}propanol + 0.5\ mole\ acetophenone} = \frac{1}{1.5} = \frac{2}{3}.$$

This means that the P_{vapor} of 2-propanol is $2/3$ (48 torr) = 32 torr, and the P_{vapor} of acetophenone is $1/3$ (12 torr) = 4 torr. You should pick **C** for best results.

37. **Choice B is correct.** Acetophenone is 50% by mass of the 120 grams. The mass of acetophenone is (0.5)(120 g) = 60 g. The MW of acetophenone can be calculated by adding up the atomic weights of the formula given in the problem:

$$C = 12\ g/mol,\ H = 1\ g/mol,\ and\ O = 16\ g/mol.\ 8\ (12\ g/mol) = 96\ g/mol\ and\ 8\ (1\ g/mol) = 8\ g/mol$$

$$96 + 8 + 16 = 120\ g/mol\ \therefore\ moles\ of\ acetophenone = 60\ grams\ (\frac{1\ mole}{120\ g}) = 0.50\ moles$$

Choose **B** for best results. Of course, the 60 grams is given in the passage, and the 120 is given in Table 1.

38. **Choice B is correct.** At reduced pressure (500 torr is less than 1 atm.), the boiling point is reduced to a value less than the normal boiling point. The normal boiling point of acetophenone is listed in the chart as 203°C, so choices A and C are eliminated. Because boiling point is defined as the temperature at which vapor pressure equals atmospheric pressure, a reduced atmospheric temperature makes it easier to reach the boiling point. The best answer is choice **B**.

39. **Choice B is correct.** The equation for the mole fraction of acetophenone is: $X_{acetophenone} = \dfrac{moles_{acetophenone}}{moles_{total}}$. The total number of moles in the mixture is the sum of the moles of acetophenone and 2-propanol. The mole fraction of acetophenone is:

$$\frac{0.5 \text{ mole acetophenone}}{1 \text{ mole 2-propanol} + 0.5 \text{ mole acetophenone}} = \frac{0.5}{1.5} = \frac{1}{3}$$

Choice **B** is the best answer.

40. **Choice D is correct.** The vapor pressure of pure acetophenone is less than the vapor pressure of 2-propanol at all temperatures below the boiling point of acetophenone. This means that 2-propanol evaporates faster than acetophenone. With each successive aliquot, there is a larger percentage of acetophenone. This means that the mole fraction of acetophenone is greater above Aliquot 10 than above Aliquot 5. This eliminates choices B and C. Because Aliquot 5 contains a greater percentage of 2-propanol, there is a greater vapor pressure above Aliquot 5 than above Aliquot 10. The correct choice is answer **D**.

41. **Choice A is correct.** Because 2-propanol has a lower boiling point than acetophenone, it evaporates more quickly than acetophenone, and thus the mole fraction of 2-propanol in the original solution reduces over time. As the mole fraction of 2-propanol in solution decreases, the mole fraction of acetophenone in solution increases, and thus the vapor pressure of acetophenone also increases. The sum of the two mole fractions is equal to 1.0 (a constant), so if the mole fraction of one decreases, then the mole fraction of the other must increase. As a point of interest, as the vapor pressure due to acetophenone increases, the vapor pressure due to 2-propanol decreases. Pick **A** to reach correctness nirvana.

42. **Choice A is correct.** Because the mole fraction of 2-propanol increases with the addition of 60 grams of 2-propanol, the mole fraction of acetophenone must be reduced. The sum of the mole fractions of the components in the mixture must equal 1.0 (i.e., the sum of the parts is the whole). A lower mole fraction of acetophenone results in a reduction in the vapor pressure for acetophenone. The best answer is choice **A**.

43. **Choice D is correct.** Because the vapor pressure above the original mixture is initially 32 torr for 2-propanol and 4 torr for acetophenone, the amount of 2-propanol in the vapor phase (and thus Aliquot 1) relative to the total vapor is $^{32}/_{36}$. This fraction reduces to $^8/_9 = 1 - ^1/_9 = 1 - .111 = .889$. The percentage of 2-propanol is therefore 88.9%, making the percentage of acetophenone 11.1%. Given this, choose **D**. Rule choice A out, because the mole fraction of 2-propanol is greater than the mole fraction of acetophenone. Choice C would be true if the mole fractions were equal, because the pure vapor pressure of 2-propanol is four times that of acetophenone. This eliminates choices A, B, and C.

Passage VII (Questions 44 - 50)   Raoult's Law

44. **Choice B is correct.** A positive deviation from Raoult's ideal behavior is due to unfavorable interactions in the solution phase. Unfavorable interactions are repulsive interactions that have a positive ΔH value. Because the material dissolves into solution, the ΔG for solvation must be negative. The favorability of the dissolving process is thus due to entropy. The correct combination of signs for the thermodynamic values is choice **B**. From the second paragraph of the passage, a positive ΔH value can be inferred.

45. **Choice B is correct.** The largest negative deviation would involve the greatest increase in the intermolecular forces upon mixing. Acetone in solution by itself cannot exhibit hydrogen bonding (it does not have a protic hydrogen). Once ethanol has been added to the acetone, the acetone can form hydrogen bonds using one of its lone pairs on the carbonyl oxygen. The increased attraction between molecules due to hydrogen bonding results in stronger interactions in the liquid phase, which reduces the vapor pressure above the solution. Choose **B** for blissful feedback. Carbon tetrachloride, hexane, and cyclohexene are essentially nonpolar and exhibit no hydrogen bonding.

46. **Choice D is correct.** From a 50% by moles mixture of the two liquids, the vapor due to methanol above the first flask is $^{87}/_{(87 + 29)}$. When the vapor is condensed, collected, and placed into the second flask, the condensed solution is 75% methanol by moles. The vapor pressure of methanol above the second flask is greater than 75%, because methanol evaporates more readily than butanol evaporates. To be the star you want to be, pick **D**. This question presents the principle behind fractional distillation. By continuously condensing and re-distilling, the distillate becomes richer with regard to the component with the lower boiling point.

47. **Choice C is correct.** Positive deviations are associated with a mixture that generates a vapor pressure greater than expected according to Raoult's law. A positive deviation is due to reduced intermolecular forces in solution, which can be correlated with repulsion. Because mixing the liquids results in repulsion (which can be thought of as bond-breaking), the dilution endothermic, so ΔH is positive. This is stated in the passage, so no background knowledge is needed. The best answer is choice **C**.

48. **Choice B is correct.** The ideal vapor pressure of Component B is calculated by multiplying the mole fraction of Component B by its pure vapor pressure. The mole fraction of Component B is 0.40 and its pure vapor pressure is 75 torr. The math is as follows: 0.40×75 torr $= 4.0 \times 7.5$ torr $= 2.0 \times 15$ torr $= 30$ torr. If the solution was ideal, exhibiting no intermolecular forces, the vapor pressure of Component B would be 30 torr. However, according to Figure 1, Component A and Component B exhibit repulsive forces in solution, causing an increase in the amount of vapor formed. This can be read directly from the graph, which shows that the actual vapor pressure is higher than the ideal vapor pressure. Choice A is eliminated. The answer must be around 30 torr (30 torr + a little bit), so choices C and D are eliminated. The best answer is choice **B**.

49. **Choice C is correct.** Compound D has a higher pure vapor pressure than Compound C (as shown in the graph by the higher vapor pressure for pure Compound D than pure Compound C), so Compound D evaporates more readily. This must be read from the second graph. The vapor pressure when the mole fraction of Compound D is equal to 1.0 is greater than the vapor pressure when the mole fraction of Compound C is 1.0. Therefore, as Compound D evaporates, Compound C does not evaporate as readily, and so the solution loses Compound D more readily than it loses Compound C. With time, the solution becomes enriched in Compound C from a mole percent perspective. The mole fraction of Compound C increases while the mole fraction of Compound D decreases. This is choice **C**. With evaporation, the moles of both Compound C and Compound D decrease, but the question asks for the mole fraction, not moles. The sum of the mole fractions must always be 1.0.

50. **Choice A is correct.** A drastic negative deviation results in a sharp drop in the vapor pressure. This implies that more than just an increase in intermolecular forces has transpired. A sharp drop in vapor pressure can be attributed to dimerization between the molecules (which is caused by a bond-forming reaction). Choice **A** explains this best. Changes in polarity would cause only minor deviations in vapor pressure, not major ones, so choices C and D should have been eliminated. The product has a greater molecular mass than the original molecules, making it harder to vaporize than the original molecules.

Passage VIII (Questions 51 - 56)   Desalination and Osmotic Pressure

51. **Choice A is correct.** Because the $P_{\text{applied external}}$ exceeds the P_{osmotic}, the applied pressure forces the water to flow from the salt solution (the more concentrated solution) through the semipermeable membrane and into the pure water (the less concentrated solution). This is because the net force is from the saltwater solution to the pure water cell. This makes both choice C and choice D invalid. As water leaves the aqueous magnesium chloride solution, the $MgCl_2$ concentration increases, because the volume of water is decreasing, while the moles of salt are remaining constant. This makes choice **A** the best answer.

52. **Choice C is correct.** The solution with the greatest osmotic pressure is the solution with the greatest total ion concentration. The greatest total ion concentration results from the highest combination of molarity (salt concentration) and ionizability (i). Choice A yields a total ion concentration of 0.4 molar, because the salt solution is 0.20 molar, and there are 2 ions per NaCl salt molecule. Choice B yields a total ion concentration of 0.6 molar, because the salt solution is 0.30 molar, and there are 2 ions per KCl salt molecule. Choice **C** is the best choice, because the salt solution is 0.25 molar and there are 3 ions per salt molecule. This results in 0.75 molar solution in total ion impurities, assuming the salt is fully soluble. The solubility products are listed to show that the salts are either fully soluble or partially soluble. Choices A, B, and **C** all dissolve completely, because their solubility product, and therefore their molar solubility, are greater than 1.0. Answer choice D is tempting, because if you blindly considered the concentration listed, you would get the largest value. But for lead chloride D ($PbCl_2$), the solubility product is 1.6×10^{-5} M^3, so the molar solubility is 1.6×10^{-2} M.

$$\text{Molar solubility} = \sqrt[3]{\frac{K_{sp}}{4}} = \sqrt[3]{\frac{1.6 \times 10^{-5}}{4}} = \sqrt[3]{4.0 \times 10^{-6}} = \sqrt[3]{4.0} \times 10^{-2}$$

This means that not all of the lead chloride solid added to the water dissolves. According to the molar solubility, the molarity of the ions in fully saturated aqueous lead chloride is 0.048 M. For this reason, lead chloride is eliminated from the answer choices. Choice **C** is the best answer choice.

53. **Choice C is correct.** This question is asking about dilution, for which one normally uses the equation $M_1V_1 = M_2V_2$. Because the osmotic pressure of the solution decreases as the volume of solvent (and thus solution) increases, the equation can be rewritten as: $\pi_1V_1 = \pi_2V_2$. The osmotic pressure of the solution decreases, because the salt concentration decreases (and osmotic pressure depends on the molarity of the solution). If the mathematical approach does not make sense, it should intuitively make sense that decreasing the solution concentration would reduce the osmotic pressure, because osmotic pressure is directly proportional to molarity ($\pi = MiRT$). To reduce the osmotic pressure to 0.4 times its original value, the concentration must be reduced to 0.4 times its original value, and thus the volume must increase by a factor of $^{1.0}/_{0.4} = 2.5$. The final volume of solution should be 250 mL. For the final volume to equal 250 mL, 150 mL of water must be added to the initial 100 mL of solution. The calculation is as follows:

$$\pi_1V_1 = \pi_2V_2, \text{ making } V_2 = V_1\left(\frac{\pi_1}{\pi_2}\right). \text{ Thus } V_2 = 100\,\text{mL}\left(\frac{25\text{ atm.}}{10\text{ atm.}}\right) = 250\,\text{mL}.$$

Again, 250 mL is the final volume, so 150 mL water must be added to the original 100 mL of brine solution to reach a total volume of 250 mL. This is choice **C**.

54. **Choice D is correct.** To stop osmosis, the external pressure must equal the osmotic pressure. The osmotic pressure (π) can be calculated using the equation $\pi = MiRT$ (as presented in the passage). The osmotic pressure is thus:

$$\pi = 1.0\text{ mole L}^{-1} \times 2\text{ ions} \times 0.0821\text{ L atm. mole}^{-1}\text{ K}^{-1} \times 304\text{ K} = 2 \times 25\text{ atm.} = 50\text{ atm, choice } \mathbf{D}$$

55. **Choice B is correct.** In desalination, applied external pressure forces the flow of water from the cell of higher concentration to the cell of lower concentration. Once the applied pressure is reduced, nature takes over and the flow of water reverses so that it flows from the cell of lower concentration to the cell of higher concentration. This is best stated in answer choice **B**.

56. **Choice B is correct.** Water can be extracted from salt water by exploiting the other colligative properties of the solution. Water could be distilled away (boiled off and then recondensed). It can also be frozen away, although the freezing point of the salt water is lower than the freezing point of pure water. This makes choice **B** the best answer.

Passage IX (Questions 57 - 63)   Freezing Point Depression Comparison

57. **Choice D is correct.** The aqueous salt solution in Flask #3 has the highest concentration of all of the solutions, because NaCl has a lower molecular mass than KCl, and Flask #3 has the greatest mass of solute per least mass of solvent. Because the freezing point is depressed by the addition of solute, the freezing point is the lowest in the most concentrated solution, which happens to be the one in Flask #3. As the ice freezes out of the solution, it freezes relatively pure (salt-free); thus, as ice freezes from the solution, the solution becomes more concentrated in terms of solute. As the solution becomes more concentrated, the freezing point is lowered even further, so choice **D** is the best answer.

58. **Choice B is correct.** The presence of a solute, in addition to lowering the freezing point, also elevates the boiling point of a solvent. This means that the most concentrated salt solution is associated with the highest boiling point. $\Delta T = k_bim$, so the salt of choice once again is NaCl (since it has the smallest mass), and the solution we want is the one with the largest molality. The most concentrated NaCl solution is the one in Flask #3 (most grams and least volume). Choice **B** is the correct answer.

59. **Choice B is correct.** The solutions in Flask #1 and Flask #4 look comparable, but because KCl has a higher molecular mass than NaCl, there are more moles of salt in Flask #1 than in Flask #4. This means that the solution in Flask #1 has more ions than the solution in Flask # 4, so the solution in Flask #1 has a higher electrical conductivity than the solution in Flask #4. Choice A is a valid statement. The solution in Flask #2 has more solute particles than the solution in Flask # 5, so the solution in Flask #2 has less water vapor escaping than the solution in Flask #4. This results in a lower vapor pressure, so choice **B** is an invalid statement, and thus the best answer. The solution in Flask #3 has more solute particles than the solution in Flask # 6. Osmotic pressure (π) is calculated using $\pi = MiRT$, so the solution in Flask #3 has a higher osmotic pressure than the solution in Flask # 6. Choice C is a valid statement. The solution in Flask # 6 has a higher concentration of KCl than the solution in Flask # 4, so the solution in Flask # 6 has a more depressed (lower) freezing point than the solution in Flask #6. The solution in Flask # 4 has a higher freezing point, so choice D is a valid statement.

60. **Choice B is correct.** The lowest boiling point is associated with the solution that has the smallest number of solute ions in solution. All of the salts dissociate completely in aqueous solution, so the smallest product of molality and ionizability ($m \times i$ value) yields the smallest concentration of solute ions in solution. This ultimately results in the lowest boiling point of the solutions. The lowest concentration of the choices is 0.2 m and the smallest i value is 2, so 0.2 m $NaCl_{(aq)}$ (with the lowest concentration and smallest i value of the choices) yields the fewest solute ions. Answer choice **B** is the best answer.

61. **Choice D is correct.** To determine the exact freezing point of a solution, the molality of the solution, the i value of the salt, and freezing point depression constant of the solvent must be known. The question gives the freezing point depression constant (k_f) of water as 1.86 °C/molal. Sodium chloride breaks into two ions, so the i value for the salt is 2. The molality of the salt solution in flask #3 is:

$$\text{molality} = \frac{(4 \text{ g solute})(\frac{1 \text{ mole solute}}{58.4 \text{ g solute}})}{0.1 \text{ kg solvent}} = \frac{40}{58.4} \frac{\text{mole solute}}{\text{kg solvent}} \cong \frac{40}{60} \frac{\text{mole solute}}{\text{kg solvent}} \; 0.67 \text{ m}$$

Determining the freezing point requires first calculating the freezing point depression value, which can be calculated from $\Delta T = k_f i m$.

$$\Delta T = k_f i m = (1.86 \text{ }^\circ C/\text{molal})2(0.67 \text{ molal}) = 1.86 \times 1.34 ^\circ C > 1.86 ^\circ C$$

The boiling point of the solution is the normal boiling point of the solvent (in this case 0°C) minus the freezing point depression value, calculated as 1.86 °C. The freezing point of the solution is:

$$T_{bp} = T_{nbp} - \Delta T = 0 - 1.86 = -1.86, \text{ so } T_{bp} < -1.86 \text{ }^\circ C$$

The freezing point of the solution is lower than -1.86 °C and only choice **D** is less than -1.86°C, so choice **D** is the best answer.

62. **Choice A is correct.** As more solute is added to the solution, the concentration of the solution increases. The freezing point decreases with increasing concentration, which makes choice **A** the best answer. The density is assumed to increase, because the addition of solute increases a solution's mass without significantly affecting its volume.

63. **Choice A is correct.** The presence of a solute depresses (lowers) the freezing point of a solvent, so the most concentrated solution of salt water must have the lowest freezing point. Choices B and D are eliminated, because the volume of water is greater than in choices A and C, given equal mass salt quantities. This leaves answers A and C as possibilities. $\Delta T = k_f i m$, hence the salt with the largest molality (m) has the greatest temperature depression. The greatest temperature depression results in the lowest freezing point. NaCl has a larger number of moles than KCl, because NaCl has a lower molecular mass than KCl, and both NaCl and KCl are present in equal mass quantities. The lowest freezing point is associated with Flask #1. For the highest point result, choose answer **A**. Note that all of the salts have an i value of 2.

Passage X (Questions 64 - 70)   Freezing Point Depression Experiment

64. **Choice B is correct.** The thermometer may possibly be off by a few degrees, but that is important only in determining the normal freezing point. The important value in this experiment is the difference in temperature, which is the same whether the thermometer is off by a few degrees or not. By using the same thermometer throughout the experiment, any consistent error should cancel itself out. Choice **B** is the best answer.

65. **Choice A is correct.** If the impurity dissociates into two particles, then there are twice as many impurities as would normally be expected, so the freezing point is depressed by twice the amount that would normally be expected. This makes choice **A** correct, so choice **A** is your choice for a brighter tomorrow.

66. **Choice C is correct.** From 0 seconds up to 160 seconds, the temperature changes by an average of 0.4 °C per 20 seconds. From 180 seconds up until the experiment is terminated, the temperature changes by an average of 0.9 °C per 20 seconds. It was between the 160-second mark and the 180-second mark that the rate of temperature change was not one these two values (but was some value between those two numbers). Because the rate of increase changed, it can be assumed that the slope of the graph corresponding to the data would show an inflection point between the 160- and 180-second marks. This means that the melting point occurred somewhere between these two marks, which means that it occurred during the third minute of the experiment. The best answer is choice **C**.

67. **Choice B is correct.** In the proposed experiment, the mixture is observed as it cools. Because the temperature decreases as it is observed over time, choices A and C (which show an increase in temperature over time) are eliminated. The curve for cooling should be the inverse of the curve observed with cyclohexanol in the menthol experiment, so the best choice is answer **B**. Choice D is incorrect, because it shows a relatively flat line to start, followed by a rapid temperature change during the phase change process. As seen with heating curves for pure substances, the temperature change during a phase change process should be zero. The curves representing the cooling of a pure compound versus one with solute impurities is drawn below. Notice the similarities between the two graphs in terms of slope changes.

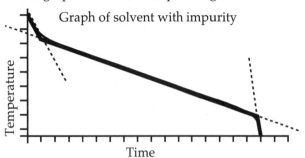
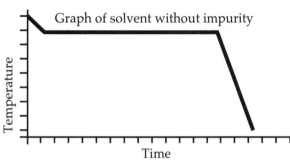

68. **Choice A is correct.** The same mass of camphor was added to Test tube #1 as the mass of menthol that was added to Test tube #2. Because menthol has a larger molecular mass, the moles of camphor added are greater than the moles of menthol added. This means that the molality of camphor is greater than the molality of menthol, thus eliminating choices B and C. The freezing point for the camphor solution is somewhere between 17.1°C and 17.8°C, according to the data in Table 1. The freezing point of the menthol solution is 17.8°C, according to the graph, so the freezing point for the camphor solution is less than the freezing point for the menthol solution. This makes choice **A** correct.

69. **Choice B is correct.** Using twice as much solvent as was used in the menthol experiment would result in a solution with half the molality of the menthol solution in the experiment. This results in a ΔT value (decrease in freezing point) that is half as large as the ΔT from the experiment. The freezing point still drops from its normal freezing point of 22.6 °C (eliminating choice A), but not by as much as what was observed in the experiment. The freezing point is greater than 17.8 °C, thus eliminating choices C and D. The only choice left is answer **B**. The observed ΔT in the experiment was 22.6 - 17.8 = 4.8. The observed ΔT, if 20.000 grams of cyclohexanol were used instead of 10.000 grams, would be 2.4. The freezing point would therefore be 22.6 - 2.4 = 20.2°C. Either way, pick choice **B**.

70. **Choice D is correct.** The solution shows a decrease in freezing point as impurities are added to solution, so choices A and C can be eliminated immediately. With impurities present in solution, the lattice cannot form as easily, because the impurities can interfere with the lattice structure as it grows. In addition, the impurities in solution attract the molecules building the lattice structure, retaining them in the solution phase. The best answer is choice **D**.

Passage XI (Questions 71 - 76)   Dumas Experiment

71. **Choice D is correct.** As is stated in the first paragraph of the passage, organic vapors dissolve rubber and plastic, so the cap cannot be made of these substances. The best answer is choice **D**. The plastic cap may expand during the experiment, but that would not necessarily harm the results. Choice A is good, but it is not the best answer. The pore size is not too small, as long as vapor can pass through the pore, so choice B is eliminated. Air flow is in both directions, so choice C is eliminated.

72. **Choice A is correct.** The molecular mass is measured in terms of grams per mole. This means that mass (m) must be in the numerator of the calculation. Because the mass (m) is in the denominator, rather than numerator, choices C and D are eliminated. From the equation $PV = nRT$, we see that the moles (n) equal PV divided by RT. This means that the inverse of moles $(1/n)$ equals RT/PV. The molecular mass is $m \times 1/n = m \times RT/PV$, which makes choice **A** the best answer.

73. **Choice A is correct.** If not all of the organic liquid had vaporized, then there would be excess liquid remaining in the flask at the end of the condensing step, so the mass of liquid in the flask would be too high. This would result in a calculated mass that was also too high. The correct answer is choice **A**.

74. **Choice C is correct.** For choice A, a permanent cap that can be opened and closed would allow for the flask to be sealed, so that no vapor could escape while the flask cools. A closed system is more stable than an open system. Choice A would make the experiment more accurate. For choice B, the electric heating mantle would distribute the heat more uniformly around the flask than a flame. This would allow for even heating and a homogeneous mixture, making the measurement more accurate. For choice C, an increased pore size would make the system more open and thus allow more vapor to escape as the system cools back down. This would result in a loss in the moles of gas and consequently, the measurement would *not* be more accurate. Pick choice C for happiness and correctness on this particular question. For choice D, the more spherical the shape of the flask, the less heat that is lost to the environment. A spherical container offers the smallest amount of surface area per unit volume (of any container shape), and therefore the least area through which the heat is lost. The less heat that can be lost, the more accurate the measurement of temperature is, and thus the more accurate the experiment.

75. **Choice A is correct.** The organic liquid that has the smallest measurement error is the one that doesn't readily evaporate from the flask during the final massing. The organic liquid should condense completely back to its liquid form at room temperature. This is a characteristic associated with a less volatile liquid (a liquid with a high boiling point). This eliminates choices B and D. To minimize error, the molecular mass should be high, so that any measurement error in the experiment would be small relative to the actual mass of the organic compound. Choice A is the best answer.

76. **Choice C is correct.** The densest vapor forms from the liquid with the greatest molecular mass. All gases at standard conditions have roughly the same molar volume, so the greatest mass per volume is found in the compound with the greatest molar mass. The molecular mass of propanol (choice A) is 60 grams per mole, the molecular mass of chloropentane (choice B) is 106.5 grams per mole, the molecular mass of bromohexane (choice C) is 165 grams per mole, and the molecular mass of 2,2-dimethylpropanol (choice D) is 88 grams per mole. Choice C has the greatest molecular mass.

Passage XII (Questions 77 - 84)   Physical Properties of Liquids

77. **Choice D is correct.** The vapor pressure above a liquid depends on intermolecular forces within the liquid and the mass of the molecule. Hydrogen bonding increases the intermolecular forces, and thus lowers the amount that vaporizes. As hydrogen bonding increases, the vapor pressure decreases, so choice A is eliminated. Polarity increases the intermolecular forces, thereby lowering the amount that vaporizes. As the polarity of the molecule increases, the vapor pressure decreases, so choice B is eliminated. As the molecular mass increases for a compound, the energy required to convert the molecule into its gaseous form increases. The vapor pressure thus decreases as the molecular mass of the compound increases, so choice C is eliminated. As the surface area increases, the amount of vapor formed is greater, but the area over which it is distributed is also greater. The result is that the amount of vapor striking a unit area (pressure) does not change. The surface area of a liquid affects the rate at which it evaporates away, but it does not affect the vapor pressure above the liquid, so choice D is the best answer.

78. **Choice B is correct.** For the non-hydrogen bonding liquids in Table 1 (comprising all of the liquids except glycerol and water) the sequence of relative viscosities is: $CHBr_3 > CCl_4 > CHCl_3 > C_6H_{14}$. For the non-hydrogen bonding liquids in Table 1 the sequence of relative surface tensions is: $CHBr_3 > CCl_4 = CHCl_3 > C_6H_{14}$, but the trend in the vapor pressure is: $CHCl_3 > CCl_4 > C_6H_{14} > CHBr_3$. Surface tension follows roughly the same trend as viscosity, but the vapor pressure deviates from the trend. It is an inverse trend, except for the hexane, which means that it shows no distinct trend. Staying within the parameters of the answer choices, the best answer is choice B.

79. **Choice B is correct.** Gravity is the same in all of the trials, so the ball that falls fastest, is the one in the solution where there is the least resistance to flow. This is observed in the solution with the lowest viscosity. According to Table 1, carbon tetrachloride has the lowest viscosity of all the choices. The correct answer is choice B.

80. **Choice D is correct.** The piece of paper stays atop the solvent with the greatest surface tension (even after it has absorbed solvent). This is assuming that the density of the paper is greater than that of all of the solvent choices. Of those choices, the solvent with the greatest surface tension is water. The best answer is choice D.

81. **Choice D is correct.** Beads form when a compound has a high surface tension, because its molecules are highly attracted to one another. This eliminates choices A and C. Beading is most exaggerated when the surface on which the bead sits has different properties than the beading liquid, so there is little or no attractive force between the liquid (beading solvent) and the surface. The best answer is choice D, where the solvent is polar and the surface is nonpolar. It may help to think of water beads that form when water is dropped on wax paper.

82. **Choice D is correct.** The lower vapor pressure of carbon tetrachloride compared to chloroform results from less carbon tetrachloride vaporizing than chloroform. Carbon tetrachloride is nonpolar, so it cannot be more polar than chloroform (which is a polar solvent), eliminating choice A. Neither carbon tetrachloride nor chloroform forms any hydrogen bonds, so choice B is eliminated. According to Table 1, carbon tetrachloride and chloroform have the same surface tension, so choice C is eliminated. Carbon tetrachloride does have a greater molecular mass than chloroform, so it requires more energy to vaporize than chloroform. This results in a lower vapor pressure for carbon tetrachloride. The best answer is choice **D**.

83. **Choice A is correct.** According to the data in Table 1, the vapor pressure is less for carbon tetrachloride than for chloroform, while the viscosity is greater for carbon tetrachloride than for chloroform. Chloroform is polar, and carbon tetrachloride is nonpolar, so the nonpolar compound has both the lower vapor pressure and greater viscosity, both of which are normally associated with stronger intermolecular forces. This deviation can be attributed to the greater molecular mass associated with carbon tetrachloride than with chloroform. In the case of carbon tetrachloride compared to chloroform, the molecular mass is more important than polarity in determining both the vapor pressure and viscosity. The best answer is choice **A**. Picking **A** should give you much happiness, extreme joy and deep satisfaction in your soul. If not, it should at least give you a point on the exam.

84. **Choice A is correct.** To determine the physical properties of dichloromethane (CH_2Cl_2), it must be compared to chloroform and carbon tetrachloride (the other chlorohydrocarbons in Table 1). The molecular mass of carbon tetrachloride is greater than the molecular mass of chloroform, which is greater than the mass of dichloromethane. Because dichloromethane is lightest, it has the highest vapor pressure (and undergoes vaporization to the greatest extent), which makes the vapor pressure greater than 173 torr. This eliminates choices B and D, which are invalid. The surface tension should be some value around 2.5×10^{-2} J per m^2, making choice **A** the best answer. To confirm that choice **A** is best, the viscosity of dichloromethane should be a value just under 5.8×10^{-4} kg per m·s.

85. **Choice D is correct.** The density of a material depends on the closeness of the particles of which it is composed. This makes choice **D** the best answer. Choice A is eliminated, because double bonds are shorter than single bonds. Because diamond is denser than graphite, atoms are closer in diamond, so despite the fact that carbon atoms touch and there exists layering in graphite, choice B does not explain why diamond is denser than graphite. Carbon atoms are the same size, regardless of the molecular packing and bonding. Choice C is eliminated.

86. **Choice B is correct.** Allotropes are made from the same element, so all of the atoms have the same electronegativity. Choice D is eliminated. Being made of only one type of atom means that allotropes are nonpolar. This eliminates choice A. While it is true that allotropes have different interatomic bonding, bonds are not broken during a phase change, so a difference in melting point cannot be explained this way. Choice C is eliminated. The best explanation for the difference in melting point between allotropes is found in differences in molecular mass and lattice packing. This makes choice **B** the best answer.

87. **Choice A is correct.** A species that appears black in the presence of white light is one that absorbs all light that strikes its surface. This eliminates choices B and D. As seen in Figure 1 in the passage, graphite has significant amount of conjugation. The best answer is choice **A**.

88. **Choice D is correct.** Electrons travel through delocalized molecular orbitals, so the reason an organic material can conduct electricity is rooted in its conjugation. In the case of carbon-based allotropes, conductivity would occur through conjugated π-bonds. Graphite has the most conjugation (from one end of the sheet to the other) of any carbon allotrope, so graphite would be the best conductor of the carbon-based allotropes. The best answer is choice **D**.

89. **Choice C is correct.** As stated in the passage, all carbons in graphite have sp^2-hybridization. This means that all carbons have trigonal planar geometry about them and all of the bond angles are 120°. The best, and correct, answer is choice **C**.

90. **Choice A is correct.** Allotropes are most commonly solids, so it is unlikely that a compound that exists predominantly in the gas phase has allotropes. Argon is an inert gas, so it is the *least* likely to form allotropes. Choice B is eliminated based on the information about carbon allotropes listed in the passage. Phosphorus and sulfur can form isotopes.

91. **Choice B is correct.** Phosphorus, P, is directly below nitrogen in the periodic table, so it should exhibit similar behavior as nitrogen. Like nitrogen, phosphorus desires to make three bonds (in cases where there is no expanded octet). In choice A, each phosphorus makes only two bonds, so choice A can be eliminated. In choice C, two phosphorus atoms make three bonds and two phosphorus atoms make two bonds, so choice C can be eliminated. In choice D, one phosphorus atom makes four bonds and three phosphorus atoms make two bonds, so choice D can be eliminated. In choice **B**, each phosphorus makes exactly three bonds, so choice **B** is the best answer.

92. **Choice D is correct.** A stated in the last sentence of the passage, molecular mass of an allotrope is the most significant factor in the energy required to undergo a phase change. Heavier molecules exhibiting equal intermolecular forces will require more energy to enter the gas phase than lighter molecules. This means that the greatest number of carbons in the allotrope will result in the greatest sublimation point. The best answer is C_{72}, choice **D**.

(Questions 93 - 100) Not Based on a Descriptive Passage

93. **Choice A is correct.** Conductivity of electricity through water is dependent on the number of ions present in the aqueous solution. A greater number of ions results in better conductivity. Because the conductivity of the KCl solution is greater than the conductivity of AgCl solution, the 0.10 M KCl(aq) solution has more ions than the 0.10 M AgCl(aq) solution. This means that KCl is more soluble than AgCl in water. This also means that the 0.10 M KCl(aq) solution has a greater osmotic pressure than a 0.10 M AgCl(aq) solution. This makes choice **A** the correct answer.

94. **Choice C is correct.** Energy is absorbed by the system when the compound goes from a lower energy state to a higher energy state. Choices B and D can be eliminated, because in each case the compound is going from a higher energy state to a lower energy state. The conversion from a solid into a gas requires a greater amount of energy than the conversion from a liquid to a gas requires. This means that more energy is absorbed during sublimation than is absorbed during evaporation. This makes choice **C** correct, which makes it the choice you want to pick for correctness.

95. **Choice A is correct.** This is a simple question hidden amongst some extraneous and intimidating facts. Part of your preparation is extracting what is necessary from a pool of information. All you need to know is that the boiling point is defined as the temperature at which the P_{vapor} equals $P_{atmosphere}$. Reduced atmospheric pressure (which occurs at higher elevations, like the mountains) means that a lower vapor pressure is necessary to reach the boiling point. Consequently, less average kinetic energy is needed to achieve boiling. This lowers the boiling point from the value of the normal boiling point (127°C for Compound A). Only choice **A** is less than 127°C; therefore, choice **A** is the best answer.

96. **Choice A is correct.** Ionic interactions, intermolecular affinity, and H-bonding can be disregarded when dealing with CH_4 and SiH_4, because both compounds are symmetric and thus nonpolar. The fact that CH_4 has a lower boiling point than SiH_4 is because SiH_4 is a heavier molecule than CH_4. Heavier molecules have more mass to put into motion when the molecules vaporize, and thus heavier molecules require more kinetic heat energy to escape from the liquid phase into the gas phase. In conclusion, more heat is required for heavier molecules to vaporize and reach their boiling point than lighter molecules. The boiling point is greater for SiH_4 than CH_4, because the silicon compound is heavier than the carbon compound. The best answer is "lower molecular mass", choice **A**.

97. **Choice D is correct.** A solid is defined as having its component atoms (or molecules) in fixed positions, undergoing no translational motion (displacement). This means that a solid has a definite shape and a definite volume. A solid is rigid unless subjected to extreme pressures, and it maintains a lattice structure. As such, solids do not flow, they have a distinct shape (and thus are *not* amorphous), and their molecules undergo no net displacement over time. This eliminates choices A, B, and C. Because the shape of a solid remains constant at a fixed temperature and pressure, it maintains set dimensions. Solids have static dimensions, so choice **D** is the best answer.

98. **Choice C is correct.** This question requires that you spew back the definition of a liquid from your memory. A liquid has no definite shape (which is why a liquid is able to flow), but it does have a definite volume (because the molecules that make up a liquid are always in contact with neighboring molecules, giving it a distinct size). This is reflected in choice **C**.

99. **Choice B is correct.** Because the unknown liquid has a lower vapor pressure than water at 60°C, the unknown liquid should also have a lower vapor pressure than water has at room temperature. Because the vapor pressure is determined as a natural log function, the vapor pressure of the unknown should be only slightly lower at the lower temperature than the vapor pressure of water. This makes choice **B** the intuitively correct choice. The graph below shows the vapor pressure as a function of temperature for the unknown liquid compared to water.

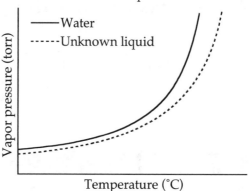

100. **Choice C is correct.** For a compound to be a liquid at room temperature, its boiling point must be greater than room temperature (otherwise, it would be a gas), and its melting point must be lower than room temperature (otherwise it would be a solid). The only choice with a melting point less than 20°C and a boiling point greater than 20°C is answer **C**. This in itself is not necessarily an MCAT-style question, but it is necessary to be able to read charts on the exam. At times, the phase of a substance must be determined, making it necessary to evaluate the phase based on the physical properties of the substance. For instance, if you are asked to decide whether a compound can be distilled, you must first determine whether it is a liquid at the given temperature.

         Section VII Detailed Explanations

Section VIII

Thermochemistry

by Todd Bennett

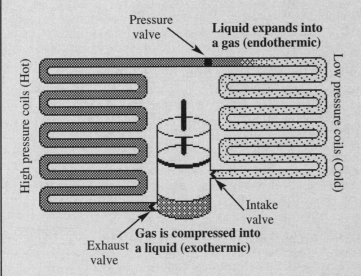

Terminology and Graphs

- a) Energy Diagrams
- b) Free Energy
- c) Enthalpy
- d) Entropy
- e) Hess's Law
- f) Bond Energies

Calorimetry

- a) Heat Energy
- b) Heat Capacity
- c) Heat of Phase Changes
- d) Calorimetry Experiments
- e) Heat Transfer
  - i. Convection
  - ii. Conduction
  - iii. Radiation
  - iv. Evaporation/Condensation

Heat and Work

- a) Energetics
- b) Carnot Cycle
- c) Refrigerator (Heat Pump)
- d) Heat Engine
- e) Enginie Efficiency

Thermochemistry Section Goals

① Know the definitions of free energy, enthalpy, and entropy.

The test asks questions that require you to have a conceptual definition of the basic terms used in thermodynamics. *Free energy* (G) is the accessible energy of the system, *enthalpy* (H) is the heat energy of the system, and *entropy* (S) is the disorder of the system. The three are related to each other by the equation: $\Delta G = \Delta H - T\Delta S$.

② Know the common thermodynamic equations.

Thermodynamics is the study of energy distribution in a chemical reaction or equilibrium system. There are six fundamental equations that you must know. These are:

A. $\Delta G = \Delta H - T\Delta S$ **B.** $\Delta G = \Delta G° + RT \ln Q_{rx}$ **C.** $\Delta H_{reaction} = \Delta H_{product} - \Delta H_{reactants}$

D. $\Delta G° = -RT \ln K_{eq}$ **E.** $\Delta G = RT \ln Q_{rx}/K_{eq}$ **F.** $\Delta H = $ bonds broken - bonds formed

③ Be able to determine the enthalpy change for a reaction from other information.

The change in enthalpy associated with a reaction can be determined in one of three ways. The first method is calorimetry (direct measurement of the heat change during the reaction). This involves surrounding the system with a solution capable of absorbing or releasing a large supply of heat energy. By measuring the change in the surroundings, the change in enthalpy of the system can be inferred. The second method involves Hess's law, which states that the enthalpy change for a reaction is the sum of the enthalpy changes for any component set of reactions. The third method involves the bond energies and is very common in organic chemistry. Energy must be added to a system to break bonds, and energy is released from a system when bonds are formed. The result is that the heat of the reaction can be determined from the change in bonds and bond energies.

④ Be able to determine the equilibrium constant from thermodynamic data.

The equilibrium constant for a reaction can be determined from the free-energy change associated with the reaction, starting with 1.0 M reactants and 1.0 M products (referred to as $\Delta G°$). The equilibrium constant can be used also to find $\Delta G°$.

⑤ Understand heat capacity and its application to calorimetry.

The heat absorbed by a material can be determined from the change in temperature. Each material has an associated heat capacity (known more precisely as *specific heat*). The heat capacity is defined as the heat required to raise the temperature of 1.00 gram of a material by 1.00 °C. Specific heat is this same value relative to water. Water is assigned a heat capacity of 1.00 calories per gram·Kelvin by definition. Heat capacity is used to determine the heat change in a calorimetry experiment.

⑥ Know the basic operations of an engine and a refrigerator.

The Carnot cycle is the theoretical mechanics linking the interconversion of work energy and heat energy. When heat energy is converted into work energy, a typical application of it is to run a motor. Consider the steam engine and the combustion engine. The steam engine is a closed system, while the combustion engine is an open system. When work energy is converted into heat energy, a typical application of it is to run a refrigerator. The heat engine and heat pump use evaporation and condensation to store and release heat. Associated with the phase change in matter in these devices is a drastic volume change, which can perform work.

⑦ Be able to work with energy diagrams of all types.

There are standard energy diagrams, that show the heat of a reaction as it proceeds along the reaction pathway. There is also the heating curve, which shows a phase-change process and the associated change in temperature over a period of time. You should be familiar with both types of graphs and understand the fundamental information that each presents. Energy diagrams are critical in organic chemistry.

Thermochemistry

Thermochemistry is the study of the energy associated with a chemical reaction. Thermochemistry answers the fundamental question "How much is involved in a reaction?" By using thermochemistry principles, we can determine the quantity of products formed, the quantity of energy released (or absorbed), and the quantity of reactants left unreacted for a given reaction. Energy diagrams show thermochemistry values. The net change in an energy diagram shows the enthalpy and free energy changes associated with the overall reaction.

Thermochemistry tells us whether a reaction is favorable or unfavorable and whether it is exothermic or endothermic. Exothermic reactions release heat, so the temperature of the system rises as the reaction proceeds. Endothermic reactions absorb heat, so the temperature decreases as the reaction proceeds. In this section, we shall focus on the heat and energy associated with a reaction.

Once a reaction has released or absorbed heat, the surroundings change. Thermodynamics is the study of the energy associated with a system and surroundings. There are three fundamental laws of thermodynamics. Each addresses a different aspect of energy as it relates to all systems. We accept these laws at the general chemistry level, although some physicists theorize that the first law is incorrect, given that energy and matter can be interchanged.

First Law of Thermodynamics: *The energy of the universe is constant.*

Second Law of Thermodynamics: *In any spontaneous process, there is always an increase in the entropy of the universe.*

Third Law of Thermodynamics: *The entropy of a perfect crystal at 0 kelvins is zero.*

The first law of thermodynamics is applied to the internal energy of a system. Kinetic energy can assume the form of mechanical work or heat. The Carnot cycle takes advantage of the first law of thermodynamics by addressing the interconversion of work energy and heat energy. The heat engine and the heat pump are the theoretical models of this conversion process. In the heat engine, because energy is conserved, the heat that is absorbed by a system is converted into work. The net energy change of the system is zero. In the heat pump, because energy is conserved, the work that is applied to a system is converted into heat that is removed from the system. Again, the net energy change of the system is zero. In chemical reactions, the heat energy associated with a reaction is a result of the interconversion of kinetic energy and potential energy in the form of bonds.

The second law of thermodynamics is applied to explain the universe's tendency to reach a *natural state*. This is to say, that nature proceeds to the most probable state, which is one of disorder. So while the energy of the universe is constant, it is heading towards disorder. In a chemical process, the hope is that the entropy of the universe remains constant. The change in the entropy of the universe is a sum of all changes in entropy for a process. Equation 8.1 shows this relationship.

$$\Delta S_{universe} = \Delta S_{system} + \Delta S_{surroundings} \qquad \textbf{(8.1)}$$

The third law of thermodynamics is the standard against which other entropy values can be measured. A perfect crystal at zero kelvins has its atoms arranged in an organized lattice, in which the motion of all atoms has ceased. Disorder cannot exist under these conditions. This is a theoretical situation, because zero kelvins is unattainable. This law also sets a standard for measurement, in this case ensuring that entropy is always a positive term.

Terminology and Graphs

Energy Diagrams

Energy diagrams show the relationship between the energetics of a system and the reaction steps (listed along the reaction coordinate). The diagrams can be used for kinetic purposes (by looking at the activation energy) or thermodynamic purposes (by looking at the energy difference between the reactants and the products). Two energy diagrams are given in Figure 8-1 below. The first graph shows the energy of a reaction as function of the reaction pathway for either a spontaneous (exergonic) or exothermic (heat releasing) reaction. We cannot identify whether it is exergonic or exothermic unless the type of energy is specified. If it is free energy (G), we use the term *exergonic*. If it is heat energy (H), we use the term *exothermic*. The second graph shows the energy of a reaction as a function of reaction pathway for either a non-spontaneous (endergonic) or endothermic (heat absorbing) reaction. If it is free energy (G), we use the term *endergonic*. If it is heat energy (H), we use the term *endothermic*. The first graph (left) distinguishes between the kinetic region and the thermodynamic region. The kinetic region is where activation energy can be read. The thermodynamic region is where the free energy change can be read. The second graph (right) shows the same features, but with the regions labeled more specifically. Although it may not seem so, the graphs are labeled in a similar fashion.

Exergonic reaction ($\Delta G < 0$)
or
Exothemic reaction ($\Delta H < 0$)

Endergonic reaction ($\Delta G > 0$)
or
Endothemic reaction ($\Delta H > 0$)

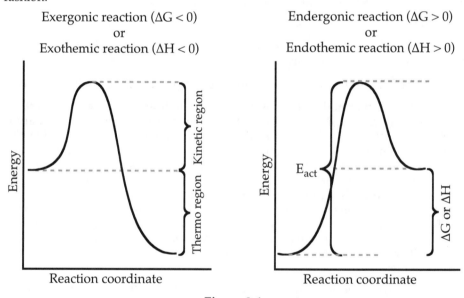

Figure 8-1

The energy diagrams shown in Figure 8-1 represent one-step reactions. Multi-step reactions have graphs with multiple apexes. The reaction coordinate represents the chronological steps that the molecules take during the reaction pathway from reactants to products. The kinetic region defines the activation energy, and thus defines the rate of a reaction. The thermochemistry region defines the energy change for the reaction. These two regions are generally the most significant aspects of an energy diagram. Activation energy is read from a free energy diagram, not from a heat energy diagram based on enthalpy. The free energy and enthalpy are related according to Equation 8.2, which requires that temperature be given in kelvins.

$$\Delta G = \Delta H - T\Delta S \qquad \textbf{(8.2)}$$

Free Energy

Gibb's free energy, associated with a closed system, is the accessible energy in a system that allows chemical reactions to proceed to a state of equilibrium. The free energy (G) of the system accounts for both the entropy (S) and the enthalpy (H) of the system. The free energy change for a chemical reaction or physical process depends on the enthalpy change and the entropy change. Equation 8.2 shows that these three thermodynamic variables, along with the temperature, are all related and thus can be used to predict the value of one another. The free energy change of a reaction is used primarily to determine the favorability of the reaction. If a chemical reaction has a negative value for ΔG, then the reaction is defined as being favorable in the forward direction. If a chemical reaction has a positive value for ΔG, then the reaction is defined as being unfavorable in the forward direction (or favorable in the reverse direction.) Table 8.1 shows different combinations of thermodynamic values as they relate to Equation 8.2.

Case	Result
ΔS positive, ΔH negative	Favorable at all temperatures
ΔS positive, ΔH positive	Favorable at high temperatures
ΔS negative, ΔH negative	Favorable at low temperatures
ΔS negative, ΔH positive	Unfavorable at all temperatures

Table 8.1

Table 8.1 summarizes the four possible combinations of values for ΔH and ΔS. In two of the cases, the temperature must be known in order to determine the sign of the free energy change (ΔG). This means that to determine the favorability of a reaction, temperature must be known in many cases. A reaction that is favorable at low temperatures may not necessarily be favorable at higher temperatures. A great example of this is the liquid-to-gas phase change, which is unfavorable at temperatures below the boiling point, but favorable at temperatures above the boiling point. This is the mathematical reasoning behind the dependence of the equilibrium constant (K_{eq}) of a reaction on the temperature.

Example 8.1

A reaction that is favorable at 25°C but unfavorable at 200°C has what signs for ΔH and ΔS?

A. Both ΔH and ΔS are positive.
B. Both ΔH and ΔS are negative.
C. ΔH is positive, and ΔS is negative.
D. ΔH is negative, and ΔS is positive.

Solution

A favorable reaction has a negative ΔG, while an unfavorable reaction has a positive ΔG. ΔG is negative at lower temperatures (25°C) and positive at higher temperatures (200°C), so ΔG increases with T. Temperature is measured in kelvins, so T is always a positive value. Using Equation 8.2, $\Delta G = \Delta H - T\Delta S$, the value of ΔS must be negative, (negative number), because only the $T\Delta S$ term changes with temperature. As T increases, ΔG increases, so $\Delta G = \Delta H - T$(negative number). ΔH must be negative for ΔG to be negative at lower temperatures, because (negative number) = $\Delta H - T$(negative small number). Both ΔH and ΔS are negative, so choice **B** is the best answer. Table 8.1 can confirm this.

Reactions that are favorable in the forward direction are said to be *spontaneous*. Spontaneity refers to the favorability of a reaction, not to the rate of a reaction, despite what the word may imply. If the reaction is favorable in the forward direction (proceeds in the forward direction to reach equilibrium), then the reaction is spontaneous in the forward direction. This is a thermodynamic perception of the reaction, which means it is based solely on the free energy change (ΔG) for the reaction. Whether a reaction is observed may also depend on kinetic factors. If there is not enough activation energy present in the system (that is, if the temperature is too low), then the reaction cannot proceed in the forward direction even though it is spontaneous.

There is also the standard free energy change ($\Delta G°$) to consider, which is the free energy change when a reaction goes from standard conditions to equilibrium. Standard conditions are defined as 1 atm. of pressure, and a temperature of 25°C, and all solute species (reactants and products) present at 1.00 M concentration. Under conditions where all solute concentrations are equal to 1.00 M, the value of Q_{rx} is 1.0, so ln Q_{rx} is zero. In such a case, only K_{eq} needs to be considered when determining the free energy change, which leads us to Equation 8.3.

$$\Delta G° = - RT \ln K_{eq} \qquad \qquad (8.3)$$

When the $\Delta G°$ value for a reaction is close to zero, the reaction has an equilibrium constant of roughly 1.0. Reactions with K_{eq} roughly equal to 1.0 are driven forward by the addition of excess reactant or the removal of products, which changes the value of ΔG, but not the value of $\Delta G°$. These techniques exploit Le Châtelier's principle to shift the equilibrium to the product side of the reaction. The technique is illustrated mathematically using Equation 8.4.

Example 8.2
If ln $K_{eq} = 5.0$ and the temperature is 25°C, what is the value of $\Delta G°$?

A. +12.5 kJ
B. +8.3 kJ
C. -8.3 kJ
D. -12.5 kJ

Solution
To solve for the numerical value, use Equation 8.3, $\Delta G° = -RT \ln K_{eq}$. The answer is in kJ, so R is 8.314 J/mole K. We are given ln K_{eq}, not K_{eq}, so the math is easier.

$$\Delta G° = - (8.314)(298)(5) \text{ J} \cong - (10)(250)(5) \text{ J} = -(2.5)(5) \text{ kJ} = - 12.5 \text{ kJ}$$

The best answer is choice **D**. Some of you may have approximated the value as follows:

$$\Delta G° = - (8.314)(298)(5) \text{ J} \cong - (8)(300)(5) \text{ J} = -(2.4)(5) \text{ kJ} = - 12 \text{ kJ}$$

The answer choices are spaced far enough apart that any reasonable approximation will lead to the best answer. Math is simplified on the MCAT, so it is also important to understand relative ΔG calculations where number crunching is not directly involved.

There are several equations for determining free energy change. They differ in their starting point for the reaction. The free energy change of a reaction accounts for the free energy change from the initial conditions of the reaction to the equilibrium conditions of the reaction. A reaction going from initial conditions to equilibrium conditions can be broken into two partial reactions: initial conditions to standard conditions, and standard conditions to equilibrium conditions. The derivation below summarizes this reasoning in Equation 8.4:

$$\Delta G_{rx} = \Delta G_{(\text{initial conditions} \to \text{equilibrium conditions})}$$

$$\Delta G_{rx} = \Delta G_{(\text{initial} \to \text{standard conditions})} + \Delta G_{(\text{standard} \to \text{equilibrium conditions})}$$

$$\Delta G_{(\text{initial conditions} \to \text{standard conditions})} = RT \ln Q_{rx} - RT \ln 1 = RT \ln Q_{rx}$$

$$\Delta G_{(\text{standard} \to \text{equilibrium conditions})} = RT \ln 1 - RT \ln K_{eq} = - RT \ln K_{eq}$$

$$\Delta G_{rx} = RT \ln Q_{rx} - RT \ln K_{eq} = - RT \ln K_{eq} + RT \ln Q_{rx}$$

Substituting in $\Delta G°$ for $- RT \ln K_{eq}$ yields Equation 8.4

$$\Delta G_{rx} = \Delta G° + RT \ln Q_{rx} \qquad (8.4)$$

This same derivation can be altered slightly to generate Equation 8.5:

$$\Delta G_{rx} = RT \ln Q_{rx} - RT \ln K_{eq} = RT (\ln Q_{rx} - \ln K_{eq}) = RT \ln \frac{Q_{rx}}{K_{eq}}$$

$$\Delta G_{rx} = RT \ln \frac{Q_{rx}}{K_{eq}} \qquad (8.5)$$

You may recall from the equilibrium section that Q_{rx} defines the reaction state, and K_{eq} defines equilibrium. When Q_{rx} is less than K_{eq}, the Q_{rx}-to-K_{eq} ratio is less than 1.0. The log of a number less than 1 is negative, so according to Equation 8.5, ΔG_{rx} must be negative. This means that the reaction is favorable in the forward direction. When the value of Q_{rx} is less than K_{eq}, the reaction has too many reactants and too few products, so it proceeds forward to reach equilibrium, reaffirming that the reaction is favorable as written.

Example 8.3
A reaction that is spontaneous in the forward direction corresponds with which of the following features?

A. It has an equilibrium constant that is greater than 1.0.
B. The reaction is spontaneous in the reverse direction.
C. It has a ΔG_{rx} that is positive for the reaction as written.
D. It has a ratio of Q_{rx} to K_{eq} that is less than 1.

Solution
"Spontaneous in the forward direction" means that the reaction is favorable as written, which implies that there is an excess of reactants and a shortage of products relative to equilibrium. This tells us nothing about the value of the equilibrium constant. The value of K_{eq} may or may not be greater than 1.0. Choice A may seem tempting, but it is not the best answer. A reaction that is spontaneous in the forward direction is non-spontaneous in the reverse direction. This eliminates choice B. A reaction is spontaneous in the forward direction when ΔG is negative. This eliminates choice C. When the ratio of Q_{rx} to K_{eq} is less than 1, there is an excess of reactants, so the reaction must proceed forward to reach equilibrium. When Q_{rx} to K_{eq} is less than 1, the log of the ratio in Equation 8.5 is negative, so ΔG_{rx} is negative. A reaction is spontaneous in the forward direction when ΔG_{rx} is negative, so choice **D** is the best answer.

Enthalpy

Enthalpy (H) is defined as the quantity of heat present in a system. Enthalpy change (ΔH) is the heat that is either lost from or added to a system (a reaction) during a chemical reaction or physical process. There is an enthalpy change associated with every chemical reaction or physical process. The value of ΔH is positive when heat is absorbed by the reaction (as is the case in an endothermic reaction) and negative when heat is given off by the reaction (as is the case in an exothermic reaction). The ΔH value of a reaction is determined by the system's heat change, not the heat change of the surroundings. The difference between the energy change of the system and the surroundings is just a sign, because the total quantity of energy released by the system is the same as the amount of energy absorbed by the surroundings. The sign convention is based on the idea that the ΔH value describes the change in heat for the chemical reaction. Although enthalpy change alone does not describe the favorability of a reaction, just the heat, the value of ΔH plays a significant role in determining ΔG.

Example 8.4

Which of the observations below is NOT associated with an exothermic reaction?

A. An increase in the temperature of the solution
B. The formation of products that are more stable than the reactants
C. A net loss in the heat energy of the surroundings
D. A value for the change in enthalpy that is negative

Solution

An *exothermic reaction* is defined as a reaction that releases heat energy from the system to the surroundings. This results in an increase in the heat energy of the surroundings, so choice A is valid. Energy is released by the reaction, because the products are at a lower energy level (are more stable) than the reactants. This makes choice B valid. An exothermic reaction has a negative value for ΔH, so choice D is valid. The false statement of the answer choices is choice **C**, because heat energy is gained by the surroundings, not lost from it. This means that the correct answer (the statement that is NOT true) is choice **C**.

Example 8.5

If the solvation of $NH_4Cl(s)$ by water solvent results in the cooling of the solution, then the sign of the ΔH value for the solvation reaction is:

A. positive at all temperatures.
B. negative at all temperatures.
C. positive at low temperatures and negative at high temperatures.
D. positive at high temperatures and negative at low temperatures.

Solution

Because the solution becomes cooler after the reaction, heat must have been absorbed by the system from the surroundings. The aqueous solution is considered to be the surroundings, as that is where the heat is absorbed from. When heat is absorbed, the enthalpy change is positive, making choice **A** correct. The reaction is thus endothermic. This means that the driving force behind the dissociation of ammonium chloride into water must be linked to the favorable change in entropy, not the unfavorable change in enthalpy. The sign of the enthalpy change does not change with temperature, so choices C and D should be eliminated immediately.

Energy diagrams sometimes refer to heat energy, in which case the heat of reaction can be extracted from the graph. When heat is absorbed, the reaction is endothermic. It is uphill from the reactants to products in the energy diagram. When heat is released, the reaction is exothermic. It is downhill from the reactants to products in the energy diagram. Figure 8-2 shows the enthalpy diagrams for an endothermic reaction and for an exothermic reaction.

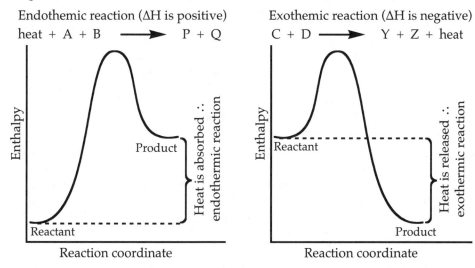

Figure 8-2

***

Example 8.6
Combustion of a hydrocarbon in the presence of excess oxygen gas is BEST classified as which of the following?

A. An exothermic reaction
B. An endothermic reaction
C. An exoconductive process
D. An endoconductive process

Solution
Because the temperature of the surroundings increases during a combustion reaction (combustion is the complete oxidation of a reactant, in this case a hydrocarbon, heat is given off by the system to the surroundings. When heat energy is released, the enthalpy change for the chemical reaction is negative. A negative enthalpy change is associated with an exothermic reaction, which makes choice **A** correct. The terms "exoconductive" and "endoconductive" are contrived terms that have no useful meaning in chemistry. The oxidation of a hydrocarbon is a reaction, not a process, so for several good reasons, choices C and D should both be eliminated.

***

The heat change for a reaction may be determined in many ways. It can be found from the ΔH values for component reactions that sum to the overall reaction. This is Hess's law. The change in heat energy may also be determined from differences in the bond-energy values for the bonds that are broken and bonds that are formed. Heat energy is needed to break bonds, while heat energy is released when bonds are formed. The last method to consider is an experimental one, where the heat change for a chemical reaction is measured by calorimetry. In calorimetry, the change in temperature for a known quantity of surrounding material is measured. This temperature change can be converted into a heat change for the surroundings, which is the negative of the system's heat change.

***

Entropy

Entropy (S) is the measure of randomness (disorder) within a system. Entropy takes into account molecular randomness (degrees of rotational freedom for each atom within a molecule), which reflects the ability of a molecule to rotate freely about its bonds. Cyclic compounds have less entropy than linear compounds, because they are more rigid and cannot rotate as freely. Cyclic structures are thus less favorable entropically than linear structures. Alkanes are more random than alkenes, because alkenes have a double bond (π-bond in particular), about which the molecule may not rotate. Entropy also accounts for the overall randomness of a system (freedom for the molecules to move in a translational manner). Gases have the most entropy of the three common phases, because their molecules are freest to move throughout the container. The gas phase is entropically the most favorable. Entropy (in a more the advanced definition presented in physical chemistry) is the reversible heat change of the system ($q_{reversible}$) divided by its temperature.

An increase in entropy (and disorder) is defined as a positive change in entropy (ΔS). We are typically more interested in the entropy change for a chemical reaction or physical process than we are in the absolute entropy of any component. Entropy can be thought of as organizational potential energy. When you organize something, it has the potential to become disordered, and release that organizational energy. This organizational energy becomes part of the free energy of the system.

Example 8.7

Which of the following processes is NOT associated with its correct sign for ΔS?

- **A.** ΔS_{system} for a liquid-to-gas phase change is positive.
- **B.** ΔS_{system} for a reaction in which the volume increases is positive.
- **C.** ΔS_{system} for a reaction in which a π-bond is formed is negative.
- **D.** ΔS_{system} for sublimation is negative.

Solution

Increases in the randomness of a system (molecular chaos) have a positive ΔS_{system} value. Conversely, decreases in the randomness of a system (molecular chaos) have a negative ΔS_{system} value. Because the molecules are becoming more random in a liquid-to-gas phase change, the entropy change for the process (ΔS_{system}) is positive. Choice A is a valid statement, so it is eliminated. When the volume of the system increases, the molecules are capable of occupying a greater number of points in space, making the molecules more random. The entropy change for the process (ΔS_{system}) is positive. Choice B is a valid statement, so it is eliminated. When a π-bond is broken, the molecule has more ability to rotate freely, which makes the system more random. Thus, when a π-bond is formed, the molecule loses some ability to rotate freely, which makes the system less random. The entropy change for the reaction (ΔS_{system}) is negative. Choice C is a valid statement, so it is eliminated. Sublimation is the physical process whereby a solid is converted into a gas. Because the molecules are becoming more random in a solid-to-gas phase change, the entropy change for the reaction (ΔS_{system}) is positive, not negative. This makes choice **D** an incorrect statement and the best answer. Positive entropy changes are often associated with increases in the number of molecules and phase changes to phases of lower density (greater volume).

Example 8.8

What can be said about the entropy of cyclohexane(l) as compared to cyclohexane(s)?

A. The entropy of cyclohexane(s) is greater than cyclohexane(l).
B. The entropy of cyclohexane(l) is greater than cyclohexane(s).
C. The entropy of cyclohexane(l) is equal to that of cyclohexane(s).
D. Neither cyclohexane(l) nor cyclohexane(s) has any entropy, because entropy applies only to non-cyclic molecules.

Solution

While cyclic molecules have lower entropy than their linear counterparts, they still have entropy. Choice D is eliminated. Cyclohexane is the same molecule, no matter what phase it is in. The randomness of the molecule itself is unchanged, so there is no change in the degrees of freedom (ability to rotate about bonds and change angles.) The difference in entropy between the two systems is due to the phase difference. The solid phase is more structured than the liquid phase, so in the solid phase the molecules are more ordered (less random). Because the molecules are more random in the liquid phase, choice **B** is correct. You should be aware that the sequence of relative entropy in the three phases is as follows: $S_{gas} > S_{liquid} > S_{solid}$. Every compound is defined as having some positive entropy, according to the third law of thermodynamics.

There is an entertaining and simple example of entropy in action that you can do with a rubber band. It involves stretching and relaxing of the rubber band. When a rubber band is stretched and held in the stretched state for a few moments, its temperature equilibrates with the environment. Using your lip as a thermometer, place the stretched rubber band against your lip to gauge its temperature. When you are convinced that it is at room temperature, remove the rubber band from your lip and let it return to its natural state of relaxation. Then, immediately place it against the same lip. The rubber band will feel cold. The reason for this is rooted in the thermodynamics of the process. The rubber band naturally tends to go from a stretched state to relaxed one, making $\Delta G_{stretched-to-recoiled}$ a negative number. The rubber band becomes cold when it goes from stretched to relaxed, making $\Delta H_{stretched-to-relaxed}$ a positive number (endothermic processes absorb heat and therefore feel cold). Because ΔG is negative and ΔH is positive, ΔS must be a positive number. This means that as the rubber band goes from stretched to relaxed, it becomes more disordered. This may seem odd at first, but when you consider any net (like a tennis net or a volleyball net), you should note that when it is stretched, it is orderly. When bundled up, it is disordered. In essence, a rubber band is a microscopic net. The driving force for relaxing from a stretched state is entropic in nature.

Hess's Law

Hess's law states that the ΔG, ΔH, or ΔS for a particular reaction can be determined by summing the ΔG, ΔH, or S values for any cumulative series of subreactions for that particular reaction (or in the case of ΔS, you can sum the entropy values for each reactant and product in the reaction). Typical MCAT questions about this include summing the $\Delta G°_{form}$, $\Delta H°_{form}$, or $S°$ for the reactants and products (reversing the reactant values is necessary to add correctly). The overall ΔG, ΔH, or ΔS can be found by *subtracting* the $\Delta G°_{form}$, $\Delta H°_{form}$ or $S°$ for the *reactants* from the $\Delta G°_{form}$, $\Delta H°_{form}$, or $S°$ for the *products*. Equations 8.6, 8.7, and 8.8 are the application of Hess's law using formation values to calculate free energy, enthalpy, and entropy, respectively.

$$\Delta G°_{reaction} = \sum \Delta G°_{formation\ products} - \sum \Delta G°_{formation\ reactants} \qquad \textbf{(8.6)}$$

$$\Delta H°_{reaction} = \sum \Delta H°_{formation\ products} - \sum \Delta H°_{formation\ reactants} \qquad \textbf{(8.7)}$$

$$\Delta S°_{reaction} = \sum S°_{products} - \sum S°_{reactants} \qquad \textbf{(8.8)}$$

The free energy change of formation ($\Delta G_{formation}$) is the change in free energy that transpires when a compound is formed from its component elements in their most stable state at standard temperature (25°C) and pressure (1.00 atmosphere). The enthalpy of formation ($\Delta H_{formation}$) is the heat change that transpires when a compound is formed from its component elements in their most stable state. There is no entropy of formation for compounds, as they are defined by themselves as having a set amount of disorder (entropy). In most general chemistry textbooks, there are exhaustive tables of free energies and heats of formation, so the values are common information. The $\Delta G_{formation}$ and $\Delta H_{formation}$ for an element in its most stable form is 0. This applies to oxygen gas, which is found in combustion reactions. Combustion reactions are among the common MCAT examples using Hess's law with the heats of formation.

Example 8.9
What is the formation reaction for $C_2H_5Br(g)$?

A. $2\,C(gr) + 2\frac{1}{2}\,H_2(g) + \frac{1}{2}\,Br_2(g) \longrightarrow C_2H_5Br(g)$

B. $2\,C(gr) + 2\frac{1}{2}\,H_2(g) + \frac{1}{2}\,Br_2(l) \longrightarrow C_2H_5Br(g)$

C. $2\,C(gr) + 2\frac{1}{2}\,H_2(g) + Br(g) \longrightarrow C_2H_5Br(g)$

D. $2\,C(gr) + 2\frac{1}{2}\,H_2(g) + Br(l) \longrightarrow C_2H_5Br(g)$

Solution
Bromine is found in nature as a diatomic liquid under standard conditions. You may recall this from an organic chemistry lab, in which you added Br_2 in CCl_4 to an unknown organic compound to test for the presence of an alkene π-bond. Bromine (Br_2) adds anti across a carbon-carbon π-bond that is present in the molecule, which results in the disappearance of the bromine liquid. Because the bromine liquid is brown, the presence of an alkene is supported by the disappearance of the brown color from the solution. Based just on the phase and molecular state of bromine in the answer choices, the best choice is answer **B**. There are certain miscellaneous facts that you should know for some questions on the MCAT. Although the test writers give you a great deal of information, there is other required information (background knowledge) that you must have, such as carbon being most stable as graphite, hydrogen being most stable as a diatomic gas, and bromine being most stable as a diatomic liquid.

To apply Equations 8.6, 8.7, and 8.8 correctly, the overall reaction must be balanced first. Stoichiometric coefficients are critical to Hess's law, as each component is multiplied by its stoichiometric coefficient prior to summing the values. Example 8.10 shows the application of Equation 8.7 in calculating the enthalpy for the combustion of methane. The solution is a step-by-step process that serves as a case-based derivation of Equation 8.7.

Example 8.10
What is the standard enthalpy of combustion for methane?

A. $\Delta H°_{formation}$ CO_2 + $\Delta H°_{formation}$ H_2O - $\Delta H°_{formation}$ CH_4

B. $\Delta H°_{formation}$ CO_2 + 2 $\Delta H°_{formation}$ H_2O - $\Delta H°_{formation}$ CH_4

C. $\Delta H°_{formation}$ CH_4 - $\Delta H°_{formation}$ CO_2 - $\Delta H°_{formation}$ H_2O

D. $\Delta H°_{formation}$ CH_4 - $\Delta H°_{formation}$ CO_2 - 2 $\Delta H°_{formation}$ H_2O

Solution
The first step is to balance the overall reaction:

Balanced reaction: $1 CH_4(g) + 2 O_2(g) \rightarrow 1 CO_2(g) + 2 H_2O(g)$

The next step is to view the formation reactions and standard enthalpy of formation for each compound in the balanced equation:

$\Delta H°_{formation}$ $CH_4(g)$ = $\Delta H°_{rxn}$ for: $1 C(gr) + 2 H_2(g) \rightarrow CH_4(g)$

$\Delta H°_{formation}$ $O_2(g)$ is not applicable, because $O_2(g)$ is in its most stable state

$\Delta H°_{formation}$ $CO_2(g)$ = $\Delta H°_{rxn}$ for: $C(gr) + O_2(g) \rightarrow CO_2(g)$

$\Delta H°_{formation}$ $H_2O(g)$ = $\Delta H°_{rxn}$ for: $H_2(g) + \frac{1}{2} O_2(g) \rightarrow H_2O(g)$

The final step is to sum up the formation reactions in a way that equals the overall reaction. This requires multiplying reactions by their stoichiometric coefficients, reversing the reaction for compounds on the reactant side, and crossing out molecules that appear on both sides of the subreactions:

$1 CH_4(g)$	$\rightarrow$ $1 C(gr) + 2 H_2(g)$	$-1 (\Delta H°_{formation} CH_4(g))$
$1 C(gr) + 1 O_2(g)$	$\rightarrow$ $1 CO_2(g)$	$1 (\Delta H°_{formation} CO_2(g))$
$2 H_2(g) + 1 O_2(g)$	$\rightarrow$ $2 H_2O(g)$	$2 (\Delta H°_{formation} H_2O(g))$

$1 CH_4(g) + 2 O_2(g) \rightarrow 1 CO_2(g)$ $2 H_2O(g)$ $\Delta H°_f CO_2$ + $2 \Delta H°_f H_2O$ - $\Delta H°_f CH_4$

The best answer is choice **B**. Because the formation reactions for reactants are reversed, the equation for calculating any thermodynamic value from the formation values involves **formation values for products minus formation values for reactants**. Equation 8.7 shows this for determining the enthalpy of reaction from the enthalpy of formation values.

For examples 8.11 through 8.14, use the values in Table 8.2.

Compound	$\Delta H°_f$ (kJ/mol)	S° (J/mol·K)	Compound	$\Delta H°_f$ (kJ/mol)	S° (J/mol·K)
CO(g)	-111.2	198	CO_2(g)	-393.5	214
H_2O(g)	-242	189	H_2O(l)	-286	70
C_2H_5OH(l)	-278	161	$C_5H_8O_2$(s)	-1011	196
$C_6H_{12}O_6$(s)	-1278	212	O_2(g)		205

Table 8.2

Example 8.11
What is the standard enthalpy change for the water shift reaction?
$$CO_2(g) + H_2(g) \rightarrow CO(g) + H_2O(g)$$

A.   +40.3 kJ/mole
B.   +3.7 kJ/mole
C.   -3.7 kJ/mole
D.   -40.3 kJ/mole

Solution
This question requires Equation 8.7, $\Delta H°_{reaction} = \sum \Delta H°_{form}$ products - $\sum \Delta H°_{form}$ reactants. The reaction is balanced as given, so we can proceed directly to the insertion of numerical values:

$$\Delta H°_{reaction} = \Delta H°_{form} CO + \Delta H°_{form} H_2O - \Delta H°_{form} CO_2 - \Delta H°_{form} H_2$$

$$\Delta H°_{reaction} = (-111.2) + (-242) - (-393.5) - 0 \approx -350 + 390 = +40 \text{ kJ/mole}$$

The best answer is choice **A**.

Example 8.12
What is the standard enthalpy change for the combustion of ethanol?
$$C_2H_5OH(l) + O_2(g) \rightarrow CO_2(g) + H_2O(l)$$

A.   -1367 kJ/mole
B.   -1235 kJ/mole
C.   -795 kJ/mole
D.   -401.5 kJ/mole

Solution
This question requires Equation 8.7, $\Delta H°_{reaction} = \sum \Delta H°_{form}$ products - $\sum \Delta H°_{form}$ reactants. The reaction must first be balanced:

$$C_2H_5OH(l) + 3 O_2(g) \rightarrow 2 CO_2(g) + 3 H_2O(l)$$

From here, we can proceed to the insertion of numerical values:
$$\Delta H°_{reaction} = 2 \Delta H°_{form} CO_2 + 3 \Delta H°_{form} H_2O - \Delta H°_{form} C_2H_5OH - 3 \Delta H°_{form} O_2$$

$$\Delta H°_{reaction} = 2 (-393.5) + 3 (-286) - (-278) - 3 (0)$$

$$= 2 (-400 + 6.5) + 3 (-300 + 14) + 300 - 22$$

$$= -800 + 13 -900 + 42 + 300 -22 = -1400 +33 = -1367 \text{ kJ/mole}$$

The correct answer is choice **A**.

Example 8.13
What is the standard enthalpy change for the combustion of glucose?

$$C_6H_{12}O_6(s) + O_2(g) \rightarrow CO_2(g) + H_2O(l)$$

A. +598.5 $kJ/mole$
B. -1523 $kJ/mole$
C. -2799 $kJ/mole$
D. -5355 $kJ/mole$

Solution
This question requires Equation 8.7, $\Delta H°_{reaction} = \sum \Delta H°_{form}$ products - $\sum \Delta H°_{form}$ reactants. The reaction must first be balanced:

$$C_6H_{12}O_6(s) + 6\,O_2(g) \rightarrow 6\,CO_2(g) + 6\,H_2O(l)$$

From here, we can proceed to the insertion of numerical values. Oxygen is most stable as O_2 under standard conditions, so it is omitted from the expression:

$$\Delta H°_{reaction} = 6\,\Delta H°_{form\;CO_2} + 6\,\Delta H°_{form\;H_2O} - \Delta H°_{form\;C_6H_{12}O_6}$$

$$\Delta H°_{reaction} = 6\,(-393.5) + 6\,(-286) - (-1278) = 6\,(-679.5) + 1278$$

$$= 6\,(-700 + 20.5) + 1300 - 22 = -4200 + 123 + 1300 - 22 = -2900 + 101$$

$$= -2799\ kJ/mole$$

The correct answer is choice **C**.

Example 8.14
What is the change in entropy for the combustion of pentyl lactone ($C_5H_8O_2(s)$)?

$$C_5H_8O_2(s) + 6\,O_2(g) \rightarrow 5\,CO_2(g) + 4\,H_2O(l)$$

A. +370 $J/mole\cdot K$
B. +2 $J/mole\cdot K$
C. -74 $J/mole\cdot K$
D. -117 $J/mole\cdot K$

Solution
This question is solved using Equation 8.8, $\Delta S°_{reaction} = \sum S°_{form}$ products - $\sum S°_{form\;reactants}$. The reaction is balanced as given, so we can proceed directly to the insertion of numerical values:

$$\Delta S°_{reaction} = 5\,S°_{CO_2} + 4\,S°_{H_2O} - S°_{C_5H_8O_2} - 6\,S°_{O_2}$$

$$\Delta S°_{reaction} = 5\,(214) + 4\,(70) - (196) - 6\,(205) = 1070 + 280 - 196 - 1230$$

$$= 1350 - 1424 = -74$$

The correct answer is choice **C**. Be sure to pay attention to the phase, especially for water, because inadvertently using the value for $H_2O(g)$ instead of $H_2O(l)$ would lead you to pick choice A.

Bond Energies

Heat of reactions can be calculated using the heat added to the system to break the bonds and the heat released when new bonds are formed. It takes energy to break a bond, and energy is given off when a bond is formed. This information can be applied to an energy diagram, as shown in Figure 8-3 below:

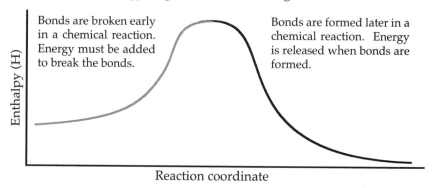

Figure 8-3 shows an exothermic reaction. Enthalpy data helps to determine relative bond strengths. In an exothermic reaction, net energy is released, so the bonds that are formed are stronger than the bonds that are broken. Equation 8.9 can be used to calculate the enthalpy change for a reaction from bond energies.

$$\Delta H_{reaction} = Energy_{bonds\ broken} - Energy_{bonds\ formed} \qquad \textbf{(8.9)}$$

A great example of bond energies is found in biochemistry. Energy is stored when adenosine diphosphate (ADP) is converted into adenosine triphosphate (ATP). This energy can be released when ATP is converted back to ADP, shown as Reaction 8.1 below:

$$ATP + H_2O \rightarrow ADP + P_i + heat$$

Reaction 8.1

The release of energy is predictable from the relative energies of the bonds broken and the bonds formed. Reaction 8.1 is shown in more detail in Figure 8-4.

Bonds broken: O—P and O—H   Bonds formed: O—H and O—P

Figure 8-4

By general chemistry conventions, because the bonds broken are the same as the bonds formed, we predict that the ΔH for the reaction is zero. However, this reaction is used to provide cellular energy, so we know it is actually heat releasing. The discrepancy is explained by examining the bonds in more detail. Because the reaction is exothermic, the bonds broken must be weaker than the bonds formed. The unusually weak bond in the ATP molecule is the O—P bond. Because of electrostatic repulsion by the oxygen atoms, the O—P bond is elongated. Longer bonds are weaker, so the O—P bond of ATP is a weak bond.

The O—P bond in ATP is referred to as a *high-energy bond* in biochemistry. This presents a slight naming problem, because in chemistry, a high bond-energy describes a bond that is strong. A "high-energy bond" (note the inversion of the word sequence) is not a bond with high dissociation energy. The high-energy bond in the phosphate linkage is actually a weak chemical bond. Perhaps it is best to think of a high-energy bond as a bond that is high on the energy diagram, making it unstable (reactive). It is that very weakness that leads to the overall release of energy when this bond is cleaved in the hydrolysis of ATP. You should note that the energy comes from the overall hydrolysis reaction, <u>not</u> from breaking the phosphodiester bond. Bond breaking requires energy. Example 8.15 shows how the bond energies are used to quantify the change in enthalpy.

Example 8.15
What is ΔH for the following reaction, given that the bond energy for C=O is 795 kJ/mole, for H—H is 428 kJ/mole, for C—O is 361 kJ/mole, for C—H is 411 kJ/mole, and for O—H is 468 kJ/mole?

$$H_3CCHO(g) + H_2(g) \rightarrow H_3CCH_2OH(g)$$

A. -90 kJ/mole
B. -17 kJ/mole
C. +17 kJ/mole
D. +90 kJ/mole

Solution
The first step is to determine the bonds that are broken and the bonds that are formed. The diagram below shows the bonds that are broken and formed:

Broken: C=O, H- H   Formed: C- O, C- H,O- H

In reality, only the π-bond of the carbonyl is broken, but we are given numbers in terms of single and double bonds, so we consider the entire C=O double bond to be broken and the single C—O bond to be reformed. Using Equation 8.9:

$$\Delta H_{reaction} = BE_{C=O} + BE_{H-H} - BE_{C-O} - BE_{C-H} - BE_{O-H}$$

$$\Delta H_{reaction} = 795 + 428 - 361 - 411 - 468$$

$$\Delta H_{reaction} = 800 - 5 + 400 + 28 - 400 + 39 - 400 - 11 - 500 + 32$$

$$1200 - 1300 + 99 - 16 = -100 + 83 = -17 \, ^{kJ}/_{mole}$$

The correct answer is choice **B**. The reaction is exothermic, which means that the bonds broken are weaker than the bonds formed. This implies that π-bonds are weaker than σ-bonds.

The values given in Example 8.15 are for heterolytic bond dissociation in the gas phase. There are some assumptions in general chemistry that are not true. In general chemistry, all C-H bonds are treated as equal in strength, although we know from organic chemistry that they are not. For instance, a 3° (tertiary) carbon forms a weaker bond with hydrogen than a 2° (secondary) or 1° (primary) carbon forms with hydrogen. The bond energy also varies with hybridization, where bonds involving *sp*-hybridized carbons are stronger than bonds involving sp^2-hybridized carbons, which are in turn stronger than bonds involving sp^3-hybridized carbons. Bond energies are also considered in organic chemistry, but in more detail.

Calorimetry

Heat Energy

Calorimetry is the measurement of the heat released from or absorbed by a chemical reaction or physical process. The heat change can be measured by carrying out a reaction in a sealed reaction vessel that is surrounded by some material (a liquid is best) that is capable of absorbing the heat given off by an exothermic reaction, or capable of supplying heat to an endothermic reaction. Once the heat has been transferred, the liquid (known as the *heat sink*) either increases in temperature due to the gain of heat energy or decreases due to the loss of heat energy. A decrease in temperature is observed if the reaction is endothermic. The heat of the reaction can be calculated from the change in temperature for the system using the heat capacity and mass of the solution. Equation 8.10 shows the relationship between heat energy (q) and the change in temperature (ΔT). The mass of the solution is represented by m, and the heat capacity of the solution is represented by C.

$$q = mC\Delta T \qquad\qquad (8.10)$$

By using measured values of reactants, the enthalpy change per mole for the reaction can be calculated, assuming that the enthalpy change for the reaction is equal to the heat energy of the reaction (q). The stereotypical lab experiment from general chemistry, lab involves the running of a reaction in a styrofoam cup filled with an aqueous solution and a thermometer. A stirring rod is also provided to ensure that there is homogeneous distribution of heat throughout the system. The temperature is read in consistent intervals and then plotted as a function of time. The true final temperature after the complete mixing of the reactants and the end of the reaction cannot be read from the thermometer directly, because by the time that the thermometer has actually reached the temperature of the solution, heat has already been exchanged with the environment. This means that to determine the final temperature after reaction, a line must be extrapolated from the data points on the graph back to the temperature axis at the t = 0 mark. This technique is common in laboratory procedures. The plotting of temperature as a function of time must be carried out in uniform increments (intervals) in order to get useful data.

Example 8.16

How many calories does your body use to heat up 100 g of water from 0°C to 37°C?

A.　7400 calories
B.　3700 calories
C.　740 calories
D.　370 calories

Solution

To determine the heat needed to raise the temperature of 100 g of water, Equation 8.10 is used. The mass is 100 g, ΔT is 37°C, heat capacity for water is 1.0 cal/g·K, and so q can be found by basic multiplication. Plugging known values into q = mCΔT yields: (100 g)(1.0 cal/g·K)(37K) = 3700 cal. Choice **B** is the best answer. If you drink all of your beverages at icy temperatures, you will expend calories heating them to body temperature. If you were to drink two liters of ice water a day, that would result in the expenditure of 74 nutritional calories to heat water.

Example 8.17

What is the final temperature of a solution made by mixing 30 mL of H_2O at 30.0°C with 60 mL of H_2O at 60.0°C?

A. 52.5°C
B. 50.0°C
C. 45.0°C
D. 42.5°C

Solution

Because the larger volume has the greater temperature, the final temperature is greater than the mean temperature (45°C). This eliminates choices C and D. To decide between choices A and **B**, we must rely on a more rigorous calculation. The answer can be found by one of two methods. The first method is to use a weighted average of the two volumes and their temperatures. The final volume of water = 90 mL, so $\frac{30\,mL}{90\,mL}$ (one-third) of the solution starts at 30°C and $\frac{60\,mL}{90\,mL}$ (two-thirds) of the solution starts at 60°C. The weighted average is calculated as follows:

$$\frac{1}{3}(30°C) + \frac{2}{3}(60°C) = 10°C + 40°C = 50\ °C$$

Choice **B** is the correct answer. The second method is based on Equation 8.10. It equates the heat lost by the warmer solution to the heat gained by the cooler solution. If no heat is lost to the environment, then $E_{cooling} + E_{heating} = 0$. This can be manipulated to read: $E_{heating} = -E_{cooling}$. Substituting Equation 8.10 for energy on each side of the equation yields the following:

$$mC\Delta T_{heating} = -mC\Delta T_{cooling}$$

$$m\Delta T_{heating} = -m\Delta T_{cooling}$$

$$30\ g\ (T_f - 30) = -60\ g\ (T_f - 60) = 60\ g\ (60 - T_f)$$

$$30\ (T_f - 30) = 60\ (60 - T_f) \therefore T_f - 30 = 2\ (60 - T_f)$$

$$T_f - 30 = 120 - 2T_f \therefore 3\ T_f = 150 \therefore T_f = 50$$

Holy smokes m-Catman, it's choice **B** yet again.

Heat Capacity

Heat capacities are just what the name implies; they are a measurement of the storage capacity of absorbed heat for a given material. The unit for heat capacity is energy per mole·Kelvin. Energy can be measured in either joules or calories and the temperature change is the same whether measured in kelvins or Celsius. Heat energy is kinetic energy, which for our considerations shall include only translational energy and vibrational energy. For the most part, solids have lower heat capacities than liquids, because they have only vibrational kinetic energy.

Heat capacities are used in the calculation of transferred heat, which is usually transferred within a material via conduction. Conduction involves the transfer of heat by way of collision when molecules are in direct contact with one another. As two atoms within a molecule vibrate about a bond, the atoms may collide with a neighboring atom and transfer some of the vibrational kinetic energy to that neighboring atom. That is the essence of conductive heat transfer on the microscopic level. The greater the amount of energy required to increase the vibrational energy of a substance, the greater its heat capacity.

The rate of temperature change for a material depends on its heat capacity. A material with a high heat capacity requires more time to reach a target temperature than a material with a lower heat capacity, when heat is applied at a uniform rate. Because of this, materials with high heat capacities generally experience small temperature increases. This is why the temperature near a body of water is relatively consistent compared to temperature fluctuations in more arid regions. Water has a high heat capacity, so it absorbs a great deal of heat on hot days, preventing the air temperature from increasing that much. On cold days, water can release heat to the environment, preventing the air temperature from decreasing that much, making it warmer than it would be in an arid environment.

Example 8.18
What is the heat capacity of a material that requires 3.0 kcal to increase a 15.0 g sample from 25°C to 75°C?

A. $1.0 \, ^{cal}/_{g \cdot K}$

B. $2.0 \, ^{cal}/_{g \cdot K}$

C. $3.0 \, ^{cal}/_{g \cdot K}$

D. $4.0 \, ^{cal}/_{g \cdot K}$

Solution
To calculate the heat capacity (C) from heating data, Equation 8.10 is used. The mass is 15.0 g, ΔT is 50°C, and q is 3000 cal, so C is found following basic multiplication. Plugging known values into $q = mC\Delta T$ yields:

$$3000 \text{ cal} = (15 \text{ g})(C)(50 \text{ K}) \quad \therefore \quad C = \frac{3000 \text{ cal}}{(15 \text{ g})(50 \text{ K})} = \frac{3000 \text{ cal}}{750 \text{ g} \cdot \text{K}}$$

After manipulating the numbers to isolate C, the value is found to be $4.0 \, ^{cal}/_{g \cdot K}$. Choice **D** is the best answer.

Example 8.19
Which of the following observations is valid when comparing two materials of equal mass starting at the same temperature?

A. The material with the greater heat capacity has a higher melting point.
B. The material with the greater heat capacity has a higher boiling point.
C. The material with the greater heat capacity reaches a higher temperature when they are both exposed to the same amount of heat energy.
D. The material with the greater heat capacity reaches a lower temperature when they are both exposed to the same amount of heat energy.

Solution
Phase change processes have little to do with heat capacity. They both relate to intermolecular forces to an extent, but they are not related to one another. As such, heat capacity cannot be used to estimate melting point or boiling point, so choices A and B are eliminated. If the two materials are exposed to the same amount of heat energy (q) and both have equal masses (m), then the compound with the greater heat capacity (C) experiences the smaller temperature change (ΔT), according to Equation 8.10. A smaller temperature change results in a lower final temperature, so choice **D** is the best answer.

$$q \ = \ m \ \times \ C \ \times \ \Delta T$$
$$\text{same} \quad \text{same} \times \text{larger} \times \text{smaller}$$

Heat of Phase Changes

Heat can be exchanged when a material undergoes a phase change. However, during a phase change, the temperature of the system does not change. Phase changes are reversible physical processes. If a phase-change process is endothermic, then the reverse process is exothermic, yielding the same absolute value of energy. For instance, the melting of a solid into a liquid is endothermic, with an enthalpy change of ΔH_{fusion}. The freezing of that same liquid into a solid is exothermic, and the enthalpy change for freezing has the same magnitude as ΔH_{fusion}, but it is a negative number.

The heat exchanged during a phase change can explain some seemingly bizarre phenomena. As strange as it may seem, when water freezes, the surrounding environment becomes warmer. An interesting application involves frozen lakes. As water freezes downward from the bottom of the ice layer at the surface of the lake, heat is released to the surrounding water. This warms the water just below the surface of the ice. Water is densest at 4°C, so as the water warms from 0°C to 4°C, it becomes denser. Warm water (if you can call water between 0°C and 4°C "warm") sinks to the bottom of the lake. This is responsible for the circulation of water under frozen lakes.

The heat of phase changes can also be applied to the concept of refrigeration. The enthalpy of vaporization is significantly greater than the heat of fusion, so a phase change between liquid and gas can be used to absorb or release a great deal of heat. For instance, steam burns are far more severe than hot water burns, even when the steam and water are both at 100°C. A large amount of heat is associated with condensation and evaporation. This is also the idea behind perspiration. When we perspire, the moisture on our skin evaporates, absorbing a large amount of heat from the surface of our body. This works only in environments that are arid. In a humid environment, moisture from the air can condense on your skin, which negates the perspiration process. This is why a "dry heat" feels preferable to a "hot and muggy" climate for most people. Our bodies are physiologically equipped to deal with heat in a dry climate.

Example 8.20

How much energy is required to melt 30 grams of ice at 0°C? ($\Delta H_{fusion} = 6.0$ kJ/mole)

A. 5.4 kJ
B. 6.0 kJ
C. 9.0 kJ
D. 10.0 kJ

Solution

In this question, ΔH_{fusion} is expressed in units of energy per mole, so the amount of water in the ice should also be expressed in terms of moles, rather than grams. We must start by converting grams of ice into moles of ice. Upon dividing the 30 grams by water's molecular mass (18 grams per mole), we get 1.667 moles of ice. The math is simply: 1.667 moles × 6.0 kilojoules per mole = 10 kJ. The correct answer is choice **D**. When you consider the amount of calories needed to melt ice, you might conclude that snacking on ice is a great diet strategy from a caloric standpoint. However, from a nutritional standpoint, a diet of nothing but ice chips would probably not be the best for anyone in the long run.

Calorimetry Experiments

The enthalpy change values we are given in general chemistry textbooks are the results of calorimetry studies. A calorimetry study involves carrying out a reaction in a container surrounded by a heat sink (usually water) to absorb or provide heat energy. One passage on the MCAT several years ago presented a typical calorimetry experiment using a styrofoam cup, an experiment that is conducted in most general chemistry laboratory classes. The reaction is an exothermic reaction between a strong acid and strong base. A styrofoam container is chosen because it is a good thermal insulator, and it fits within most laboratory budgets. The styrofoam calorimeter experiment is shown in Figure 8-5 below:

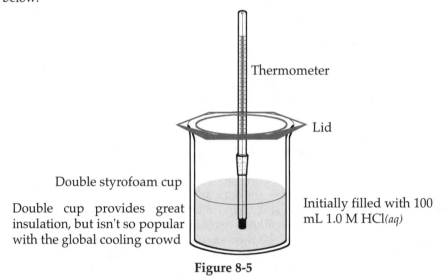

Figure 8-5

A baseline temperatures for the hydrochloric acid solution in the styrofoam cup and for the 100 mL 1.0 M KOH(*aq*) in a second container are determined. Once a steady baseline temperature for each solution is established, the potassium hydroxide solution is added to the hydrochloric acid solution in the styrofoam cup. The temperature is then recorded at regular twenty-second intervals. Because the reaction is exothermic, the temperature of the system increases. A double styrofoam cup system is often used to increase insulation. Figure 8-6 shows data that were collected and graphed at regular time intervals.

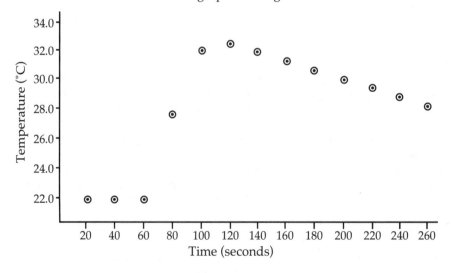

Figure 8-6

Analysis of the data has the goal of determining a value for ΔT for the mixture. The reaction is not instantaneous and the heat is not transferred instantly, so the thermometer does not register the final temperature right away. Heat is lost from the system to the environment by the time the thermometer catches up and reads the actual solution temperature. To compensate for this loss of heat, the data points are used to extrapolate a line back to the time of mixing (the 70-second line in this experiment). This leads to a value for ΔT, which can then be plugged into Equation 8.10, $q = mC\Delta T$. The value used for ΔT is the change in temperature from initial temperature (at the time when the solutions are first mixed) to the projected temperature (extrapolated back to the time of mixing from the data), as shown in Figure 8-7 below:

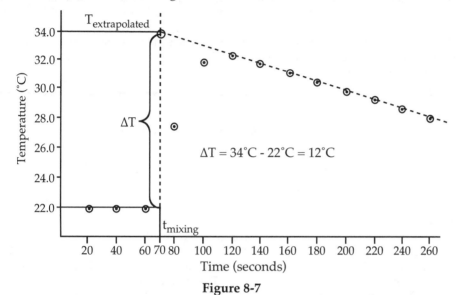

Figure 8-7

The styrofoam cup is not a perfect insulator, so some heat is lost to the environment, which accounts for the drop in solution temperature over time. With better insulation, the slope of the extrapolated line is closer to zero (a flat line). There are several conceptual and error-analysis questions that can accompany this experiment, which makes it an ideal topic for the MCAT.

Example 8.21
Why is the solution stirred after mixing?

A. To generate the activation energy needed for the reaction
B. To prevent the mixture from forming a biphasic system
C. To increase the effectiveness of insulation
D. To distribute the heat evenly throughout the system

Solution
Stirring does not introduce much energy into the system, so choice A is eliminated. Two aqueous solutions do not form a biphasic layer, so choice B is eliminated. Insulation depends on the material, not the motion of the solution, so choice C is eliminated. Solutions are stirred to generate homogeneity of solute molecules and heat. Heat must be evenly distributed through the solution. If the solution were not stirred, then the temperature of the solution at the point where the thermometer rests might not be accurate, because heat pockets in the solution could exist. Choice **D** is the best answer.

Example 8.22
What would be observed if the concentrations of HCl and KOH were cut in half?

A. The change in temperature would be the same.
B. The change in temperature would increase by a factor of two.
C. The change in temperature would decrease by a factor of two.
D. The change in temperature would decrease by a factor of four.

Solution
If the concentrations of both solutions were cut in half, assuming that their volumes stayed the same, then the moles of reactants would be cut by half. With a reduction to half the quantity of reaction, the amount of heat released is cut in half. This would reduce ΔT by half, and makes choice **C** the best answer. If either reactant is decreased, then the amount of heat released must also decrease. In this case, both reactants are decreased by the same amount, so neither one becomes the limiting reagent.

Example 8.23
Why is styrofoam chosen for a simple calorimetry experiment?

A. For its high heat capacity
B. For its isothermal compressibility
C. For its thermal insulating capability
D. For its ability to conduct heat

Solution
The goal in a calorimetry experiment is to measure the heat associated with a reaction. Paramount in this task is the ability to retain all energy within the container, minimizing the interaction with the surrounding medium. Styrofoam is chosen, because it is a good insulator. This makes choice **C** the best answer. You do not want the container to absorb heat, so choice A is eliminated. The experiment entails monitoring a temperature change, so no "isothermal" property is pertinent. This eliminates choice B. Styrofoam is not very dense, so it is assumed that its molecules are relatively far apart from one another. Molecules that are far apart (not in direct contact with one another) do not conduct heat very well. Thus, styrofoam reduces heat loss through conduction. This eliminates choice D. A thermos design is used in more accurate calorimetry experiments. The design of a thermos includes an evacuated chamber between the inner container and the outer wall. An evacuated space prevents heat transfer either through convection or conduction.

Example 8.24
Why must a lid be used in the calorimetry experiment?

A. To prevent heat loss via conduction
B. To prevent heat loss via convection
C. To prevent heat loss via evaporation
D. To prevent heat loss via radiation

Solution
The lid serves as a barrier to prevent gaseous molecules from escaping. This reduces both convective heat loss and evaporative heat loss. The greatest amount of heat is lost through evaporation, so the more significant role of a lid is to prevent evaporative heat loss. Choice **C** is the best answer.

Heat Transfer

Heat is naturally transferred from a warmer object to a cooler object. A greater difference in temperature between the two objects, results in more heat being transferred per unit time. Heat is transferred in four ways: convection, conduction, radiation, and evaporation-condensation. These terms are defined below, along with examples of each type of heat transfer.

Convection (via fluid medium): Convection is the movement of heat through a fluid medium. The particles of the medium collide with the surface of the hot object, resulting in the transfer of heat from the hot object to the medium. The medium can flow, allowing it to travel through the space between the hot and cold objects. When a warm medium strikes the surface of a cold object, heat is transferred through collision to the cold object. The net result is that heat is transferred from the warmer surface to the cooler surface through the fluid medium. The heat is said to travel via *thermal currents*.

Convection example: Convection ovens function by creating thermal currents, which heat food. The heat source (electric coil or flame) is placed in the bottom of the oven where the cooler (denser) air is found. The cooler air collides with the heat source, increasing its thermal energy. As the air becomes warmer, it becomes less dense, and thus rises. The food is typically placed near the top, above the heat source. The warmer air strikes the container holding the food and transfers heat to the container. This cools the air, which then becomes denser, and sinks back to the bottom. The flow of the warm and cool air creates thermal currents. Convection ovens are the conventional ovens found in most kitchens. Some convection ovens augment the airflow with fans that help circulate the warm and cool air.

Conduction (via direct contact): Conduction is the transfer of heat through direct contact (vibrational energy is transferred via collisions between neighboring molecules). The particles of a solid vibrate faster as the object becomes warmer. Vibrating molecules can transfer heat energy to neighboring molecules when they collide. This allows neighboring molecules to equilibrate. Heat is transferred from the warmer point to the cooler point in the object. Because of the continual heat transfer and equilibration of vibrational kinetic energy between neighbors, *heat gradients* are formed.

Conduction example: When heating a metal rod (as when roasting marshmallows over an open flame), the end of the rod in the flame becomes hot. However, although one end is placed in a heat source energetic enough to cook food, the other end of the metal rod is not too hot to hold. This is because the temperature is not uniform throughout the rod. There is a gradient of temperatures between the hot end and the cold end of the rod.

Radiation (absorption and emission of IR photons): Radiation is the emission of photon energy in the form of electromagnetic waves. The energy of the photon varies with the temperature of the object that emits it, as expressed in physics by Wien's displacement law. An object becomes cooler and its molecules move less energetically as it continues to radiate infrared energy.

Radiation examples: Heat-seeking devices are designed to detect regions of high infrared emission. Heat is responsible for making molecules vibrate, and IR photons, when absorbed, stimulate a molecule to reach an excited vibrational state. This means that hot objects emit infrared photons. Microwave ovens function by irradiating food with EM waves of a specific frequency that rotates the water molecules inside the food. By heating the water molecules selectively, water molecules can transfer heat to neighboring food molecules through conduction.

Evaporation-Condensation: Evaporation is an endothermic process in which a liquid absorbs heat and is converted into a gas. Condensation is an exothermic process whereby heat is released from a gas as it is converted into a liquid. A hot body can be cooled when a liquid evaporates from its surface. A cold body can be warmed when a gas condenses on its surface.

Evaporation-condensation example: Perspiration involves the evaporation of a thin film of liquid on the surface of the skin to cool the body. To maximize the effects, surface area must be maximized. In very humid environments, where the rate of condensation equals the rate of evaporation, evaporation is ineffective in cooling the body. For instance, when you first enter a gym, it feels hot and sticky. This is the perspiration from the other inhabitants condensing on the surface of your skin (you unsuspecting cold body you.)

When designing many kinds of machinery, engineers must consider all forms of heat transfer. A good example is the *Miracle Meat Thawer*™, as seen on some of the finer infomercials television has to offer. The Miracle Meat Thawer™ takes advantage of several principles of heat transfer. It is a metal tray with a black top, and ridges. The dark surface absorbs light energy more effectively than a light surface would. The ridges increase the surface area, optimizing the absorption of photons. Being made of metal allows for easier conduction of heat energy. The metal should have a low heat capacity, so that minimal heat is retained by the metal itself. A frozen piece of meat placed on the surface of the thawer acts as a heat sink for all of the energy absorbed by the metal tray. A well-designed tray has a slight slope and a drainage hole leading to a basin. If water collected on the surface of the plate, then heat energy would be wasted in evaporating the water. The apparatus does not work as well if the object being thawed covers the entire surface, because fewer photons can be absorbed.

An engine radiator is another example of a device designed to transfer heat. It works by moving a fluid through the core of a hot engine. The fluid absorbs heat, provided that the coils through which it moves have enough contact with the hot engine. The fluid then passes through more coils in the front of the car, which are covered with thin fins. The purpose of the fins is to maximize the surface area from which heat may be lost via convection. As air passes over the fins, heat from the engine is released to the air.

Example 8.25

Which of the following is NOT a reason why the space surrounding the resistive coil in an incandescent light bulb is evacuated?

A. To maximize energy loss via radiation
B. To prevent pressure buildup at higher temperatures
C. To prevent oxidation of the filament
D. To maximize energy loss via convection

Solution

A light bulb is designed to convert heat (generated through resistance in the coil) into light. By evacuating any gas from the bulb, we reduce the amount of heat energy transferred from the coil through convection. The result is that energy is dissipated as light, and not heat. This maximizes radiation and minimizes convection, making choice A valid and choice **D** invalid. Choice **D** is the best answer. If the bulb contained gas, the gas could expand upon heating, and the bulb might blow up. This makes choice B a valid statement. In an evacuated bulb, there is no oxygen, so oxidation is eliminated. This makes choice C valid.

Heat and Work

Energetics

Energy is a topic common to both chemistry and physics. In a sense, chemistry is the study of energy production while physics is the study of energy application. In chemistry, we think of energy in terms of heat, which is defined by the calorie unit. Heat is absorbed or released during chemical reactions. In physics, we think of energy in terms of work, which is defined by the joule unit. Work is done by either the system or the surroundings in a physical process.

Energy can be converted between heat and work. Heat may be absorbed by a system, expanding the gas contained within, which in turn does work on the surroundings as it expands. This is the essence of any piston-based machine that converts heat directly into work. In this case, heat is defined in chemistry as positive, because heat energy is *gained* by the system. Work, however, is defined in chemistry as negative, because work is *done by the system on the surroundings*. The total energy of a system is a sum of the heat and work. Equation 8.11 defines the change in energy for the system.

$$\Delta E = q - P\Delta V \qquad \qquad (8.11)$$

E is the energy of the system, q is heat, P is pressure, and V is volume. Work can be described as either $F\Delta d$ or $P\Delta V$, depending on the system. For a piston system, the volume changes, so work is $P\Delta V$. As a piston expands (positive ΔV), energy is released by the system to the surroundings, so work is defined as $-P\Delta V$. Values are defined from the system's perspective in chemistry. When q is positive, heat flows from the surroundings into the system. When q is negative, heat flows from the system out to the surroundings. When w is positive, work is done on the system by the surroundings. When w is negative, work is done by the system on the surroundings. When a piston returns to its original position, the energy of a system does not change ($\Delta E = 0$). This is to say that energy is neither absorbed nor released by the system, but converted between work and energy ($q = |P\Delta V|$).

Some terms that describe the conditions involved in energetics are listed below:

Adiabatic: A process where there is no change in heat (q = 0). Heat is neither gained nor lost. The system is perfectly insulated thermally.

Calorie: A unit of energy defined as the heat energy required to raise 1.000 gram of water by 1.000 °C (specifically from 14.50°C to 15.50 °C).

Energy (E): The capacity to do work or to produce heat. There are two types of energy with which we shall concern ourselves: kinetic (energy of motion) and potential (position of an object or chemical composition).

Heat (q): The form of energy involving the motion of molecules. Motion includes translational displacement, and vibrational and rotational movement. The heat associated with a process depends on the pathway.

Joule: A unit of energy defined as the work energy exerted when one Newton of force is applied to an object to move it a distance of one meter.

Surroundings: The surroundings are defined as the environment neighboring a chemical reaction or physical process. The surroundings can either donate energy to the system or absorb energy from the system.

System: The system is defined as the contents of a chemical reaction or physical process that produce or absorb energy. We often study the system, when we look at a chemical reaction.

Work (w): The ability to move an object over a given distance by applying a force. This form of energy is harnessed to move mass. Like heat, work depends on the pathway. $w = F \cdot d = -P \cdot \Delta V$

Carnot Cycle

The Carnot cycle is a cyclic process carried out in a piston, where heat is converted into work or work is converted into heat. Practical examples of the Carnot cycle include engines and refrigerators. We inherently know the concept behind the Carnot cycle. When we blow on a hot liquid, it is done so with pursed lips. Consider blowing on the skin on the back of your hand. If you exhale through your mouth with a normal relaxed degree of aperture, your breath comes out at body temperature. But if you exhale through your mouth with a small opening, the air feels cooler as it passes across your skin. That is due to the compression of the gas (exothermic) as it passes through your lips, and the expansion of the gas (endothermic) once it leaves your mouth. The air feels cooler, because it is expanding as it passes across the surface of your skin. When a gas expands, the molecules increase their intermolecular distance, which breaks intermolecular forces. Just as bond breaking is endothermic, so is the expansion of a gas.

The process of blowing air on your skin through pursed lips results in heat transfer from a cold body (your skin) to a hot body (your mouth). This is unnatural heat flow, so it is similar to the function of the Carnot heat pump. We shall look at a heat pump (refrigerator) in more detail. The Carnot cycle, in a practical sense, can be applied in the form of a heat pump or applied in reverse in the form of a heat engine. It involves phase changes, so the process can be drawn overlaid onto a phase diagram, but the traditional lines of the phase diagram are often removed. Figure 8-8 shows a typical phase diagram on the left and then the Carnot cycle for a heat pump overlaid onto that same phase diagram on the right.

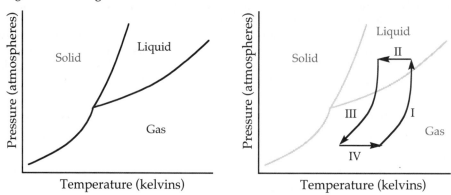

Figure 8-8

A heat pump follows a counterclockwise path about the phase change process cycle. The following lists the phase details of the four-step cycle shown in Figure 8-8:

I.   A material that is normally a gas at room temperature and pressure is compressed into a liquid. Condensation is an exothermic process, so the material heats up and finishes as a liquid at a higher temperature and pressure than it originally had.

II. The material is maintained at a high pressure, so it remains a liquid. It is allowed to cool back to room temperature by dissipating heat to the environment. It finishes at a lower temperature, but the same high pressure.

III. The pressure on the system is returned to normal, so the material expands from a liquid into a gas. Evaporation is an endothermic process, so the material cools down. It finishes as a gas at a lower temperature and pressure than it originally had.

IV. The material is maintained at normal pressure, so it remains a gas. It is allowed to warm back to room temperature by absorbing heat from the environment. It finishes at a higher temperature, but the same pressure.

After the four-step process, the material returns back to its original state. As such, the internal energy does not change. Figure 8-9 shows the energetics of the heat pump cycle shown in Figure 8-8.

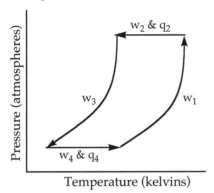

Figure 8-9

As you follow the heat pump around in its counterclockwise path, you see that work is done so that heat energy can be released. The following is a list of the energy details of the four-step cycle shown in Figure 8-9:

I. As the material is compressed into a liquid, work is done on the system (w_1). Heat is released from the molecules as they form stronger intermolecular forces. The heat remains a part of the system in this step, so we cannot consider it transferred yet.

II. Heat is released from the system as the material cools to ambient temperature (q_2). As it cools at constant pressure, the volume decreases slightly (liquids do not exhibit significant volume changes), so a small amount of work is done by the surroundings on the system (w_2).

III. As the material expands back into a gas, work is done by the system (w_3). Heat is absorbed by the molecules as they form weaker intermolecular forces. The heat is not replenished into the system in this step.

IV. Heat is absorbed by the system as the material warms to ambient temperature (q_4). As it heats at constant pressure, the volume increases, so work is done by the system on the surroundings (w_4).

After the four-step process, the material returns to its original state. Overall, more heat is released than absorbed and more work is done on the system than by the system. The net result is that work goes into the system and heat flows out from the system. Another common graph associated with Carnot heat pumps shows pressure on the y-axis and volume on the x-axis. The process is the same, but a phase diagram cannot be understood easily with such axes.

Refrigerator (Applied Heat Pump)

The refrigerator, in its simplest form, uses work to absorb heat as a fluid passes through the four stages in a closed system. In a refrigerator, a change in volume is ultimately a change in heat. The basic idea behind the refrigerator is to put work energy into the system to compress a gas and condense it into a liquid. Compression of a gas and condensation are both exothermic, so heat is released. The system is then allowed to thermally equilibrate with the environment by releasing heat to the surroundings. Following thermal equilibration, the liquid evaporates and the gas expands back to its natural state. Evaporation and the expanding of a gas are both endothermic, so heat is absorbed.

Condensation and evaporation are carried out at different pressures, so it takes more work energy to compress and condense the gas than the work energy released when the liquid evaporates and the gas expands. Ideally, the difference in work energy equals the heat energy released, assuming that energy is conserved in the overall process. Figure 8-10 shows a simplistic schematic diagram for the process, where some material flows repeatedly counterclockwise through the system.

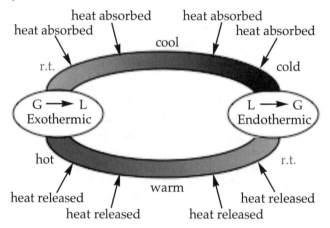

Figure 8-10

Translating from the theoretical schematic in Figure 8-10 into the actual refrigerator requires a piston and a network of coils. A piston is used to compress the gas into a liquid. This is represented by the gas-to-liquid conversion shown in the exothermic oval of Figure 8-10. This region equates to the compressor in a refrigerator. The compressor converts the refrigerant gas to its liquid form, which is an exothermic process. After compressing the refrigerant, the liquid refrigerant flows into a high-pressure reservoir coil, which is represented by the shaded tube from which heat is released in Figure 8-10. Because the reservoir coil is hot, the outer surface is fitted with fins to enhance convection. In order to keep the material a liquid, the warm coil must be pressurized. This is accomplished using a pressure valve at the end of the coil.

Once the liquid refrigerant has cooled to ambient room temperature (RT), it passes through the pressure valve, and then expands into a gas within a low-pressure sealed aluminum coil. As the liquid refrigerant expands within the low-pressure coil to form a gas, heat is absorbed from the environment during this endothermic process. Heat is absorbed from the coils, so the coils become cold. In turn, the coils absorb heat from the surrounding air. Any gas, liquid, or solid in contact with the coils loses heat by transferring it to the walls of the coils. The cold coils are placed in an insulated, sealed container, so the core of the container becomes cool. This is the interior of the refrigerator. The compressor and high-pressure coils must be kept as far away from the core of the container as possible, because of the heat they release. Figure 8-11 is a more detailed pictorial representation of the refrigeration process shown in Figure 8-10.

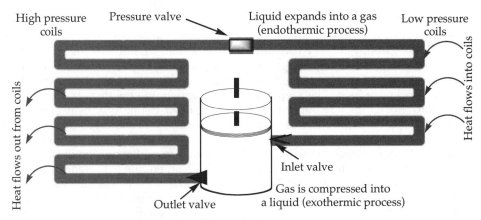

Figure 8-11

The four stages of the refrigerator shown in Figure 8-11 are listed below:

1. Freon gas flows from the low-pressure coils into the piston of the compressor through an inlet valve at the top of the piston. The piston is then compressed. The increased pressure exerted on the freon gas converts the freon gas into its liquid phase. As the piston descends further, the hot freon liquid is forced through an outlet valve. The liquid is hot due to the condensation process. (Check a compressor if you wish to verify this).

2. When the piston reaches the bottom of its cycle, the outlet valve is forced open, and hot freon liquid escapes into the high-pressure coils. Because freon liquid is hot (condensation is a heat-releasing process), the high-pressure coils are hot. They are found on the back (exterior) of the refrigerator, often covered by a metal grid or thin plate. The freon liquid cools and equilibrates with the air by dissipating the heat to the external environment through the walls of the coils. Coils are chosen to maximize surface area.

3. Freon liquid at ambient temperature is forced from the high-pressure coils through a pressurized outlet valve into the low-pressure coils. The freon liquid is forced into the low-pressure coils by the increased hydraulic pressure generated when hot freon liquid is forced into the high-pressure coils through the inlet valve by the compressor.

4. Freon liquid evaporates to form freon gas in the low-pressure coils. Freon evaporates by the absorption of heat from the core of the container in which the low-pressure coils reside. During this step, heat is absorbed from the inside of the refrigerator. The freon gas fills the low-pressure coil once it has evaporated. The cycle repeats.

The net result is that work is applied at the compressor, and heat flows out from the high-pressure coils, so heat is removed from the core of the refrigerator to the environment. The compressor acts as a pump, and freon flow is in one direction through the system. Heat is absorbed and released at different points.

Air conditioners and freezers have the same mechanics as a refrigerator. The difference between freezers, air conditioners, and refrigerators is the temperature of the internal coils. Because a phase change from liquid to gas is responsible for absorbing heat, the temperature of the cold coils depends on the boiling point of the refrigerant. A refrigerant is selected on the basis of its boiling point and the target temperature of the system. The temperature in a freezer is less than the temperature of a an air conditioner or refrigerator, so the boiling point of the refrigerant used in a freezer is lower than the refrigerant used in an air conditioner or a refrigerator.

Heat Engine

The Carnot heat engine is the reverse of a Carnot heat pump. This is to say that when a heat pump is run backwards (heat is added in and work is released), a heat engine is created. The diagram for a heat engine, Figure 8-12, shows arrows in a clockwise loop, as opposed to the heat pump, which has its arrows in a counterclockwise loop, like Figure 8-9. The heat engine operates by converting heat into work. In its simplest definition (Carnot definition), heat is used to expand a gas in a closed system within a piston. When the gas expands, the walls of the container move. Because the container is a piston, only one wall moves. Work is associated with force times distance, so the motion of the wall is harnessable work. The basic concept behind a heat engine is rooted in the ideal gas equation $PV = nRT$, where altering one variable changes another variable. In an engine, a change in heat is ultimately a change in volume. This means that no change in internal energy transpires, only the conversion from heat into work. The following is the operation of a Carnot heat engine:

1. The first step starting from the upper left corner of the diagram in Figure 8-12 below is the reversible isothermal expansion of the gas from state a to state b. During this step, work (defined as w_{a-b} in the diagram) is done by the piston on the surroundings (defined as negative for the system); and heat (q_1) is absorbed by the gas. In a combustion engine, it is the explosion of the gasoline that generates this heat.

2. The second step is the reversible adiabatic expansion of the gas from state b to state c. As implied by the term "adiabatic," no heat is gained or lost by the system. As a consequence of no heat transfer, the temperature drops as the expanding gas absorbs heat energy. In this step, the piston does work (w_{b-c}) on the surroundings. In a combustion engine, this is that small period of time after the gasoline has exploded where the piston is still rising.

3. The third step is the reversible isothermal compression of the gas from state c to state d. During this compression step, the surroundings do work (w_{c-d}) on the gas (defined as positive for the system), and heat (q_2) flows out of the engine. In a combustion engine, this is the venting of the piston allowing the hot exhaust to escape followed by cool air and gasoline vapor flowing in.

4. The fourth step (which completes the cycle) is the reversible adiabatic compression of the gas from state d back to state a. During this step, the surroundings do work (w_{d-a}) on the gas as the piston descends, but heat is not gained or lost. In a combustion engine, this is the equilibrating of the piston chamber back to its resting state just before the spark ignites the gas.

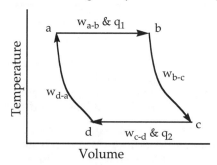

Figure 8-12

The graph may also be diagrammed as pressure as a function of volume. The volume term is important, because work is defined by the equation: $w = -P\Delta V$.

A good example of the application of the principles behind the heat engine is the single-piston steam engine. In the steam engine, we start by considering a reservoir filled with hot water (water at 100°C). Water is taken through a four-step process that changes its phase and pressure and then returns it to its original state. The following steps outline the operation of a steam engine:

1. Water evaporates to form steam as heat is stoked in the boiler. During this step, heat is added from the surroundings (defined as heat energy into the system). The steam builds up pressure in the reservoir.

2. Steam flows from the reservoir into the piston when the inlet valve to the piston is opened. The pressure exerted by the steam that enters causes the piston to rise from its lowest point to its highest point (apex). As the piston rises, work is done by the system on the surroundings (defined as energy out from the system).

3. When the piston has reached the top of its cycle, the outlet valve is opened, and the steam escapes into the exhaust column and collects in the condenser, where the pressure is reduced upon condensation. The piston returns to its lowest point through inertia and the force of a counterweight (in a one-piston engine). As the piston falls, work is done by the surroundings on the system (defined as work energy into the system).

4. The steam condenses in the condenser and is pumped back into the boiler. During this step, heat is released to the surroundings (defined as heat energy out from the system) as the steam condenses back into water. The cycle then repeats step one again.

The condenser reduces the pressure so that when the exhaust valve is opened, the steam within the piston can flow from a region of higher pressure (the piston) to a region of lower pressure (the condenser). Heat is released from the condenser, so an efficient engine finds a way to recycle that emitted heat. Figure 8-13 shows a pictorial diagram of a steam engine.

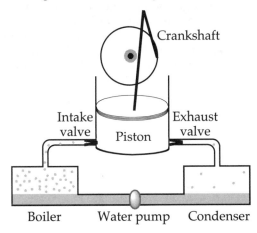

Figure 8-13

The steam engine is a closed system through which water circulates. A combustion engine differs from the Carnot heat engine and steam engine in that it is an open system. Petroleum mist and air are injected into the piston. The mixture is ignited, and the piston rapidly expands. The power stroke of the piston does work on the crankshaft, turning the crank 180 degrees. Exhaust is removed from the piston and released to the atmosphere. The conversion of explosive linear work into circular motion requires a crankshaft.

One of the more important physics-based features of an engine is the timing of the valves. Because the motion generated by an engine is periodic, there must be periods (timing) for each operation of the machine. The inlet valve must open and close (allowing fuel and air to enter the chamber) before the spark can ignite the mixture, followed by the opening of the exhaust valve to vent the products from the chamber once burning has ceased. This is what is referred to as the *timing* of the engine. Modern engines have each piston fitted with four valves (two intake and two exhaust), so that the gas diffuses more evenly in the chamber. Because the up-and-down motion of the piston ultimately turns a crank, torque must be invoked. To maximize torque, a lever arm system is used. This allows the rod to be attached at the edge of the crank (maximizing moment arm) and allows the rod to move in same direction as the piston, for the most part. This maximizes the applied force of the system shown in Figure 8-13.

Engine Efficiency

The efficiency of an engine is simply the output over the input. Work energy is produced from heat energy, so engine efficiency is work out divided by heat in. The most efficient engines have low exhaust temperature (minimal heat is wasted), few moving parts (minimizes friction), and low weight (work energy produced is not wasted in moving the engine). Efficient engines are multi-piston systems rather than a single piston connected to a counterweight. A good analogy involves a bicycle crank. The pedals are placed out of phase for greatest efficiency. A bicycle could be designed with two pedals in phase attached to a crank housing a counterweight that is out of phase with the two pedals. The counterweight system works well in theory, but this would not be an enjoyable bike to ride uphill because of its extreme mass.

Refrigerators, Engines, and Carnot Cycle Reality Check

This is one of the most difficult topics tested on the physical sciences section of the MCAT. As such, their questions must be modified to a level that will generate a bell curve. Although the passages may seem overwhelming, if you have a very fundamental perspective that a refrigerator takes in work (applied to a piston) and releases heat while an engine takes in heat (to expand a gas in a piston) and releases work, you should do fine on their questions. Do not over-study this topic, even if you feel like you only partially comprehend it.

Thermochemistry Passages

13 Passages

100 Questions

Suggested Thermochemistry Passage Schedule:

I: After reading this section and attending lecture: Passages I - III, VI, & XI
Grade passages immediately after completion and log your mistakes.

II: Following Task I: Passages IV, V, IX, & X (28 questions in 36 minutes)
Time yourself accurately, grade your answers, and review mistakes.

III: Review: Passages VII, VIII, XII - XIII & Questions 93 - 100
Focus on reviewing the concepts. Do not worry about timing.

The BERKELEY REVIEW®

Specializing in MCAT Preparation

Thermodynamics Study Passages

Thermochemistry Scoring Scale

Raw Score	MCAT Score
84 - 100	13 - 15
66 - 83	10 - 12
47 - 65	7 - 9
34 - 46	4 - 6
1 - 33	1 - 3

Passage I (Questions 1 - 7)

Drawn below are two energy diagrams for two separate processes. Figure 1 shows the energy diagram for Reaction 1, and Figure 2 shows the energy diagram for Reaction 2. For Reaction 1, there are two pathways drawn leading to two separate products, X and Y. Both pathways represent two-step reaction mechanisms. In Reaction 2, there are two steps to the reaction, as represented by the two peaks, but only one reaction pathway is shown on the energy diagram.

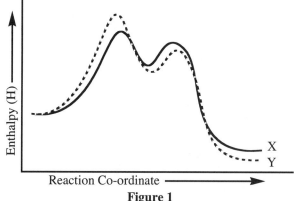

Figure 1

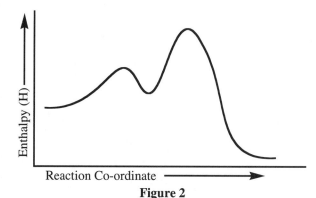

Figure 2

In Reaction 1, either pathway can occur, depending on the conditions. The pathways are referred as the *kinetic* and *thermodynamic pathways*. Lower activation energy is associated with the kinetic pathway, while a more stable product is associated with the thermodynamic pathway. At low temperatures, the reaction is forced to take the pathway that requires the least activation energy. This means that the kinetic product is observed at lower temperatures. At elevated temperatures, the thermodynamic product is observed.

1. In Reaction 1, what is true of the rate-determining step?

 A. The first step is rate-determining, because it has the highest activation energy.
 B. The first step is rate-determining, because it has the lowest activation energy.
 C. The second step is rate-determining, because it has the highest activation energy.
 D. The second step is rate-determining, because it has the lowest activation energy.

2. If ΔS is positive for Reaction 2, then as the temperature is increased, what is observed?

 A. Both the K_{eq}-to-Q ratio and ΔG increase.
 B. The K_{eq}-to-Q ratio decreases, while ΔG increases.
 C. The K_{eq}-to-Q ratio increases, while ΔG decreases.
 D. Both the K_{eq}-to-Q ratio and ΔG decrease.

3. For Reaction 1, what can be said about the enthalpies of both pathways?

 A. ΔH for Pathway X is positive; more energy is released from Pathway X than Pathway Y.
 B. ΔH for Pathway X is positive; less energy is released from Pathway X than Pathway Y.
 C. ΔH for Pathway X is negative; more energy is released from Pathway X than Pathway Y.
 D. ΔH for Pathway X is negative; less energy is released from Pathway X than Pathway Y.

4. At higher temperatures, what is true about Pathway X and Pathway Y of Reaction 1?

 A. Pathway X is the kinetic pathway and is more probable than Pathway Y.
 B. Pathway X is the thermodynamic pathway and is more probable than Pathway Y.
 C. Pathway Y is the kinetic pathway and is more probable than Pathway X.
 D. Pathway Y is the thermodynamic pathway and is more probable than Pathway X.

5. What is observed in Reaction 2?

 A. The intermediate builds up to a detectable level, because the rate-determining step is the first step.
 B. The intermediate builds up to a detectable level, because the rate-determining step is the second step.
 C. The intermediate cannot build up to a detectable level, because the first step is rate-determining.
 D. The intermediate cannot build up to a detectable level, because the second step is rate-determining.

 GO ON TO THE NEXT PAGE

6. Which of the graphs represents the percentages of products X and Y as the temperature is increased?

A.

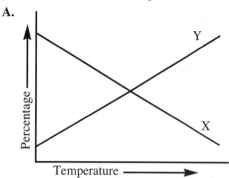

B.

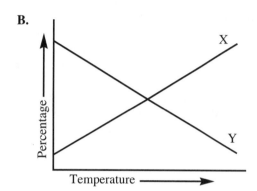

C.

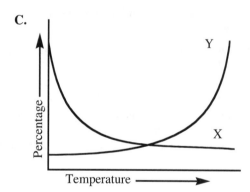

D.

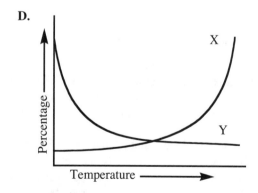

7. If Reaction 1 is favorable at lower temperatures but unfavorable at higher temperatures, then what is true about the change in enthalpy and entropy?

A. $\Delta H > 0; \Delta S > 0$

B. $\Delta H > 0; \Delta S < 0$

C. $\Delta H < 0; \Delta S > 0$

D. $\Delta H < 0; \Delta S < 0$

GO ON TO THE NEXT PAGE

The enthalpy of a reaction can be found using the bond energies. The change in enthalpy can be attributed to the difference between the energies of the bonds broken and the energies of the bonds formed. Equation 1 shows how enthalpy change is obtained from bond energies.

$$\Delta H = B.E._{(bonds\ broken)} - B.E._{(bonds\ formed)}$$

Equation 1

Table 1 lists the bond energies of some of the more common bonds within organic molecules.

Bond	B.E. (KJ/mole)	Bond	B.E. (KJ/mole)	Bond	B.E. (KJ/mole)
H—C	413	C—C	347	N—C	305
H—H	432	C—H	413	N—H	391
H—N	391	C—N	305	N—N	160
H—O	467	C—O	358	N—O	201
H—F	565	C—F	485	N—F	272
H—Cl	427	C—Cl	339	N—Cl	200
H—Br	363	C—Br	276	N—Br	243
H—I	295	C—I	240	N—I	171

Table 1

Table 2 lists the bond energies of some of the less common bonds within organic molecules. Both tables fail to account for hybridization or the effects of neighboring substituents on the stability of a bond. The kJ unit is converted into kcal by dividing by 4.18.

Bond	B.E. (KJ/mole)	Bond	B.E. (KJ/mole)	Bond	B.E. (KJ/mole)
O—O	146	F—F	154	C=C	614
O=O	495	Cl—Cl	239	C=N	615
S—H	347	Br—Br	193	C=O	799
S—S	128	I—I	149	N=N	418
S—F	XXX	Cl—F	253	N=O	607
S—Cl	258	Br—Cl	218	C≡C	839
S—Br	218	I—Cl	208	C≡N	891
S—I	266	I—Br	175	N≡N	941

Table 2

8. Which bond is the WEAKEST in diethyl peroxide?

   A. H—C
   B. C—O
   C. O—O
   D. C—C

9. The second π-bond in nitrogen gas has:

   A. a bond energy of 258.0 kJ per mole.
   B. a bond energy of 390.5 kJ per mole.
   C. a bond energy of 313.7 kJ per mole.
   D. a bond energy of 523.0 kJ per mole.

10. Why does an $sp^2C{-}sp^3C$ bond have a higher bond energy than an $sp^3C{-}sp^3C$ bond?

    A. An sp^2 orbital is shorter than an sp^3 orbital, hence the $sp^2C{-}sp^3C$ bond is shorter and thus stronger.
    B. An sp^2 orbital is shorter than an sp^3 orbital, hence the $sp^2C{-}sp^3C$ bond is longer and thus weaker.
    C. An sp^2 orbital is less electronegative than an sp^3 orbital, hence the $sp^2C{-}sp^3C$ bond is more polar and thus stronger.
    D. An sp^2 orbital is more electronegative than an sp^3 orbital, hence the $sp^2C{-}sp^3C$ bond is more polar and thus stronger.

11. The breaking of an H—H and an F—F bond to form two H—F bonds is:

    A. highly endothermic.
    B. slightly endothermic.
    C. slightly exothermic.
    D. highly exothermic.

12. How can the bond energy trend of the sulfur-halide bond be explained?

    A. As the halide gets larger, the bond gets stronger.
    B. As the halide gets more electronegative, the bond gets stronger.
    C. The strength of the bond depends on both the size and polarizability of the halide.
    D. As the electron affinity of the halide increases, the bond gets stronger.

13. What is the approximate bond energy of a Br—F bond?

    A. $261 \dfrac{kJ}{mole}$
    B. $242 \dfrac{kJ}{mole}$
    C. $206 \dfrac{kJ}{mole}$
    D. $161 \dfrac{kJ}{mole}$

14. Why is the F—F bond weaker than the Cl—Cl bond?

    A. The F—F bond is shorter, and shorter bonds are always weaker.
    B. Chlorine is more electronegative than fluorine.
    C. Fluorine atoms repel when close together.
    D. Chlorine is smaller than fluorine.

GO ON TO THE NEXT PAGE

Passage III (Questions 15 - 21)

The Born-Haber cycle refers to the energy released when a salt is formed from its most stable elements in their natural form. The enthalpy change for the overall reaction can be found by summing the individual steps of the overall process. The formation of lithium fluoride from lithium metal and fluorine gas is shown in a stepwise fashion below:

Step I: Sublimation of lithium metal:

$Li(s) \rightarrow Li(g)$ $\Delta H_{sublimation} = +153 \text{ kJ}$

Step II: Ionization of lithium gas:

$Li(g) \rightarrow Li^+(g)$ Ionization energy $= +513 \text{ kJ}$

Step III: Dissociation of F—F Bond:

$\frac{1}{2} F_2(g) \rightarrow F(g)$ Half bond energy $F_2 = +77 \text{ kJ}$

Step IV: Electron affinity of atomic fluorine:

$F(g) + 1 e^- \rightarrow F^-(g)$ Electron affinity $= -324 \text{ kJ}$

Step V: Formation of lattice from gaseous ions:

$Li^+(g) + F^-(g) \rightarrow LiF(s)$ Lattice energy $= -1045 \text{ kJ}$

Overall:

$Li(s) + \frac{1}{2} F_2(g) \rightarrow LiF(s)$ $\Delta H_{reaction} = -626 \text{ kJ}$

The total energy of the reaction is found by summing the five steps of the reaction. The lattice energy can be found using Equation 1, where Q is charge and r is the distance between ions in the lattice:

$$E = k \frac{Q_{cation}Q_{anion}}{r}$$

Equation 1

15. If sodium metal were used instead of lithium metal, what values would be affected?

   I. The sublimation energy would increase.

   II. The ionization energy would increase.

   III. The lattice energy would increase.

   A. I only
   B. II only
   C. I and II only
   D. I and III only

16. Why is only half of the bond dissociation energy used in Step III?

   A. The F—F bond is only partially broken.
   B. The table value for the bond dissociation energy is double the actual value for the bond dissociation energy.
   C. Because the bond is broken in a heterolytic fashion, the bond dissociation value is only half of the value for the homolytic breaking.
   D. The breaking of the bond produces two fluorine atoms, and only one is needed.

17. How do the lattice energies of NaCl, LiF, and MgO compare to one another?

   A. $E_{MgO} > E_{LiF} > E_{NaCl}$
   B. $E_{MgO} > E_{NaCl} > E_{LiF}$
   C. $E_{LiF} > E_{NaCl} > E_{MgO}$
   D. $E_{NaCl} > E_{LiF} > E_{MgO}$

18. If calcium metal is used instead of lithium metal, how can the value in Step II be determined?

   A. Only the value for the first ionization should be used.
   B. Only the value for the second ionization should be used.
   C. An average of the first and second ionization values should be used.
   D. The sum of the first and second ionization values should be used.

19. The electron affinity can BEST be described as:

   A. the energy associated with the excitation of an electron.
   B. the energy associated with the de-excitation of an electron.
   C. the energy associated with the loss of an electron.
   D. the energy associated with the gain of an electron.

20. Which change results in LESS energy being released in the overall process?

   A. Using a metal that is easier to sublime than lithium
   B. Using a halogen that forms a stronger bond as a diatomic molecule than fluorine.
   C. Using a halogen atom with a greater electron affinity than fluorine
   D. Using a cation that can easily lose a second electron

21. What changes would reduce the magnitude of the lattice energy?

   I. Substituting a larger cation for a smaller cation

   II. Substituting an anion of less charge for the anion

   III. Reducing the cation charge, anion charge, and distance between ions each by half

   A. I only
   B. I and II only
   C. I and III only
   D. I, II, and III

The free energy change of a reaction depends on the initial reaction conditions and the position of the equilibrium. Reactions that spontaneously proceed in the forward direction have negative free energy changes, and are defined as favorable reactions. Equation 1 shows the relationship of the free energy change (ΔG_{rx}) based on the standard equilibrium shift from equal parts products and reactants.

$$\Delta G_{observed} = \Delta G° + RT \ln Q_{rx}$$

Equation 1

The value for $\Delta G°$ can be found by measuring the ΔG_{rx} when one mole of each product and reactant are mixed together in a one liter container. The value for $\Delta G°$ is given by the following equation:

$$\Delta G° = - RT \ln K_{eq}$$

Equation 2

The free-energy change can also be found using the following equation:

$$\Delta G_{rx} = \Delta H_{rx} - T\Delta S_{rx}$$

Equation 3

The ΔH_{rx} represents the enthalpy change for the reaction, which is measured as the heat change (either gained or lost) during the reaction. The ΔS_{rx} represents the entropy change for the reaction, which is measured as the change in randomness of motion during the reaction.

22. Which process is NOT entropically favorable?

   A. Distillation of ethanol from octane
   B. Solvation of a salt by water
   C. Sublimation of iodine solid
   D. Diffusion of a pure gas into the air

23. Which of the following reactions exhibits ΔS value > 0?

   A. $NaCl(s) + H_2O(l) \rightleftharpoons Na^+(aq) + Cl^-(aq)$
   B. $PCl_3(l) + Cl_2(g) \rightleftharpoons PCl_5(s)$
   C. $2 H_2(g) + O_2(g) \rightleftharpoons 2 H_2O(l)$
   D. $N_2(g) + O_2(g) \rightleftharpoons 2 NO(g)$

24. Addition of a catalyst MOST changes:

   A. the free energy of the reaction.
   B. the enthalpy of the reaction.
   C. the entropy of the reaction.
   D. the rate of the reaction.

25. If a reaction that is spontaneous as written lowers the solution temperature as it proceeds, then the ΔS for the reaction is:

   A. negative at all temperatures.
   B. negative at low temperatures and positive at high temperatures.
   C. positive at low temperatures and negative at high temperatures.
   D. positive at all temperatures.

26. For a reaction where the reaction quotient (Q_{rx}) is greater than the equilibrium constant (K_{eq}), what is true about the reaction and $\Delta G_{observed}$?

   A. $\Delta G_{observed} > 0$; the reaction shifts to the reactant side to reach equilibrium.
   B. $\Delta G_{observed} < 0$; the reaction shifts to the reactant side to reach equilibrium.
   C. $\Delta G_{observed} > 0$; the reaction shifts to the product side to reach equilibrium.
   D. $\Delta G_{observed} < 0$; the reaction shifts to the product side to reach equilibrium.

27. The ΔH for a given reaction is 12.5 kJ/mole. The ΔS for the reaction is 25 J/mole·K. At what temperature does the equilibrium constant equal the reaction quotient?

   A. 0°C
   B. 227°C
   C. 327°C
   D. 500°C

28. The $\Delta G_{observed}$ for a reaction can be found using which of the following equations?

   A. $\Delta G_{observed} = RT \ln \dfrac{Q_{rx}}{K_{eq}}$

   B. $\Delta G_{observed} = RT \ln \dfrac{K_{eq}}{Q_{rx}}$

   C. $\Delta G_{observed} = \dfrac{Q_{rx}}{K_{eq}} e^{RT}$

   D. $\Delta G_{observed} = \dfrac{K_{eq}}{Q_{rx}} e^{RT}$

Over the past few decades, several advances have been made in rocket propulsion systems. These developments center on the engineering of the rocket equipment, as well as on advances in the fuels used to propel rockets. The perfect fuel system is lightweight and capable of providing large sustained energy bursts. An ideal fuel system is liquid hydrogen (b.p. 18 K) mixed with liquid oxygen (b.p. 91 K). Reaction 1 below shows the gas phase combustion reaction of hydrogen and oxygen.

$$H_2(g) + \tfrac{1}{2} O_2(g) \rightarrow H_2O(g); \quad \Delta H° = -242 \ \frac{kJ}{mole}$$

Reaction 1, oxidation of hydrogen gas

The oxidation of hydrogen gas has been used in the later stages of several launches of orbiting spacecraft, but it is not used for the initial launch from earth, where a greater amount of energy is required. Reactions 2, 3, and 4 can also be used to generate the energy required to move massive projectiles.

$$C_{12}H_{26}(l) + 18\tfrac{1}{2} O_2(g) \rightarrow 12 \ CO_2(g) + 13 \ H_2O(g)$$

$$\Delta H° = -7513 \ \frac{kJ}{mole}$$

Reaction 2, oxidation of kerosene

$$2 \ N_2H_4(l) + N_2O_4(g) \rightarrow 3 \ N_2(g) + 4 \ H_2O(g)$$

$$\Delta H° = -1049 \ \frac{kJ}{mole}$$

Reaction 3, hydrazine oxidation via dinitrogen tetraoxide

$$2 \ Al(s) + 6 \ NH_4ClO_4(s)$$

$$\rightarrow 1 \ NO_2(g) + 6 \ HCl(g) + 1 \ Al_2O_3(s) + 9 \ H_2O(g)$$

$$\Delta H° = -1216 \ \frac{kJ}{mole}$$

Reaction 4, $Al/(C_2H_4)_n$ oxidation via NH_4ClO_4

All four reactions generate a large amount of heat by way of oxidation. By rapidly oxidizing the fuel, a concentrated stream of energy is produced to lift the rocket and thrust it in the determined pathway.

29. The $\Delta H_{formation}$ of $H_2O(l)$ is -286 kJ per mole. The difference between this value and the value listed with Reaction 1 is because the condensation of water is:

A. endothermic, so the $\Delta H_{formation}$ for $H_2O(l)$ is more negative than $\Delta H_{formation}$ of $H_2O(g)$.

B. exothermic, so the $\Delta H_{formation}$ for $H_2O(l)$ is more negative than $\Delta H_{formation}$ of $H_2O(g)$.

C. endothermic, so the $\Delta H_{formation}$ for $H_2O(l)$ is less negative than $\Delta H_{formation}$ of $H_2O(g)$.

D. exothermic, so the $\Delta H_{formation}$ for $H_2O(l)$ is less negative than $\Delta H_{formation}$ of $H_2O(g)$.

30. What makes kerosene a better fuel for early rocket stages than hydrogen gas?

A. At standard temperature, kerosene is far denser than hydrogen, and thus more convenient to store.

B. Kerosene provides more energy per gram than hydrogen.

C. Kerosene burns at a higher temperature.

D. Oxidation of kerosene produces fewer products.

31. Which of the following describes the ideal mixture of hydrazine and dinitrogen tetraoxide?

A. 2 : 1 by mass in favor of hydrazine

B. 1 : 1 by mass of hydrazine with N_2O_4

C. 3 : 2 by mass in favor of N_2O_4

D. 2 : 1 by mass in favor of N_2O_4

32. Which of the following reactions CANNOT be used to propel rockets?

A. $C_6H_{14}(l) + 9\tfrac{1}{2} O_2(g) \rightarrow 6 \ CO_2(g) + 7 \ H_2O(g)$

B. $N_2H_4 + \tfrac{1}{2} KClO_4 \rightarrow N_2 + 2 \ H_2O + \tfrac{1}{2} KCl$

C. $Fe + (NH_4)_2CrO_4 \rightarrow$
$\tfrac{1}{2} Fe_2O_3 + H_2O + \tfrac{1}{2} Cr_2O_3 + 2 \ NH_3$

D. $H_2SO_4 + 2 \ KOH \rightarrow K_2SO_4 + 2 \ H_2O$

33. Which of the following is NOT a requirement of a rocket fuel?

A. Highly exothermic combustion reaction

B. A large heat-to-gram fuel ratio

C. Gas phase at room temperature

D. Highly reactive as an oxidant or reductant

34. In the $N_2H_4(l) + N_2O_4(g)$ reaction, what is true?

A. $N_2O_4(g)$ is a reducing agent.

B. $N_2H_4(l)$ loses four electrons per nitrogen.

C. Nitrogen-nitrogen bonds are broken.

D. Hydrazine is being oxidized.

35. What is the heat per gram value for kerosene?

A. Greater than 75.0 kJ per gram

B. Greater than 50.0, but less than 75.0 kJ per gram

C. Greater than 40.0, but less than 50.0 kJ per gram

D. Less than 40.0 kJ per gram

Thermodynamics is the study of energy and its distribution within a physical or chemical system. One of the common mathematical practices in thermodynamics is the coupling of several processes to sum up to an overall process. For example, the overall enthalpy is the sum of the individual enthalpies for each reaction. This is known as Hess's law. In addition to enthalpy, entropy and free energy can also be determined using Hess's law. The entropy and free energy change for a reaction is equal to the sum of the entropy and free energy changes for any set of reactions that sum to the same reaction.

A common application of this procedure is the summing of the heats of formation for each reactant and product to obtain the heat for the overall reaction, such as the combustion of a hydrocarbon. By definition, the heat of formation for an element in its most natural state at 25°C is 0 kJ/mole. This is to say that converting an element such as $O_2(g)$ into $O_2(g)$ (the most stable form of oxygen at room temperature) requires 0 kJ/mole. A small sampling from a chart of enthalpies of formation is listed below. The chart below can be used in conjunction with Hess's law (which is not one of the laws of thermodynamics) to calculate the values common to thermodynamics.

Compound	$\Delta H° \left(\dfrac{kJ}{mole}\right)$	$\Delta G° \left(\dfrac{kJ}{mole}\right)$
$CO_2(g)$	-393.5	-394.3
$C_2H_2(g)$	+226.8	+209.1
$C_2H_4(g)$	+52.4	+68.3
$C_2H_5OH(l)$	-277.7	-174.9
$H_2O(g)$	-241.8	-228.6
$H_2O(l)$	-285.9	-237.2

Table 1

The phase of the compound is specified, because the energies are different for each phase of the compound. The difference between the thermodynamic values associated with each phase is the thermodynamic value for the phase change process. The enthalpy of fusion (associated with melting) can be found by subtracting the enthalpy of formation for the solid from the enthalpy of formation for the liquid. The enthalpy for a reaction is found by subtracting the enthalpy of formation for all of the reactants from the enthalpy of formation for all of the products.

36. What is the free energy change for the vaporization of water under standard conditions?

A. $-44.1 \dfrac{kJ}{mole}$

B. $-8.6 \dfrac{kJ}{mole}$

C. $+8.6 \dfrac{kJ}{mole}$

D. $+44.1 \dfrac{kJ}{mole}$

37. The difference in the enthalpies of combustion for xylose (an aldopentose) and ribose (an aldopentose) can BEST be attributed to:

A. ring strain in the furanose ring.

B. steric repulsion in the furanose ring.

C. the difference in the number of O-H bonds.

D. the difference in the number of C=O bonds.

38. From the values in Table 1, what can be said about the hydrogenation of acetylene (C_2H_2) to ethylene (C_2H_4)?

A. Hydrogenation of acetylene is favorable.

B. Hydrogenation of acetylene is unfavorable.

C. The free energy change for the reaction cannot be calculated without knowing the enthalpy of formation for $H_2(g)$.

D. The free energy change for the reaction cannot be calculated without knowing the enthalpy of combustion for $H_2(g)$.

39. Which of the following is the change in enthalpy for the formation of chloroethene under standard conditions?

A. ΔH for the reaction:
$2 C(gr) + 1\frac{1}{2} H_2(g) + \frac{1}{2} Cl_2(g) \rightarrow C_2H_3Cl(g)$

B. ΔH for the reaction:
$2 C(gr) + 1\frac{1}{2} H_2(g) + \frac{1}{2} Cl_2(l) \rightarrow C_2H_3Cl(g)$

C. ΔH for the reaction:
$2 C(d) + 1\frac{1}{2} H_2(g) + \frac{1}{2} Cl_2(g) \rightarrow C_2H_3Cl(g)$

D. ΔH for the reaction:
$2 C(d) + 1\frac{1}{2} H_2(g) + 1 Cl(g) \rightarrow C_2H_3Cl(g)$

40. Which of the following is the change in enthalpy for the combustion of propene under standard conditions?

A. $3 \Delta H_f H_2O + 2 \Delta H_f CO_2 - \Delta H_f C_3H_6$

B. $3 \Delta H_f H_2O + 3 \Delta H_f CO_2 - \Delta H_f C_3H_6$

C. $4 \Delta H_f H_2O + 3 \Delta H_f CO_2 - \Delta H_f C_3H_6$

D. $\Delta H_f C_3H_6 - 3 \Delta H_f CO_2 - 3 \Delta H_f H_2O$

41. Given that $\Delta H_{formation}$ for $H_3C—CH_3$ is -87.4 $\frac{kJ}{mole}$, how can the ΔH_{rx} of -271.4 $\frac{kJ}{mole}$ for the following hydrogenation reaction be explained?

$$H_2C=CH—CH=CH_2 + 2\ H_2 \rightarrow H_3CCH_2CH_2CH_3$$

A. The value for ΔH_{rx} is more negative than expected, because the reactant is stabilized by conjugation.

B. The value for ΔH_{rx} is less negative than expected, because the reactant is stabilized by conjugation.

C. The value for ΔH_{rx} is more negative than expected, because the product is stabilized by conjugation.

D. The value for ΔH_{rx} is less negative than expected, because the product is stabilized by conjugation.

42. Which of the following statements is true about the heat produced from burning one gram of ethyne and one gram of ethene in the presence of excess oxygen gas under standard conditions?

A. 1.0 g $C_2H_2(g)$ yields more heat than 1.0 g $C_2H_4(g)$.

B. 1.0 g $C_2H_2(g)$ yields less heat than 1.0 g $C_2H_4(g)$.

C. 1.0 g $C_2H_2(g)$ yields as much heat as 1.0 g $C_2H_4(g)$.

D. The amount of heat cannot be calculated without first knowing the $\Delta H_{formation}$ of oxygen gas.

43. Which of the following is the free energy of combustion for ethanol (C_2H_5OH) under standard conditions?

A. -1325.3 $\frac{kJ}{mole}$

B. -1368.3 $\frac{kJ}{mole}$

C. -1675.1 $\frac{kJ}{mole}$

D. -1920.1 $\frac{kJ}{mole}$

Passage VII (Questions 44 - 49)

The enthalpy of a reaction can be calculated empirically using data from calorimetry experiments. In the standard procedure, referred to as *bomb calorimetry*, a known quantity of a compound is burned in a containment vessel surrounded by a liquid with a known heat capacity (usually water). The heat absorbed by the surroundings is assumed to equal the heat released by the reaction. This indirectly gives the ΔH for the reaction. An error that arises using this method is the loss of heat to the environment. To avoid this, the liquid is encased in an insulated container.

The results of calorimetry experiments can be combined to determine the ΔH for other reactions using Hess's law. Hess's law states that the ΔH for a reaction is equal to the sum of the ΔH values for any series of reactions that sum up to the overall reaction.

A researcher conducts the following two experiments to determine the molar heat of formation for magnesium oxide:

Experiment 1

A researcher places into an insulated beaker 1.00 kg of 0.10 M HCl solution (C = 4.34 J/g·K) at 22°C. This beaker is labeled Beaker 1. 2.43 grams of magnesium metal (24.3 grams/mole) are then added to the solution. A thermometer calibrated in 0.10°C increments is placed into the beaker. The temperature at uniform time intervals is recorded in Figure 1. Reaction 1 is shown below:

$$Mg(s) + 2\ H^+(aq) \rightarrow Mg^{2+}(aq) + H_2(g)$$

Reaction 1

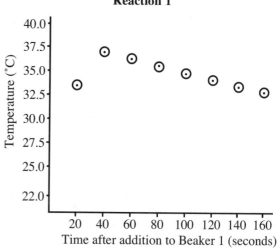

Figure 1

Experiment 2

A second beaker, identical to that in Experiment 1, is set up and labeled Beaker 2. 4.03 grams magnesium oxide (40.3 grams/mole) is then added to the solution. A thermometer calibrated in 0.10°C increments is placed into the beaker. The temperature at uniform time intervals is recorded in Figure 2. Reaction 2 is shown below:

$$MgO(s) + 2\ H^+(aq) \rightarrow Mg^{2+}(aq) + H_2O(l)$$

Reaction 2

GO ON TO THE NEXT PAGE

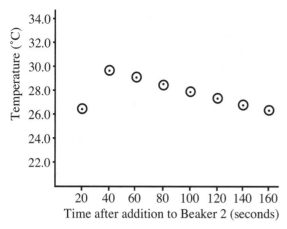

Temperature (°C)

Time after addition to Beaker 2 (seconds)

Figure 2

The same researcher conducts the following experiment to study an endothermic reaction:

Experiment 3

A third beaker is filled with 1.00 kg pure water also at 22°C and labeled Beaker 3. 5.35 grams ammonium chloride (53.5 grams/mole) is then added to the water. A thermometer calibrated in 0.10°C increments is placed into the beaker. The temperature at uniform time intervals is recorded in Figure 3. Reaction 3 is shown below:

$$NH_4Cl(s) + H_2O(l) \rightarrow NH_4^+(aq) + Cl^-(aq)$$

Reaction 3

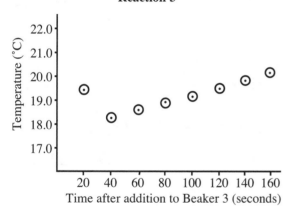

Temperature (°C)

Time after addition to Beaker 3 (seconds)

Figure 3

Each graph shows that the thermometer lags for about thirty seconds, before equilibrating with the solution. To obtain the highest solution temperature, a line must be extrapolated through the data points to the y-axis. This is used to determine the change in temperature, which ultimately is used to calculate the ΔH for the reaction.

44. Which of the following statements is a valid conclusion from the observations of Beaker 3?

A. Solvation of $NH_4Cl(s)$ is exothermic.

B. Solvation of $NH_4Cl(s)$ is endothermic.

C. Solvation of $NH_4Cl(s)$ is endergonic.

D. Solvation of $NH_4Cl(s)$ is unfavorable.

45. Adding 1.21 grams of Mg(s) into Beaker 1 instead of 2.43 grams would have led to a temperature increase up to what temperature?

A. 26°C

B. 30°C

C. 38°C

D. 54°C

46. Given that the enthalpy of formation for $H_2O(l)$ is -286 kJ/mole, what is the enthalpy of formation of MgO(s)?

A. $\Delta H_{(Beaker\ 1)} + \Delta H_{(Beaker\ 2)} - 286$ kJ / mole

B. $\Delta H_{(Beaker\ 1)} - \Delta H_{(Beaker\ 2)} - 286$ kJ / mole

C. $\Delta H_{(Beaker\ 1)} + \Delta H_{(Beaker\ 2)} + 286$ kJ / mole

D. $\Delta H_{(Beaker\ 1)} - \Delta H_{(Beaker\ 2)} + 286$ kJ / mole

47. With respect to Experiment 2, what is the molar enthalpy for the following reaction?

$$MgO(s) + 2\,H^+(aq) \rightarrow Mg^{2+}(aq) + H_2O(l)$$

A. $-\dfrac{1.0 \times 4.34 \times 7.5 \times 4.03}{40.3} \dfrac{kJ}{mole}$

B. $-\dfrac{1.0 \times 4.34 \times 9.0 \times 4.03}{40.3} \dfrac{kJ}{mole}$

C. $-\dfrac{1.0 \times 4.34 \times 7.5 \times 40.3}{4.03} \dfrac{kJ}{mole}$

D. $-\dfrac{1.0 \times 4.34 \times 9.0 \times 40.3}{4.03} \dfrac{kJ}{mole}$

48. Which of the following is the gas given off in the reaction of Beaker 1 after the magnesium metal was added?

A. Carbon dioxide gas

B. Chlorine gas

C. Water vapor

D. Hydrogen gas

49. In calculations, it can be assumed that the heat capacity of 0.1 M HCl(aq) is equal to that of water. If the heat capacity of 0.1 M HCl(aq) is greater than the heat capacity of water, how is the calculated value affected?

A. The calculated ΔH is too small.

B. The calculated ΔH is too large.

C. The difference is insignificant compared to heat lost to the environment.

D. The reaction rate increases, so the thermometer does not accurately record the temperature.

GO ON TO THE NEXT PAGE

Passage VIII (Questions 50 - 55)

Heat packs are designed for commercial use to produce heat rapidly. One of the reactions employed to generate the heat is the oxidation of iron. The reaction is exothermic and, if controlled, it can produce uniform heat for several hours. This reaction is shown below as Reaction 1:

$$4\,Fe(s) + 3\,O_2(g) \rightarrow 2\,Fe_2O_3(s) \quad \Delta H^\circ = -1652 \text{ kJ/mole}$$

Reaction 1

The oxidation-reduction reaction employed is the same reaction observed when iron rusts in moist air. In dry air, iron does not rust as rapidly. The greater rate of oxidation in the presence of water is attributed to the dissolving of oxygen into water, and the consequential increase in interaction between oxygen and iron. The presence of ions in the water increases conductivity, which also escalates the rate of oxidation.

To aid in the transfer of electrons within a heat pack, the reaction is carried out in aqueous sodium chloride with sawdust, activated charcoal, and zeolite. To increase the rate of the reaction, and consequently the production of heat, the iron is finely powdered. The packet's longevity is indirectly proportional to the degree of powdering of the iron.

50. Roughly how many grams of iron should be added to the pack to produce 1000 kJ of energy?

   A. Less than 50 grams
   B. More than 50 grams but less than 100 grams
   C. More than 100 grams but less than 150 grams
   D. More than 150 grams

51. How does the weight of the pack compare before and after opening?

   A. It weighs less after opening, because of the loss of heat.
   B. It weighs more after opening, because of the loss of heat.
   C. It weighs less after opening, because of the gain of oxygen.
   D. It weighs more after opening, because of the gain of oxygen.

52. What can be concluded about the change in entropy and change in free energy for this reaction at room temperature?

   A. $\Delta S^\circ > 0$ and $\Delta G^\circ > 0$
   B. $\Delta S^\circ > 0$ and $\Delta G^\circ < 0$
   C. $\Delta S^\circ < 0$ and $\Delta G^\circ > 0$
   D. $\Delta S^\circ < 0$ and $\Delta G^\circ < 0$

53. What is the role of the minimum amount of salt water present in the heat pack?

   A. The salt water absorbs the heat produced by the reaction, so that the process is adiabatic.
   B. The salt water regulates the rate of heat production as the reaction proceeds, so that the pack does not raise to a temperature that is too high.
   C. The salt water dissolves the iron metal, providing more surface area.
   D. The salt water facilitates the transfer of electrons within the reaction.

54. Which of the following graphs represents the temperature of the heat pack versus time for both finely powdered iron and less finely powdered iron filings? Assume that equal masses of iron are present in both heat packs.

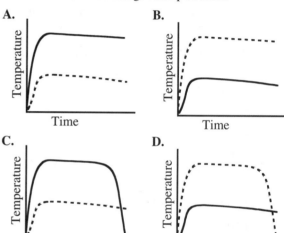

55. What is the purpose of placing the packet into a paper packet inside of a plastic wrapper?

   A. The paper allows for the flow of air to carry out the reaction. It is kept in plastic to prevent oxidation from the air before it is opened.
   B. The paper is impermeable to air, preventing oxidation of the activated charcoal.
   C. The paper allows for the flow of air to carry out the reaction. The plastic prevents iron from vaporizing out of the packet.
   D. The paper is semipermeable to air, allowing only the activated charcoal to be oxidized.

The heat released from an exothermic reaction can be determined accurately by carrying the reaction out in a bomb calorimeter. The bomb calorimeter is comprised of a sealed lead reaction vessel encased in a water bath. A thermometer is measures the temperature change for the surrounding circulating water. The heat released from the reaction is assumed to equal the heat absorbed by the calorimeter. A typical steel-walled bomb calorimeter is shown in Figure 1.

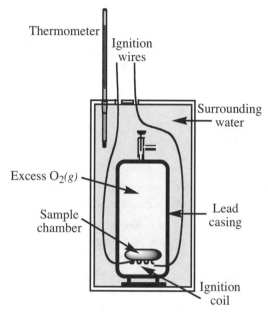

Figure 1

The sample is placed in a cup that contains an ignition coil connected to the ignition wires of a circuit. A possible error in the experiment is introduced by igniting the sample, because the amount of heat generated by resistance in the ignition coil is not measured directly. Excess oxygen gas is used in combustion reactions to ensure that oxygen is not the limiting reagent. The temperature of the water is recorded against time from the start of the reaction until the calorimeter has cooled back to room temperature.

The exact time at which the reaction starts must be estimated. The final temperature of all of the components in the calorimeter is assumed to reach the same temperature as water. To approximate adiabatic conditions, the water temperature should rise only a small amount, thereby minimizing the effects of convection and conduction.

56. What is the role of the stirrer in the experiment?

A. To help to form more stable products so that the reaction reaches an even more favorable equilibrium

B. To provide activation energy to initiate the reaction

C. To lower the pressure and thus push the reaction forward

D. To homogenize the heat distribution throughout the solution

57. What liquid could be substituted for water in this experiment?

A. Decane b.p. 174.1°C, heat capacity 1.44 $\frac{cal}{g \cdot °C}$

B. Diethyl ether b.p. 34.6°C, heat capacity 0.70 $\frac{cal}{g \cdot °C}$

C. Isopropanol b.p. 82.3°C, heat capacity 0.96 $\frac{cal}{g \cdot °C}$

D. Pentanol b.p. 138.2°C, heat capacity 1.33 $\frac{cal}{g \cdot °C}$

58. Why are the walls of the bomb made of steel?

A. Steel has a high heat capacity

B. To prevent any change in pressure

C. Rigid walls maintain the volume of the system

D. Reactive with water

59. Why is excess oxygen gas added to the container?

A. To ensure a complete reaction

B. To increase the amount of convection

C. To store the heat energy

D. To prevent the formation of CO_2

60. What ignites the sample?

A. The oxidation of the wire in the ignition coil

B. The heat generated by resistance in the wire of the ignition coil

C. The friction generated by spinning the wire of the ignition coil

D. The reaction of wire vapor with graphite after the ignition coil sublimes

61. To study a reaction that generates very little heat, what change in the apparatus will NOT help?

A. Using a liquid with a lower heat capacity than water

B. Using more reactant in the bomb

C. Increasing the stir rate

D. Using a thermometer with more calibrations

62. What reaction, assuming all reactions are favorable, is most likely to result in a decrease in temperature?

A. Oxidation of a metal by oxygen

B. Combustion of a hydrocarbon

C. Precipitation of solute from water

D. Dissolving of solute into aqueous solution

GO ON TO THE NEXT PAGE

Passage X (Questions 63 - 69)

Hot and cold packs are commercially available for things like injury treatment and food storage. These packets rely on the heat released or absorbed by a chemical reaction. The change in heat energy is referred to as the *enthalpy change* for the reaction. A typical pouch contains an anhydrous salt in one membrane and water in another membrane. Rupturing the wall between the two membranes allows for mixing, which results in either heat being absorbed (endothermic) or heat being released (exothermic). The salts should be inert and non-toxic. Two typical reactions are given below:

$$CaCl_2(s) + H_2O(l) \rightarrow Ca^{2+}(aq) + 2\ Cl^-(aq)$$

$$\Delta H_{solvation} = -82.4 \text{ kJ/mole}$$

Reaction 1

$$NH_4NO_3(s) + H_2O(l) \rightarrow NH_4^+(aq) + NO_3^-(aq)$$

$$\Delta H_{solvation} = +26.9 \text{ kJ/mole}$$

Reaction 2

The temperature change can be estimated if you multiply the moles of salt by the enthalpy (in calories) to determine the heat change, and then divide that value by the mL of water (which is roughly its mass). This estimate is close, because the heat capacity of water is 1.00 calorie per degree per gram water. As the salt dissolves into solution, however, the heat capacity of the aqueous salt solution increases. For this reason, along with the decreasing reaction rate over time, the packets show their greatest temperature change initially.

Ten grams of calcium chloride can raise the temperature of 100 mL of water approximately eighteen degrees. Ten grams of ammonium nitrate can lower the temperature of 100 mL of water approximately seven degrees. Once used, the packets cannot easily be recycled, because the anhydrous salts are difficult to regenerate. Alternative salts for heat packs include magnesium sulfate and sodium sulfate, both of which (when anhydrous) are used as dehydrating agents for organic solvents. Alternative salts for cold packs include ammonium chloride and ammonium iodide.

63. Which of the following fluids would be BEST for a generic radiator for a power plant?

   A. Distilled water
   B. Salt water
   C. Nitrogen gas
   D. Dehumidified air

64. For a heat pack designed to reach 100°C, the solvation reaction must be:

   A. exothermic and rapid.
   B. exothermic and slow.
   C. endothermic and rapid.
   D. endothermic and slow.

65. Which of the following solvation reactions could be used for a heat compress?

   A. A reaction breaking weak lattice forces and forming strong solvent-to-ion interactions
   B. A reaction breaking strong lattice forces and forming strong solvent-to-ion interactions
   C. A reaction breaking weak lattice forces and forming weak solvent-to-ion interactions
   D. A reaction breaking strong lattice forces and forming weak solvent-to-ion interactions

66. What is the highest temperature reached after 40 grams of $CaCl_2$ are added to 200 mL of water at 20°C?

   A. 36°C
   B. 56°C
   C. 72°C
   D. 92°C

67. How can a solution temperature of 107°C be explained after sodium sulfate is added to water at 50°C?

   A. The solvation reaction is highly exothermic, and the boiling point of the aqueous solution is greater than 100°C because of boiling point elevation.
   B. The solvation reaction is highly exothermic, and the boiling point of the aqueous solution is greater than 100°C because of boiling point depression.
   C. The solvation reaction is highly endothermic, and the boiling point of the aqueous solution is greater than 100°C because of boiling point elevation.
   D. The solvation reaction is highly endothermic, and the boiling point of the aqueous solution is greater than 100°C because of boiling point depression.

68. Which of the following anhydrous salts would MOST likely be found in a cold pack?

   A. $MgSO_4$
   B. $CaSO_4$
   C. $MgCl_2$
   D. NH_4Cl

69. What is true about the salts used in cold packs?

   A. Lattice forces are strong; solvation is endothermic and driven by an increased entropy.
   B. Lattice forces are weak; solvation is endothermic and driven by an increased entropy.
   C. Lattice forces are strong; solvation is exothermic and driven by an increased enthalpy.
   D. Lattice forces are weak; solvation is exothermic and driven by an increased enthalpy.

GO ON TO THE NEXT PAGE

Passage XI (Questions 70 - 78)

A two-part experiment is carried out involving four metals and four liquids. In Experiment I, 10.0-gram samples of each of the four metals are placed into an insulated heating chamber with uniform heat distribution. The initial temperature for each metal was recorded before it was placed in the heating chamber. After ten minutes in the heating chamber, the metals were removed and the temperature for each metal was immediately measured. Table 1 below shows the initial and final temperature for each metal:

Solid	Initial Temperature	Final Temperature
Metal I	22.0 °C	57.0 °C
Metal II	22.1 °C	81.2 °C
Metal III	22.0 °C	73.4 °C
Metal IV	22.0 °C	46.9 °C

Table 1

In Experiment II a 10.0-gram cylinder of Metal IV is heated to exactly 50°C from its initial temperature of 25.0°C. The metal is added to a 40.0-gram sample of unknown liquid at 25°C in an insulated container. The metal is fully submerged into the liquid, and the system is allowed to equilibrate until the two temperatures are equal. The final temperature of the solution is recorded when the liquid and Metal IV reach the same temperature. The temperature of the outside wall of the insulated container did not increase during the experiment. The experiment is repeated three more times using a different liquid each time. The results from the four trials are recorded in Table 2 below:

Solution	Final Temperature
Liquid I	28.3°C
Liquid II	29.2°C
Liquid III	28.1°C
Liquid IV	30.7°C

Table 2

The two experiments were repeated an additional four times each, to minimize any errors that may have arisen during the procedure. The numbers listed in both Table 1 and Table 2 are the data collected for the first trial only. No significant errors were detected in the subsequent trials, so the data are assumed to be valid.

70. To determine the heat capacity for any of the metals, what else must be known precisely in the first experiment?

A. The initial temperature of the heating chamber

B. The molecular mass of the metal and the initial temperature of the heating chamber

C. The initial temperature of the heating chamber and the total energy absorbed by the metal

D. The total energy absorbed by the metal

71. The metal with the GREATEST heat capacity is:

A. Metal I.

B. Metal II.

C. Metal III.

D. Metal IV.

72. If a metal and a liquid of identical heat capacities were used in the second experiment, what would the temperature be once the system reached equilibrium after the energy was fully transferred? Assume that no heat is lost to the environment.

A. Less than 25.0°C

B. Less than 37.5°C, but greater than 25.0°C

C. Exactly 37.5°C

D. Greater than 37.5°C

73. The heat capacity of Metal IV is less than the heat capacity of any liquid EXCEPT:

A. Liquid I

B. Liquid II

C. Liquid III

D. Liquid IV

74. Had Metal III been used in Experiment II instead of Metal IV, the final temperatures for the liquids would have been:

A. greater than the temperatures found using Metal IV, because more heat would have been absorbed by the solution using Metal III.

B. less than the temperatures found using Metal IV, because more heat would have been absorbed by the solution using Metal III.

C. greater than the temperatures found using Metal IV, because the heat capacity for Metal III is less than the heat capacity for Metal IV.

D. less than the temperatures found using Metal IV, because the heat capacity for Metal III is less than the heat capacity for Metal IV.

75. The GREATEST amount of transferable kinetic energy is found in which of the following?

A. Metal I at 60°C

B. Metal II at 60°C

C. Metal III at 80°C

D. Metal IV at 80°C

76. The relative heat capacities of the liquids are arranged in which of the following sequences?

A. III > I > II > IV

B. IV > II > I > III

C. IV > III > II > I

D. I > II > III > IV

77. Had the temperature of the outside wall of the container increased, how would the results have bee affected?

A. The observed final temperature would be lower than expected, and the calculated heat capacity of the liquid would be too high.

B. The observed final temperature would be lower than expected, and the calculated heat capacity of the solid would be too high.

C. The observed final temperature would be higher than expected, and the calculated heat capacity of the liquid would be too high.

D. The observed final temperature would be higher than expected, and the calculated heat capacity of the solid would be too high.

78. Which of the following relationships represents the ratio of the heat capacity of the liquid to the heat capacity of the solid in Experiment II?

A. $\dfrac{C_{liquid}}{C_{solid}} = 4\,\dfrac{\Delta T_{liquid}}{\Delta T_{solid}}$

B. $\dfrac{C_{liquid}}{C_{solid}} = \dfrac{1}{4}\,\dfrac{\Delta T_{liquid}}{\Delta T_{solid}}$

C. $\dfrac{C_{liquid}}{C_{solid}} = 4\,\dfrac{\Delta T_{solid}}{\Delta T_{liquid}}$

D. $\dfrac{C_{liquid}}{C_{solid}} = \dfrac{1}{4}\,\dfrac{\Delta T_{solid}}{\Delta T_{liquid}}$

Passage XII (Questions 79 - 85)

The basic design of a one-cylinder engine focuses on a piston and a counterweight, placed on a cyclic crank in such a way that the counterweight's maximum potential energy occurs when the piston is fully extended. The full extension of the piston turns the crank 180°, and the descent of the counterweight turns the crank the other 180° of the cycle.

Drawn below is a diagram of a basic one-cylinder engine. The boiler, when rapidly heated, creates a flow of steam that forces the piston upward. Once the piston is fully extended, the intake valve is closed and the exhaust valve is opened so that the counterweight can fall with less resistance. The steam from the piston is cooled and condensed in the condenser. The water is then pumped from the condenser to the boiler. A pump must be used because of the pressure difference between the boiler and condenser. Figure 1 shows a basic single-piston engine.

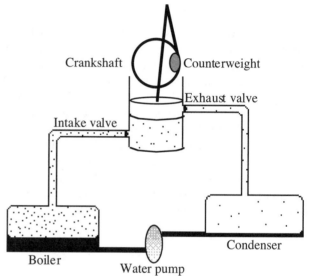

Figure 1

The one-piston engine is perhaps best recognized as the steam engine that has moved large trains and electrical generators for years. The point at which the rod connects the top of the piston to the crank is linked to the top of the piston by a hinge. The rod must be able to rock back and forth as the piston ascends and descends. The counterweight is not exactly out of phase with the piston but is slightly offset to ensure that the crank turns in only one direction.

79. Which of the following valves is a one-way valve that allows flow from left to right?

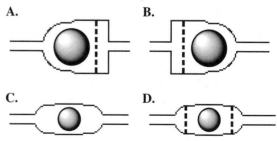

80. If a cooling fan were added to the system, where would be the BEST place for it?

A. Adjacent to the boiler

B. Adjacent to the crankshaft

C. Adjacent to the condenser

D. Inside of the piston

81. Water is chosen for which of the following reasons?

A. Water has a high heat capacity in the liquid phase.

B. Water has a high heat capacity in the gas phase.

C. Water can sublime and condense at the temperatures of the engine.

D. Water can vaporize and condense at the temperatures of the engine.

82. When the counterweight is at its lowest point on the crankshaft, the piston is not completely compressed. What is the reason for this?

A. Not all of the steam can escape rapidly enough to compress the piston completely. The residual steam offers too much resistance for full descent.

B. All of the gas escapes, so to compress the piston completely, steam must be pumped back into the chamber.

C. The exhaust valve is situated too high on the chamber wall.

D. The intake valve is situated too low on the chamber wall.

83. Which of the following statements BEST describes the flow of heat a steam engine?

A. Heat is added at the condenser and removed at the piston.

B. Heat is added at the boiler and removed at the piston.

C. Heat is added at the piston and removed at the condenser.

D. Heat is added at the boiler and removed at the condenser.

84. To raise the piston, what must be true about the two valves in the engine?

A. Both the intake and exhaust valves must be open.

B. Both the intake and exhaust valves must be closed.

C. The intake valve must be open, and the exhaust valve must be closed.

D. The intake valve must be closed, and the exhaust valve must be open.

85. What would make this engine MOST efficient?

A. If no heat were emitted from it

B. If heat radiated evenly throughout the engine

C. If heat radiated more from the condenser than from the piston

D. If heat radiated more from the boiler than the piston

GO ON TO THE NEXT PAGE

Figure 1 below shows a simplified representation of a Carnot engine. The diagram shown in Figure 2 below is a simplified representation of a Carnot heat pump. The change in energy for a system can be calculated as the sum of work and heat, as shown in Equation 1.

$$\Delta E = q + w$$

Equation 1

where q is heat and w is work (found by $w = -P\Delta V$ for the system). The actual operations of an engine and refrigerator (heat pump) are not accurately represented by the diagrams; but because the overall pathway between two points can be calculated by any combination of reversible pathways that sum to the overall pathway, it is possible to calculate the values for the Carnot engine and heat pump from these diagrams.

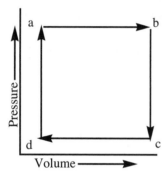

Figure 1

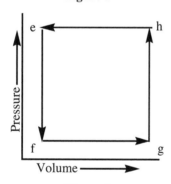

Figure 2

The arrow between any two adjacent letters refers to a step in the overall process. Each step can be treated as independent or in combination with adjacent steps for calculation purposes.

86. Which diagram from the passage represents an engine?

A. The diagram in Figure 1, because work flows into the system and heat flows out of the system.

B. The diagram in Figure 1, because work flows out of the system and heat flows into the system.

C. The diagram in Figure 2, because work flows into the system and heat flows out of the system.

D. The diagram in Figure 2, because work flows out of the system and heat flows into the system.

87. For the diagram in Figure 2, the full cycle shows:

A. $\Delta E > 0$; work in > work out

B. $\Delta E < 0$; work in < work out

C. $\Delta E = 0$; work in > work out

D. $\Delta E = 0$; work in < work out

88. If $\Delta E = 0$ for the system, and the work for the system is positive, then the heat (q) is:

A. negative for both the system and the surroundings.

B. positive for both the system and the surroundings.

C. positive for the system and negative for the surroundings.

D. negative for the system and positive for the surroundings.

89. After a hand pump has been operating, the shaft is warm and the tip of the needle is cool. This is because:

A. air is compressed in the shaft of the pump, and it expands as it enters the needle tip.

B. air is compressed in the shaft of the pump, and it expands as it leaves the needle tip.

C. air expands in the shaft of the pump, and it is compressed as it enters the needle tip.

D. air expands in the shaft of the pump, and it is compressed as it leaves the needle tip.

90. From point a to point c in Figure 1, what is true?

A. The gas expands, and $w_{system} > 0$.

B. The gas expands, and $w_{system} < 0$.

C. The gas compresses, and $w_{system} > 0$.

D. The gas compresses, and $w_{system} < 0$.

91. An efficient engine would have which of the following?

A. A high exhaust temperature and many points where energy is transferred

B. A low exhaust temperature and many points where energy is transferred

C. A high exhaust temperature and few points where energy is transferred

D. A low exhaust temperature and few points where energy is transferred

92. The arrow from point b to point c in Figure 1 represents:

A. a pure work step.

B. a pure heat step.

C. a step with both heat and work, where $\Delta E > 0$.

D. a step with both heat and work, where $\Delta E < 0$.

93. The fact that, as order is gained by a system, its surroundings are losing order is a consequence of which of the following?

A. The First Law of Thermodynamics
B. The Second Law of Thermodynamics
C. The Third Law of Thermodynamics
D. The Rutherford rules

94. How much work is done on a system when an ideal gas is expanded adiabatically from 0.4 liters to 2.4 liters under a constant pressure of 950.0 torr?

A. 5.00 liter·atmospheres
B. 2.50 liter·atmospheres
C. -2.50 liter·atmospheres
D. -5.00 liter·atmospheres

95. If ΔH is positive and ΔS is positive, then ΔG is which of the following?

A. Positive at all temperatures
B. Negative at all temperatures
C. Zero at all temperatures
D. Can be zero, positive, or negative, depending on the temperature.

96. If $P\Delta V = +24.4$ kJ and $q = 22.2$ kJ, then ΔE is equal to which of the following values?

A. -46.6 kJ
B. -2.2 kJ
C. 2.2 kJ
D. 46.6 kJ

97. What is the final temperature after 32 mL H_2O at 36.0°C is mixed with 96 mL H_2O at 64.0°C?

A. 57.0°C
B. 54.7°C
C. 51.3°C
D. 50.0°C

98. ΔS for a gas-to-solid phase change is always:

A. positive at all temperatures and pressures.
B. negative at all temperatures and pressures.
C. zero at all temperatures and pressures.
D. can be zero, positive, or negative, depending on the temperature.

99. Expansion of a gas is:

A. exothermic and entropically favorable.
B. endothermic and entropically favorable.
C. exothermic and entropically unfavorable.
D. endothermic and entropically unfavorable.

100. Which of the following relationships may be TRUE?

I. Vaporization absorbs more heat than fusion.
II. More heat is released during sublimation than condensation.
III. When a liquid freezes, the environment gets warmer.

A. I only
B. II only
C. I and III only
D. II and III only

1. A	2. C	3. D	4. D	5. B
6. A	7. D	8. C	9. D	10. A
11. D	12. C	13. B	14. C	15. A
16. D	17. A	18. D	19. D	20. B
21. D	22. A	23. A	24. D	25. D
26. A	27. B	28. A	29. B	30. A
31. C	32. D	33. C	34. D	35. C
36. C	37. B	38. A	39. A	40. B
41. B	42. B	43. A	44. B	45. B
46. B	47. D	48. D	49. A	50. C
51. D	52. D	53. D	54. C	55. A
56. D	57. C	58. C	59. A	60. B
61. C	62. D	63. B	64. A	65. A
66. B	67. A	68. D	69. A	70. D
71. D	72. B	73. D	74. D	75. D
76. A	77. A	78. D	79. A	80. C
81. D	82. A	83. D	84. C	85. A
86. B	87. C	88. D	89. B	90. B
91. D	92. B	93. B	94. C	95. D
96. B	97. A	98. B	99. B	100. C

YOU ARE DONE.

Thermochemistry Passages Answers

1. **Choice A is correct.** In Reaction 1, for both the thermodynamic and kinetic pathway, the larger activation energy (higher energy transition state) is associated with the first step of the two-step reaction. The greater the activation energy, the slower the step. The slowest step is the rate-determining step, so the transition state of highest energy corresponds to the rate-determining step. The first step is rate-determining in Reaction 1. The correct answer is choice **A**.

2. **Choice C is correct.** The value of the free energy change (ΔG) is found from the equation $\Delta G = \Delta H - T\Delta S$. The question states that ΔS is a positive value, and given that T is measured in kelvins, it too must be a positive number. This means that as the temperature increases, the value of ΔG decreases (because $T\Delta S$ is increasing). This eliminates choices A and B. Using a second equation, $\Delta G = RT \ln (Q_{rx}/K_{eq})$, it can be seen that as ΔG decreases, the Q_{rx}-to-K_{eq} ratio decreases, so the K_{eq}-to-Q_{rx} ratio increases. The best answer is choice **C**.

    If you didn't recall the second equation above, you could have also used the equation $\Delta G = \Delta G° + RT \ln Q_{rx}$, where $\Delta G° = - RT \ln K_{eq}$. The standard free energy change ($\Delta G°$) and the equilibrium constant (K_{eq}) are related according to $\Delta G° = - RT \ln K_{eq}$. As $\Delta G°$ decreases, the value of ΔG decreases and the value of K_{eq} increases, so consequently the K_{eq}-to-Q_{rx} ratio increases.

3. **Choice D is correct.** Both Pathway X and Pathway Y begin at the same point (implying that the reactants are the same). This means that only the endpoint of the two pathways must be compared to answer this question. The endpoint of Pathway Y is lower than the endpoint of Pathway X, so more energy is released from Pathway Y than Pathway X. This eliminates choices A and C. Because the endpoint of Pathway X is lower than the starting point, the enthalpy change is negative (it is an exothermic reaction). This makes choice **D** the best answer choice.

4. **Choice D is correct.** At higher temperatures, the thermodynamic pathway is preferable, because it yields the greatest amount of heat. At lower temperatures, the reaction is forced to go by the lower energy transition state. Pathway Y is the thermodynamic pathway, because it produces more energy than Pathway X. At higher temperatures, Pathway Y is preferred, so choice **D** is the best answer.

5. **Choice B is correct.** Because the second transition state (apex in the graph) is of higher energy than the first transition state, the second step of the reaction is the rate-determining step in the reaction. This eliminates choices A and C. The intermediate occurs at the nadir (low point) between the two transition states (between the first and second steps). If the second step is the rate-determining step, then the intermediate is allowed to build up its concentration. This is referred to as bottlenecking of the intermediate. The best answer is choice **B**.

6. **Choice A is correct.** As the temperature is increased, more of Product Y is formed, and therefore less of Product X is formed. This eliminates choices B and D, which both show increases in Product X and decreases in Product Y. The sum of Product X and Product Y must always be 100%, so choice C is not possible (the sum is less than 100% at the middle temperatures). The best answer is choice **A**.

7. **Choice D is correct.** Because Reaction 1 has the endpoint of the energy curve lower than the starting point, it is exothermic. This means that the value of the enthalpy change (ΔH) is negative. This eliminates choices A and B. Because the reaction is less favorable as the temperature increases, ΔG must be increasing with the temperature. The equation for the free energy change (ΔG) is $\Delta G = \Delta H - T\Delta S$. In order for ΔG to increase with temperature, the $T\Delta S$ term must be negative. The temperature is measured on the Kelvin scale, so it is always positive. Only the entropy change (ΔS) can be negative. This makes choice **D** the best choice.

8. **Choice C is correct.** This question is a "read the chart" question. At 146 kJ per mole, the O—O bond is the weakest. Even if you didn't remember what diethyl peroxide was, you could have matched the answer choices to the values in the table. Pick **C**.

9. **Choice D is correct.** The energy of the second π-bond in N≡N can be approximated by subtracting the bond energy of a nitrogen double bond from the bond energy of a nitrogen triple bond. Although the effects of the closer nuclei (associated with the shorter triple bond) may include strengthening of the sigma bond, for this question it is best to assume that the change in energy between the double and triple bond is due entirely to the new (second) π-bond. The energy difference is 941 - 418 = 523. The best answer is choice **D**.

10. **Choice A is correct.** Because of the reduced *p*-character in the sp^2-hybridized orbital compared to the sp^3-hybridized orbital, an sp^2-hybridized orbital is shorter and more electronegative than the sp^3-hybridized orbital. This eliminates choices B and C. The best answer is choice **A**, because the bond strength is more associated with bond length than the bond polarity. Choice D is a true statement, but not the best answer.

11. **Choice D is correct.** The bonds broken are both relatively weak (154 and 432), while the bonds formed are both relatively strong (565 each). The heat released is greater than 500 kJ per mole (586 - 1130), which makes the reaction highly exothermic. The best answer is choice **D**.

12. **Choice C is correct.** The energy trend of the sulfur-halide bonds is not a clear trend. The strongest halide bond to sulfur is with iodine (the largest halide), but because of the weak bond between sulfur and bromine, a trend in size cannot be drawn. This eliminates choice A. The most electronegative halide bond to sulfur is with chlorine, but because this is the second strongest bond to sulfur and the weak bond between sulfur and bromine, a trend in size cannot be drawn. This eliminates choice B. The halide with the greatest electron affinity is chlorine, so as with electronegativity, a trend in size cannot be drawn. This eliminates choice D. The best conclusion that can be drawn is that the bond strength depends on two opposing factors, which would explain why bromine has the lowest bond energy. Based on halogen size, the relative strength order would be: S—Cl > S—Br > S—I. Based on polarizability of the halogen, the relative strength order would be: S—I > S—Br > S—Cl. The actual order is S—I ≈ S—Cl > S—Br, so both effects must be involved. The best answer is choice **C**.

13. **Choice B is correct.** A Br—F bond would be stronger than a Br—Cl bond, so the bond energy is greater than 218 kJ/mole. This eliminates choices C and D. A Br—F bond would be weaker than a Cl—F bond, so the bond energy is less than 253 kJ/mole. This eliminates choice A. The only choice that fits in the energy range is **B**.

14. **Choice C is correct.** As a general rule, shorter bonds are stronger than longer bonds, because the overlap of orbitals allows for the electrons to be shared between nuclei most readily. This makes choice A a false statement. According to periodic trends, chlorine is both less electronegative than fluorine and larger than fluorine. This eliminates choices B and D. The weakness of the F—F bond can be attributed to the repulsion of the nuclei of the two fluorine atoms. As the fluorine atoms get close enough to form a bond, the two +9 nuclei begin to repel. The repulsion results in the overall weakening of the bond. The best answer is choice **C**.

Passage III (Questions 15 - 21)   Born-Haber Cycle

15. **Choice A is correct.** Because sodium metal is heavier than lithium metal, the energy required to sublime sodium is greater than the energy required to sublime lithium. This makes statement I true. As a column in the periodic table is descended, the ionization energy of the element decreases, so the first ionization energy of lithium is greater than the first ionization energy of sodium. This makes statement II a false statement. The atomic radius of sodium cation is larger than the atomic radius of lithium cation, thus the lattice energy of the sodium salt involves a larger r-value in the denominator. The lattice energy is decreased when lithium is replaced by sodium, so statement III is a false statement. The correct answer is choice **A**.

16. **Choice D is correct.** In the reaction, the F—F bond is completely broken (partial breaks are not possible), so choice A is eliminated. The bond energy for F_2 is 154 kJ/mole, although the value is not from the table. Half of the value is used, because only one fluorine atom is needed. The bond is broken in a homolytic fashion (with each atom receiving one electron), so choices A, B, and C are eliminated, making choice **D** the best answer.

17. **Choice A is correct.** The lattice energy increases with increasing charge (q) or decreasing radius (r). Magnesium carries a +2 charge, and oxygen carries a -2 charge, so the greatest lattice energy is associated with MgO. This eliminates choices C and D. Because Li^+ is smaller than Na^+ and F^- is smaller than Cl^-, the second highest lattice energy is associated with LiF. This makes choice **A** the best answer.

18. **Choice D is correct.** If calcium metal is used in lieu of lithium metal, the ionization energy changes, because calcium forms a dication, which requires two ionizations. The total ionization energy for calcium is a sum of the first and second ionization energies. As a note, the extra energy invested in the ionization is recovered by the doubling of the lattice energy. This is because the ionization energy doubles when the cation charge doubles from +1 to +2. The best answer is choice **D**.

19. **Choice D is correct.** Electron affinity involves the gaining of a free electron by a neutral atom. The excitation and relaxation (de-excitation) involve the absorption and emission of a photon when an electron moves between the ground state and an excited state. The charge of the atom does not change in either process. The ionization energy is associated with the loss of an electron, while the electron affinity is associated with the gain of an electron. The best answer is choice **D**.

20. **Choice B is correct.** Using a metal that is easier to sublime than lithium requires the input of less energy, so the overall process yields more energy. Choice A is consequently eliminated. Using a halogen that forms a stronger covalent bond than fluorine requires the input of more energy, so the overall process yields less energy. This makes choice **B** the best answer. Using a halogen with a greater electron affinity than fluorine (which is not physically possible, given that fluorine has the highest electron affinity of the halogens) releases more energy, so the overall process yields more energy. Choice C is consequently eliminated. Using a metal that can easily lose a second electron requires more ionization energy, but double the amount of energy is released in the lattice formation, so the overall process yields more energy. Choice D is also eliminated.

21. **Choice D is correct.** Substituting a larger cation for a smaller cation increases the distance between ions. This reduces the lattice energy, because the denominator has been increased. This makes statement I true. Substituting an anion of lesser charge for the current anion in the salt reduces the lattice energy, because the numerator has been decreased. This makes statement II true. Cutting the cation and anion charges by one-half each reduces the lattice energy to one-fourth its original value, because the numerator has been decreased by a factor of four. Cutting the internuclear distance by one-half doubles the lattice energy, because the denominator has been decreased by a factor of two. Overall, the effect of cutting all three values in half is that the lattice energy decreases by a factor of two, making statement III true. The best answer is choice **D**.

Passage IV (Questions 22 - 28)   Free-Energy Calculation

22. **Choice A is correct.** In distillation, a mixture is converted into pure components. Distillation results in more order for the system, which is entropically unfavorable. This makes choice **A** a correct answer. The conversion from a solid salt into two ions in solution is entropically favorable, because the system becomes more random. This eliminates choices B. In sublimation, a solid is converted into a gas, which increases the randomness, so the process is entropically favorable. This eliminates choice C. Diffusion of a gas into the air results in the loss of a pure component into a mixture, which increases the randomness. This is entropically favorable, so choice D is eliminated.

23. **Choice A is correct.** A value of $\Delta S > 0$ results from an increase in disorder. In choices B and C, the number of molecules decreases from reactant to product, so both can be eliminated. In choice D, the number of molecules remains the same, so choice D can be eliminated. In choice **A**, the salt becomes more random as it dissociates into ions. Pick **A** if you desire the jubilation and enjoyment associated with correct answers.

24. **Choice D is correct.** Addition of a catalyst does not affect the thermodynamic values of a reaction, such as free energy (ΔG), enthalpy (ΔH), and entropy (ΔS). A catalyst stabilizes the transition state, lowering the activation energy for a reaction. This affects only the reaction rate and makes the best answer choice **D**.

25. **Choice D is correct.** Because the reaction is spontaneous as written, the free energy change (ΔG) for the reaction is negative. Because the solution temperature lowers as the reaction proceeds, the reaction is endothermic. This makes the value of ΔH positive. Rearranging Equation 3 yields: $T\Delta S = \Delta H - \Delta G$; so if ΔH is positive, and ΔG is negative, then the value of ΔS must be positive at all temperatures, making choice **D** the best answer.

26. **Choice A is correct.** When the reaction quotient is greater than the equilibrium constant, too many products are present, so the reaction must shift to the reactant side in order to reach equilibrium. This eliminates choices C and D. When the reaction spontaneously shifts in the reverse direction (to the reactants), it is said to be positive, so the best answer is choice **A**.

27. **Choice B is correct.** Combining Equation 1 with Equation 2, we get $\Delta G = -RT \ln K_{eq} + RT \ln Q_{rx}$, so the value of ΔG must be zero when $K_{eq} = Q_{rx}$. This is to say that when the reaction is at equilibrium, the free energy change is zero. Equation 3, $\Delta G = \Delta H - T\Delta S$, must be used to determine the temperature at which ΔG is zero.

$$\Delta G = \Delta H - T\,\Delta S = 0 \therefore \text{ by adding } T\Delta S \text{ to both sides of the equation, } \Delta H = T\,\Delta S$$

Dividing both sides of the equation by ΔS leads to the relationship: $T = \dfrac{\Delta H}{\Delta S}$

$$\frac{\Delta H}{\Delta S} = \frac{12{,}500\ \dfrac{J}{mole}}{25\ \dfrac{J}{mole \cdot K}} = \frac{12{,}500}{25}\,K = \frac{2500}{5}\,K = 500\ K$$

Do not blindly choose answer choice D, however, because the answers are in Celsius. The temperature must be converted from Kelvin into Celsius. Subtracting 273 from the Kelvin value yields 500 K = 227°C, choice **B**.

28. **Choice A is correct.** This question is answered by combining Equations 1 and 2 into one equation as follows:

$$\Delta G_{observed} = \Delta G^\circ + RT \ln Q_{rx}$$

$$\Delta G_{observed} = -RT \ln K_{eq} + RT \ln Q_{rx} = RT \ln Q_{rx} - RT \ln K_{eq}$$

$$\Delta G_{observed} = RT (\ln Q_{rx} - \ln K_{eq}) = RT \ln \frac{Q_{rx}}{K_{eq}}$$

The best answer is choice **A**.

Passage V (Questions 29 - 35)   Rocket Fuels

29. **Choice B is correct.** The value for the water reaction in the passage involves the formation of water vapor. In the question, the value is listed for the formation of water liquid. Conversion from vapor to liquid is exothermic, so the formation of water liquid yields more heat energy than the formation of water vapor. The best answer is choice **B**.

30. **Choice A is correct.** The first stage of a rocket requires that the greatest total amount of heat be given off, because the first stage is responsible for liftoff and the acceleration away from the earth's gravitational pull. The fuel must provide a great amount of heat, while not occupying too much volume (the storage space must be minimized). It is ideal if the fuel provides a large amount of heat per gram as it burns, making the fuel most efficient without significantly increasing the mass of the rocket. Hydrogen would be ideal, because it is so light (except for the fact that it is a gas at nearly all temperatures). At room temperature, kerosene is a liquid, while hydrogen is a gas. Because liquids are denser, they are far easier to store conveniently and efficiently. This makes choice **A** a good choice. Choice B should be eliminated, because kerosene provides less energy per gram than hydrogen. This is to say that 242 divided by 2 is greater than 7513 divided by 170. Whether kerosene burns hotter than hydrogen or not should have no bearing on its use as a rocket fuel. The hotter it burns, the more heat that is wasted by loss to the environment. Choice C can be eliminated. Oxidation of kerosene produces both water and carbon dioxide, which results in more products than oxidation of hydrogen gas (which produces only water). The answer choice D is a wrong statement.

31. **Choice C is correct.** From the balanced equation, two moles of hydrazine are required for every one mole of dinitrogen tetraoxide. Hydrazine weighs 32 grams per mole, while dinitrogen tetraoxide has a molecular mass of 92 grams per mole. This means that for 64 grams of hydrazine, 92 grams of dinitrogen tetraoxide are required. This means that roughly one and one-half times as many grams of dinitrogen tetraoxide are needed as hydrazine. This is answer choice **C**.

32. **Choice D is correct.** The first three reactions are all oxidation-reduction reactions that mimic the sample reactions from the passage. The last reaction is an acid-base reaction, and it does not produce sufficient energy to propel a rocket. The correct answer choice is answer **D**. Although the passage does not blatantly state that an oxidation-reduction reaction should be used, it can be inferred from the sample reactions.

33. **Choice C is correct.** From the sample reactions in the passage, it can be seen that rocket fuels engage in highly exothermic combustion reactions, provide a large amount of heat per gram, and are highly reactive in oxidation-reduction reactions. This makes statements A, B, and D valid. A rocket fuel is better if it is a solid or liquid at room temperature, rather than a gas, so it can be stored (packed) more efficiently. This means that choice **C** is *not* a requirement of a rocket fuel. You must pick **C**, you must, you must, you must!

34. **Choice D is correct.** Dinitrogen tetraoxide gets reduced in the reaction, so it is the oxidizing agent in the reaction. Statement A can therefore be eliminated. Hydrazine is oxidized into nitrogen gas. The oxidation state of nitrogen changes from -2 to 0. This implies that the entire compound loses four electrons (two per nitrogen), not that each nitrogen loses four electrons. Choice B can therefore be eliminated. Because the final product has a nitrogen-nitrogen triple bond, it can be concluded that nitrogen-nitrogen bonds are formed during the course of the reaction, and not broken. This eliminates choice C. Hydrazine is losing hydrogens, so it is being oxidized. This makes choice **D** the best answer.

35. **Choice C is correct.** The heat per gram for kerosene can be found by dividing 7513 kJ per mole by 170 grams per mole. The value falls in the range of 40 to 50 kJ per gram. The math is set up as follows:

$$50 = \frac{8500}{170} > \frac{7513}{170} > \frac{6800}{170} = 40$$

Because the range is between 40 and 50 kJ per mole, the best answer is choice **C**.

36.   Choice C is correct. Vaporization is a change in the physical state of matter, whereby a liquid evaporates to form a gas. Writing out the reaction for the vaporization of water and using values Table 1 yields:

$$H_2O(l) \rightarrow H_2O(g) \qquad \Delta G_{formation} \, H_2O(l) = -237.2 \qquad \Delta G_{formation} \, H_2O(g) = -228.6$$

$\Delta G_{formation}$ of products - $\Delta G_{formation}$ of reactants = ΔG_{rx} ➡ -228.6 - (-237.2) = + 8.6 kJ per mole, choice **C**. Energy is required to vaporize water, so we expect a positive number. A value of 44.1 results from using ΔH numbers.

37.   Choice B is correct. Both xylose and ribose form five-membered rings, furanose rings, according to the information in the question. The five-membered rings are not subject to much ring strain (if they were, five-membered rings would not be so common in biological systems, so choice A is eliminated. Both xylose and ribose are aldopentoses, so they each have one C=O (in the form of an aldehyde) and four O-H bonds (in the form of hydroxyls on carbons two through five). This eliminates choices C and D. The only choice left is answer choice **B**. The repulsion experienced by the eclipsed hydroxyl groups in the five-membered ring appears in the enthalpy of reaction. As the repulsion within a molecule increases, the molecule is said to be less stable, and thus it will have a greater enthalpy of reaction (more heat will be released when the ring steric hindrance in the reactant is relieved). Using the enthalpy of reaction to determine the stability of structural features is common in organic chemistry. Using Hess's law with the general chemistry values does not show the other features that affect a molecule's stability. Many experiments in organic chemistry focus differences in the enthalpy changes between reactions with similar bond changes.

38.   Choice A is correct. From Table 1, the $\Delta G°$ values of + 209.1 for acetylene (the reactant) and + 68.3 for ethylene (the product) can be read from the free energy change column. Be sure that you use the values for $\Delta G°$, and not $\Delta H°$ by mistake. The free energy of formation for $H_2(g)$ is 0, because hydrogen gas is a diatomic gas at room temperature in its natural elemental state. This eliminates choices C and D. For the hydrogenation reaction, the change in free energy is found by $\Delta G_{formation}$ of products - $\Delta G_{formation}$ of reactants. The value $\Delta G°_{rx}$ equals 68.3 - 209.1, a negative number. A negative number for $\Delta G°$ makes the reaction favorable in the forward direction, so the best answer is choice **A**. The hydrogenation reaction is shown below:

$$1 \, C_2H_2(g) + 1 \, H_2(g) \rightarrow 1 \, C_2H_4(g)$$

39.   Choice A is correct. At standard conditions, carbon exists as graphite, not as diamond, eliminating choice C. Cl_2 and H_2 are gases at 25°C in their most stable elemental form, so this rules out choice B. Also, chlorine exists as a diatomic molecule in its most stable form at 25°C, so the answer is not choice D. The only answer choice left is **A**, which is a good thing considering it is the correct answer. Be sure that the equation balances.

40.   Choice B is correct. The first thing to do is to balance the combustion reaction:

$$1 \, C_3H_6 + 4.5 \, O_2 \rightarrow 3 \, H_2O + 3 \, CO_2$$

The phases are ignored, because they are not listed in the answer choices. Normally, phase is significant, because water can be listed as a liquid or a gas.

$$\Delta H_{rx} = \Delta H_{formation} \text{ of products} - \Delta H_{formation} \text{ of reactants} = 3 \, \Delta H_{form} \, H_2O + 3 \, \Delta H_{form} \, CO_2 - \Delta H_{form} \, C_3H_6$$

This is choice **B**. Oxygen gas (O_2) is ignored, because its most stable form at 25°C is the diatomic molecule O_2, so its enthalpy of formation is 0.

41.   Choice B is correct. From the values in Table 1, the hydrogenation of one π-bond (from an alkene to an alkane) produces a change in enthalpy ($\Delta H°_{hydrogenation}$) of -139.8 kJ per mole. This value is determined from the following reaction and thermodynamic data:

$$C_2H_4(g) + H_2(g) \rightarrow C_2H_6(g) \qquad \Delta H_{form} \, C_2H_4(g) = +52.4 \qquad \Delta H_{form} \, C_2H_6(g) = -87.4 \qquad \Delta H_{form} \, H_2(g) = 0$$

$$\Delta H_{hydrogenation} = \Delta H_{formation} \text{ of products} - \Delta H_{formation} \text{ of reactants} = (-87.4) - 52.4 = -139.8 \, \frac{kJ}{mole}$$

The reaction in the question involves the hydrogenation of two π-bonds in butadiene, so a good approximation is that the change in enthalpy for the complete hydrogenation of butadiene has a value of 2 (-139.8 kJ per mole) = -279.6 kJ per mole. The value is given in the question as -271.4 kJ per mole, which is less negative than expected. This eliminates choices A and C. The logic behind the reduction in heat energy released is rooted in either a increased stability in the reactant or decreased stability in the product. In this case, it is the stability of the reactant (conjugation) that causes the reduction in heat released. The best answer is choice **B**.

42. **Choice B is correct.** The heat produced for the reaction is calculated using the equation: $\Delta H_{rx} = \Delta H_{products} - \Delta H_{reactants}$. Using values from Table 1 (values are in kJ per mole), the two ΔH are calculated as follows:

$$C_2H_2 \longrightarrow H_2O + 2\,CO_2$$

ΔH: +226.8   -285.9   -393.5 $\Delta H_{rx} = [(-285.9) + 2(-393.5)] - 226.8 = -1299.7 \dfrac{kJ}{mole}$

$$C_2H_4 \longrightarrow 2\,H_2O + 2\,CO_2$$

ΔH: +52.4   -285.9   -393.5 $\Delta H_{rx} = [2(-285.9) + 2(-393.5)] - 52.4 = -1411\,2 \dfrac{kJ}{mole}$

The problem asks for heat per gram, not the heat per mole, so the values must be divided by molecular mass before comparison to one another.

$$C_2H_2 \text{ yields } \frac{1299.7\ kJ}{26\ g}, \text{ which is just less than } \frac{1300\ kJ}{26\ g}, \text{ which is } 50\ \frac{kJ}{g}$$

$$C_2H_4 \text{ yields } \frac{1411.2\ kJ}{28\ g}, \text{ which is just over } \frac{1400\ kJ}{28\ g}, \text{ which is } 50\ \frac{kJ}{g}$$

Thus, C_2H_2 produces just less than 50 kJ per gram of heat, while C_2H_4 produces a little more than 50 kJ per gram of heat, making answer **B** the correct choice.

43. **Choice A is correct.** The free energy produced for the reaction is calculated using the equation: $\Delta G_{rx} = \Delta G_{products} - \Delta G_{reactants}$. Using values from Table 1 (values are in kJ per mole), ΔG is calculated as follows:

$$C_2H_5OH \longrightarrow 3\,H_2O + 2\,CO_2$$

ΔG: -174.9   -237.2   -394.3 $\Delta G_{rx} = [3(-237.2) + 2(-394.3)] - (-174.9) \dfrac{kJ}{mole}$

$$= (-711.6) + (-788.6) + 174.9 = -1325.3 \dfrac{kJ}{mole}$$

Choice **A** is the best answer.

Passage VII (Questions 44 - 49)   **Salt-Solution Calorimetry Experiment**

---

44. **Choice B is correct.** The initial temperature of the water in Beaker 3 before the NH_4Cl salt is added to the water is 22°C. In Figure 3, the temperature decreases to a value less than 22°C (extrapolation shows that the temperature is about 17.5 °C). Once the temperature reaches its lowest point, it slowly climbs up until it levels off at ambient temperature (22°C). This means that the reaction is absorbing heat from the solution during the dissociation of NH_4Cl. Because heat is being absorbed during the solvation reaction, the solvation of NH_4Cl must be an endothermic reaction. The passage also states that the reaction is endothermic. To score big, you should pick **B**.

45. **Choice B is correct.** Adding 1.21 grams of $Mg(s)$, instead of 2.43 grams as were added in Experiment 2, results in only half of the heat being released that was released in Experiment 2. The temperature increase in Beaker 2 (using 2.43 grams) was 16°C, so the temperature increase using 1.21 grams should be about 8°C. This, when added to the starting temperature of 22°C, would yield a final temperature of 30°C. Choice **B** is the best answer, for those of you interested in best answers.

46. **Choice B is correct.** Using Hess's law, we know that the molar heat of reaction is obtained from the heats of reaction for any series of reactions that sum to the overall reaction. For this experiment, the two reactions along with the formation of water are as follows:

$$Mg(s) + 2\,H^+(aq) \longrightarrow Mg^{2+}(aq) + H_2(g) \quad \Delta H = \text{heat released from Beaker 1} \times 10 = -668.8\ \dfrac{kJ}{mole}$$

$$MgO(s) + 2\,H^+(aq) \longrightarrow Mg^{2+}(aq) + H_2O(l) \quad \Delta H = \text{heat released from Beaker 2} \times 10 = -376.2\ \dfrac{kJ}{mole}$$

$$H_2(g) + \tfrac{1}{2}\,O_2(g) \longrightarrow H_2O(l) \qquad\qquad \Delta H_{formation} = -286\ \dfrac{kJ}{mole}$$

The overall reaction is: $Mg(s) + \tfrac{1}{2}\,O_2(g) \longrightarrow MgO(s)$

We must reverse the second reaction and then sum the ΔH values for the three component reactions above, in order to obtain the overall reaction. This means that the $\Delta H_{formation}$ (MgO) = $\Delta H_{(Beaker\ 1)} - \Delta H_{(Beaker\ 2)} - 286$ kJ per mole. The best answer is choice **B**. The actual value is -669 + 391 - 286 = -564.

47. **Choice D is correct.** To solve for the molar enthalpy of this reaction, you must first solve for the heat of reaction for MgO in terms of kJ per gram (using the data from Beaker 2), and then convert from kJ per gram MgO to kJ per mole MgO. To determine the heat released during the reaction, we use the equation $E = mC\Delta T$, where m equals 1.0 kg, C = 4.34 J per g·K, and ΔT is extrapolated from the graph. To extrapolate, you draw a straight line through the data points to the time = 0 axis, in order to estimate the highest temperature of the solution.

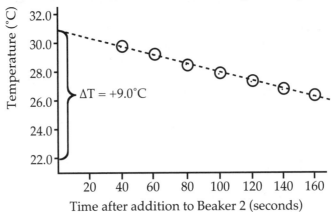

As extrapolated from the graph in Figure 2 (shown above), the apex temperature is roughly 31°C, so the value of ΔT is roughly 9°C. The heat released when 4.03 grams MgO was added to Beaker 2 is calculated as follows:

$$E = 1.0 \, kg \times 4.34 \, \frac{J}{g \cdot K} \times 9.0 \, K = 4.34 \times 9 \, kJ = 43.40 - 4.34 \, kJ = 39.06 \, kJ$$

The molecular mass of MgO is given in the passage as 40.3 grams/mole, so 4.03 grams is exactly 0.10 moles MgO. The molar enthalpy is calculated by dividing the heat of the reaction by the moles of reactant (MgO, in this case). The calculation is set up as follows:

$$\frac{1.0 \times 4.34 \times 9.0}{4.03} \, \frac{kJ}{gram} \times 40.3 \, \frac{grams}{mole} = \frac{1.0 \times 4.34 \times 9.0 \times 40.3}{4.03} \, \frac{kJ}{mole}$$

Choice **D** is correct. Because the temperature increase during the reaction, heat is given off by the reaction, so the reaction is an exothermic reaction. Because the reaction is exothermic, the sign of the enthalpy change (ΔH) is negative. All of the answer choices are negative, so this doesn't help in eliminating wrong answers.

48. **Choice D is correct.** The reaction of a metal with hydronium results in the oxidation of the metal by the H^+ ions. The reaction is as follows: $Mg(s) + 2 \, H^+(aq) \rightarrow Mg^{2+}(aq) + H_2(g)$. H_2 gas is given off, so choice **D** is best.

49. **Choice A is correct.** If the heat capacity (C) is greater for the HCl solution than water, then the value for C (4.18 for water) plugged into $E = mC\Delta T$ is too small. The calculated value is therefore too small. This makes choice **A** correct. An increased heat capacity does not allow the temperature to increase as much, which lowers the container temperature and actually decreases the reaction rate. This makes choice D invalid.

Passage VIII (Questions 50 - 55)   **Heat Pack**

50. **Choice C is correct.** According to the information for Reaction 1, four moles of iron produce 1652 kJ of heat. This means that 2 moles of iron produce 826 kJ, and 3 moles of iron produce 1239 kJ. In order to produce 1000 kJ of energy, just over two but less than three moles of iron are needed. Two and one-half moles of iron produce 826 kJ + 207 kJ, which is greater than 1000 kJ. This means that the amount of iron needed is less than 2.5 moles of iron. Iron weighs 55.85 grams per mole, so the mass needed to produce 1000 kJ of heat is greater than 111.7 grams (the mass of two moles) and less than 139.62 grams (the mass of two and one-half moles of iron). The best answer is choice **C**.

51. **Choice D is correct.** The pack initially contains iron and the solution in which the reaction transpires. Once exposed to the air, oxygen can enter the pores of the paper container and oxidize the iron. Because the product (Fe_2O_3) has gained mass from the environment, the mass after reaction is greater than the initial mass. The exact amount of mass increase is the mass of the oxygen that has reacted. The best choice is answer **D**.

52. **Choice D is correct.** Because the reaction takes place at room temperature and the iron is oxidized to completion, it is assumed that the reaction is favorable. This results in a $\Delta G°$ value less than zero, which eliminates choices A and C. The reactants are four solids and three gases that go on to form two solids. This is a loss in entropy by the system, which carries a negative $\Delta S°$. The value of $\Delta S°$ is also less than zero, making choice **D** the correct choice.

53. **Choice D is correct.** The role of salt water, as mentioned in the passage, is to increase the interaction of oxygen with iron and to conduct electricity. None of the answer choices addresses the interaction of iron with oxygen. This means that the role of the salt water of interest to us is to facilitate the flow of electrons. Salt water provides the medium through which the electrons may transfer. The best answer to this question is choice **D**. Heat is released by the reaction, so the reaction cannot be adiabatic. Choice A is thus eliminated. The salt water has no role in thermal regulation, because it does not undergo any chemical or physical changes during the reaction. Choice B is thus eliminated. Iron metal does not dissolve into water, as you perhaps have noticed when iron structures are able to stand through the rain. Choice C is thus eliminated.

54. **Choice C is correct.** The finely powdered iron has more surface area, so it reacts at a faster rate than the filings. This results in more heat being released per period of time. The finely powdered iron consequently heats up faster and reaches a higher temperature. From this, choices B and D can be eliminated. Given that equal masses of iron are present in both heat packs, the finely powdered iron is depleted before the iron filings are depleted, because the reaction proceeds faster with the powdered iron. This is best illustrated in answer selection **C**, where the sudden temperature drop back to the initial temperature indicates that no more heat is being produced, so the reaction must have stopped.

55. **Choice A is correct.** Answer choice **A** best explains the logic behind the packaging. Because oxygen gas must enter the packet to react with the iron, the membrane must be porous. Paper is porous, allowing air to flow into the heat pack. To prevent the packet from oxidizing prematurely, it must not be exposed to air. The plastic wrapper is impermeable to air, so the pack is stable in the anaerobic environment. The plastic wrapper also helps to prevent the loss of water due to evaporation.

Passage IX (Questions 56 - 62)   Bomb Calorimeter

56. **Choice D is correct.** Stirring the solution does not increase the thermodynamic values (equilibrium constant, free energy, and enthalpy), but it does allow the reaction to proceed at a faster rate. Choice A should be eliminated. The stirring does not provide enough energy to activate the reaction. The energy used to activate the reaction is provided by the system's heat energy, as measured by the temperature. Choice B is thus eliminated. The stirring of the solution has no effect on the pressure of the solution, so choice C is eliminated. The stirring of the solution allows the heat to be distributed uniformly throughout the solution, which makes choice **D** the best answer.

57. **Choice C is correct.** The liquid substituted must have a heat capacity similar to water and not have a boiling point that is too low. A low boiling point would build up pressure, as the circulating solution expands and vaporizes. Isopropanol has a boiling point and heat capacity close to those of water. If the heat capacity is too high, the ΔT is too small, and thus the accuracy of the temperature change is decreased. Choice **C** is best.

58. **Choice C is correct.** Whether steel has a high heat capacity or low heat capacity, the effects of both can be calculated for. The lower the heat capacity, the better, because water can rise to a larger temperature, but it is a trivial point. By having steel walls, the container does not expand during the reaction, so the volume remains constant while the pressure changes. This makes choice B false and choice **C** true. Hopefully, the steel is not reactive with water; otherwise, the heat change cannot be attributed solely to the reaction. The best answer (so that the heat capacity at constant volume can be used in calculation) is choice **C**.

59. **Choice A is correct.** The excess oxygen is added to ensure a complete reaction. The amount of heat generated is measured relative to the mass of the sample (the limiting reagent in the reaction). The oxygen gas increases convection, but that is not the reason for adding excess oxygen. This is a true, but irrelevant statement. Oxygen gas stores little to no heat energy, because gases have relatively low heat capacities relative to water. Choice D is eliminated, because the presence of oxygen results in CO_2 formation. The best answer is choice **A**.

60. **Choice B is correct.** The sample is ignited by heat emitted from the ignition coil. The question is, "What generates the heat in the coil?" The coils are connected to a circuit, so it is in fact a resistor. As current passes through the ignition coil, heat is generated due to resistance of the material in the heating coil. The result is that the sample is ignited when the resistor temperature is high enough. The best answer is choice **B**.

61. **Choice C is correct.** In determining a temperature change from a reaction that generates little heat, the problem is that a small ΔT results in an error in its determination. By using a liquid with a lower heat capacity than water, the ΔT is greater and thus more accurately measured. Choice A is a valid statement. If more sample (reactant) is used, more heat is generated, so the ΔT is larger and thus can be measured more accurately. Choice B is a valid statement. Increasing the stir rate helps the system to distribute the heat uniformly and more quickly. This does not help the reaction ΔT to be measured more accurately. A thermometer with more calibrations would give us a more precise measurement of ΔT. This makes choice D a valid statement. The best answer is choice **C**.

62. **Choice D is correct.** As a rule, both the oxidation-reduction reaction of a metal with oxygen and the combustion reaction of a hydrocarbon (which is an oxidation-reduction reaction) are exothermic reactions. They both result in an increase in temperature of the solution, not a temperature decrease. If the precipitation of a solute is favorable, then the ΔG that reaction is negative. In a precipitation reaction, the system becomes more ordered, so ΔS is definitely negative. The sign of ΔH must be negative to make the sign of ΔG negative, based on the equation $\Delta G = \Delta H - T\Delta S$ (negative number - T(negative number) = negative number). Dissolving a solute into solution is the only one of the choices given that can possibly be endothermic, if all of the answer choices represent favorable reactions. An endothermic reaction results in a temperature drop. The best answer is thus choice **D**.

Passage X (Questions 63 - 69) Hot and Cold Compresses

63. **Choice B is correct.** Whether the solution is for the radiator of a power plant, or any system designed to absorb great amounts of heat, the best solution is the one with the greatest heat capacity and greatest contact area with the heat source. Choices C and D should not be considered, because they are both gases. The addition of salt to water increases the heat capacity, allowing salt water to absorb more heat per degree increase, and to reach a higher temperature before boiling. This can be inferred from the passage where it states that the temperature increase begins to slow, because the heat capacity changes as more salt dissolves. This is why many power plants use salt water in their circulating radiator system. Cars use a mixture of ethylene glycol in distilled water. Using an organic compound like ethylene glycol prevents against salt buildup that would occur if salt water were used, due to the evaporation of water. The best answer is choice **B**.

64. **Choice A is correct.** For a heat pack to reach a temperature greater than room temperature, it must exploit a reaction that releases heat energy. This describes an exothermic reaction. Because the heat is needed immediately, rapid reactions are more favorable. Slow reactions allow more heat to dissipate to the environment. This combination makes choice **A** the best answer.

65. **Choice A is correct.** To be to use in a heat compress, the reaction must be exothermic. To be exothermic, the reaction must require minimal energy to break the bonds and obtain a great deal of energy when the new bonds are formed. In the case of a salt dissolving into water, this would result from weak lattice forces (bonds broken) and strong solvent to ion interactions (solvation). The best answer is choice **A**.

66. **Choice B is correct.** The passage states that 10 grams of calcium chloride raise 100 mL of water approximately eighteen degrees from room temperature. This means that 40 grams of calcium chloride should increase 200 mL water by 36°C. The final temperature is the initial temperature (20°C) plus the temperature increase (36°C), resulting in a final temperature of 56°C. The actual value is a little less, due to the reaction time being longer (allowing heat to dissipate to the environment) and the changing heat capacity of the aqueous solution as the reaction proceeds. The best answer is choice **B**.

67. **Choice A is correct.** For the temperature to increase, the reaction must be exothermic, so choices C and D are eliminated. The boiling point is greater than that of pure water (100°C), so the boiling point must have been elevated. The best answer is choice **A**.

68. **Choice D is correct.** Sulfate salts are exothermic when they dissolve, so they cannot be used in cold compresses. This eliminates choices A and B. Ammonium salts are endothermic when they dissolve, so heat is absorbed and the solution begins to cool. The best answer for an endothermic solvation involves ammonium chloride (NH_4Cl). The best answer is choice **D**. The answer is provided in the last sentence of the passage.

69. **Choice A is correct.** Cold packs absorb heat because of a chemical reaction, so the solvation reaction must be endothermic for cold packs. This causes the temperature to decrease. The favorability of a reaction depends on the value of ΔG. If the value of ΔG is negative, then the reaction is said to be favorable. An endothermic reaction has a positive value for ΔH, so the only way that the value of ΔG can be negative is if the value of ΔS is positive ($\Delta G = \Delta H - T\Delta S$). This automatically means that the salt dissociates because of increased entropy, not favorable enthalpy. This eliminates choices C and D. The lattice forces are most likely strong, requiring high energy to break. The more energy required to break the lattice bonds, the more likely that the reaction is endothermic. The best answer is choice **A**.

Passage XI (Questions 70 - 78) Calorimetry Experiment

70. **Choice D is correct.** The heat capacity depends on three values: energy absorbed (E), mass of substance (m), and the change in temperature (ΔT). The mass of each metal is known and the change in temperature is known, so only the heat absorbed, while inside the heating chamber must be known to calculate the heat capacity for each metal. This makes choice **D** correct.

71. **Choice D is correct.** Heat capacity has units of calories per gram·Kelvin in the standard case. Using the formula $E = mC\Delta T$, the heat capacity (C) for each metal sample can be found by dividing the energy absorbed by the mass of the sample and temperature change for the process. Each metal absorbed the same amount of heat energy and had an identical mass. The only difference between the metal samples was the change in temperature observed for the process. Because ΔT is in the denominator when calculating the heat capacity for each metal ($C = E/m \cdot \Delta T$), the greatest heat capacity is associated with the metal that showed the smallest increase in temperature. According to Table 1, the metal with the smallest final temperature (and therefore smallest ΔT) is Metal IV, so pick choice **D** with great pride and satisfaction.

72. **Choice B is correct.** If the heat loss for the liquid and heat gain for the metal were identical (which is true when the process is adiabatic), then the following mathematical equality holds true:

$$E_{\text{heating of liquid}} = -E_{\text{cooling of metal}}$$

$$m_{\text{liquid}} C_{\text{liquid}} (T_{\text{final}} - T_{\text{init (liquid)}}) = - m_{\text{metal}} C_{\text{metal}} (T_{\text{final}} - T_{\text{init (metal)}}) = m_{\text{metal}} C_{\text{metal}} (T_{\text{init (metal)}} - T_{\text{final}})$$

Given that the heat capacities are equal, they can be canceled from each side of the equality:

$$m_{\text{liquid}} \cancel{C_{\text{liquid}}} (T_{\text{final}} - T_{\text{init (liquid)}}) = m_{\text{metal}} \cancel{C_{\text{metal}}} (T_{\text{init (metal)}} - T_{\text{final}})$$

$$m_{\text{liquid}} (T_{\text{final}} - 25) = m_{\text{metal}} (50 - T_{\text{final}}) \quad \therefore \quad 40 (T_{\text{final}} - 25) = 10 (50 - T_{\text{final}}) \quad \rightarrow \quad 4 (T_{\text{final}} - 25) = (50 - T_{\text{final}})$$

$$4 T_{\text{final}} - 100 = 50 - T_{\text{final}} \quad \therefore \quad 5 T_{\text{final}} = 150 \quad \therefore \quad T_{\text{final}} = 30$$

The best answer is choice **B**. This could have been solved intuitively by saying that if the heat capacities for the liquid and solid are equal, then mixing equal mass quantities of the metal and liquid would lead to a temperature exactly between the two starting temperatures (the average of 25 and 50 is 37.5). Because there was excess liquid, the final temperature would be closer to the initial liquid temperature than the initial metal temperature, which makes it less than 37.5°C. The temperature must increase somewhat from the liquid's initial temperature, so the final temperature is between 25°C and 37.5°C. The best answer is choice **B**.

73. **Choice D is correct.** If the heat capacity of the liquid and metal are the same, then the final temperature is 30°C. Considering that the mass of the liquid is four times the mass of the solid, the difference in the final temperature (and thus temperature change) can be attributed to different heat capacities. If the final temperature is greater than 30°C, then the heat capacity of the liquid is less than the heat capacity of the solid. The math is below:

$$m_{\text{liquid}} C_{\text{liquid}} (T_{\text{final}} - T_{\text{init (liquid)}}) = m_{\text{metal}} C_{\text{metal}} (T_{\text{init (metal)}} - T_{\text{final}})$$

Given that $m_{\text{liquid}} = 4 \times m_{\text{metal}}$, the following substitution and subsequent cancellation can be made:

$$4 \times \cancel{m_{\text{metal}}} C_{\text{liquid}} (T_{\text{final}} - T_{\text{init (liquid)}}) = \cancel{m_{\text{metal}}} C_{\text{metal}} (T_{\text{init (metal)}} - T_{\text{final}})$$

$$4 C_{\text{liquid}} (T_{\text{final}} - 25) = C_{\text{metal}} (50 - T_{\text{final}})$$

By cross-dividing (if there is such a mathematical term), we find that:

$$\frac{T_{\text{final}} - 25}{50 - T_{\text{final}}} = \frac{C_{\text{metal}}}{4 \times C_{\text{liquid}}} \quad \therefore \quad 4 \times \frac{T_{\text{final}} - 25}{50 - T_{\text{final}}} = \frac{C_{\text{metal}}}{C_{\text{liquid}}}$$

$$\text{If } T_{\text{final}} = 30°C, \text{ then } \frac{C_{\text{metal}}}{C_{\text{liquid}}} = 1 \qquad \text{If } T_{\text{final}} > 30°C, \text{ then } \frac{C_{\text{metal}}}{C_{\text{liquid}}} > 1$$

$$\text{If } T_{\text{final}} < 30°C, \text{ then } \frac{C_{\text{metal}}}{C_{\text{liquid}}} < 1$$

This means that any liquid that shows a final temperature greater than 30°C has a heat capacity less than the heat capacity for the solid. According to Table II, this is true only for Liquid IV. If this wasn't your first thought, then your test-taking skills should have pulled you through. Only one choice is correct, so of the liquids, you should pick the one with either the highest or lowest final temperature, **never one in the middle**. The lower the heat capacity, the more the temperature increases for a given quantity of heat, so the correct choice is the liquid with the highest final temperature, Liquid IV. The best answer is choice **D**.

74. **Choice D is correct.** Because Metal IV reached a lower temperature in Experiment I than did Metal III, the heat capacity of Metal IV must be greater than the heat capacity of Metal III. This means that when both Metal III and Metal IV are at 50°C, Metal IV has more kinetic energy than Metal III. This means that when Metal III is added to the liquids, it has less energy to transfer to the liquids, so that the final temperature of each liquid must be lower than it would have been had Metal IV been used. More kinetic energy in the metal results in more kinetic energy being transferred to the liquid and thus a higher final temperature for the liquid. This is best explained in answer choice **D**. Choices A and B are eliminated, because the heat transferred from Metal III is less than the heat transferred from Metal IV.

75. **Choice D is correct.** The greatest amount of transferable kinetic energy is found with the metal with the greatest combination of temperature and heat capacity. Metal IV has the greatest heat capacity, based on information from Experiment I. Of the choices presented, Metal IV also has the greatest temperature. This makes Metal IV at 80°C the correct choice, so choose answer choice **D**.

76. **Choice A is correct.** Using your test-taking skills, you see that the correct answer involves the sequential ordering of the liquids in Table II, according to their final temperatures. Because equal amounts of heat were applied to all four liquids and the amount of liquid was identical in each trial, the lower ΔT is due to a larger heat capacity. This means that the greatest heat capacity is associated with the liquid that showed the smallest ΔT (Liquid III). The correct choice is III > I > II > IV, answer choice **A**. The answer choices should have been narrowed down to either **A** or B based strictly on test-taking skills, using the sequence of temperatures from Table 2. For optimum satisfaction, choose **A**.

77. **Choice A is correct.** If the outer wall of the calorimeter increases in temperature during the experiment, heat must be lost during the process. Any heat that is lost to the environment is not absorbed by the liquid, so the final temperature of the liquid is less than is expected. The final temperature of the solid is equal to the final temperature of the liquid at equilibrium, so the final temperature is lower than expected. This eliminates choices C and D. Because the final temperature is too low, the change in temperature for the liquid is too small, and the change in temperature for the solid is too high. Because the calculation for the energy transfer involves equating the two temperature changes, the inaccurate temperature changes affect the heat capacities. Because the temperature of the liquid does not increase as high as it should, the lower temperature change may be mistaken for a larger heat capacity for the liquid. Because the energy (E) equals mCΔT, a ΔT value that is too small will be balanced out by a C that is too large. The best answer is choice **A**.

78. **Choice D is correct.** The ratio of the heat capacities can be determined by equating the energy changes for both the liquid heating up and the solid cooling down.

$$E_{\text{heating of liquid}} = -E_{\text{cooling of solid}}$$

$$m_{\text{liquid}} C_{\text{liquid}} (T_{\text{final}} - T_{\text{init (liquid)}}) = -m_{\text{solid}} C_{\text{solid}} (T_{\text{final}} - T_{\text{init (solid)}}) = m_{\text{solid}} C_{\text{solid}} (T_{\text{init (solid)}} - T_{\text{final}})$$

$$m_{\text{liquid}} C_{\text{liquid}} (T_{\text{final}} - T_{\text{init (liquid)}}) = m_{\text{solid}} C_{\text{solid}} (T_{\text{init (solid)}} - T_{\text{final}})$$

$$40 \, C_{\text{liquid}} \, \Delta T_{\text{liquid}} = 10 \, C_{\text{solid}} \, \Delta T_{\text{solid}} \quad \therefore \quad \frac{C_{\text{liquid}}}{C_{\text{solid}}} = \frac{1}{4} \frac{\Delta T_{\text{solid}}}{\Delta T_{\text{liquid}}}$$

The best answer is choice **D**.

Passage XII (Questions 79 - 85)   Single-Piston Engine

79. **Choice A is correct.** A one-way valve allows fluid to flow in only one direction. Because the flow is asymmetric, the valve must be asymmetric. Choices C and D have symmetry, so they can be eliminated. For fluid from left to right, the valve must seal on the left and remain open on the right. Choose **A**. The valve must be viewed in three dimensions to appreciate its operation. If pressure is applied (due to the flow of fluid) from right to left, the ball seals with the port and no fluid can flow. If pressure is applied (due to the flow of fluid) from left to right, the ball does not form a seal with the port, so fluid continues to flow. This means that fluid flows in only one direction (left to right) through the valve.

80. **Choice C is correct.** A cooling fan, by definition, is designed to cool by convection. In the one-piston steam engine, cooling is required to condense the steam into liquid water. Condensation takes place in the condenser, so the fan should be set up near the condenser (so the condenser can be cooled). The best answer is choice **C**. A condenser would have many thin fins on its surface to increase the surface are and thus increase heat transfer by way of convection.

81. **Choice D is correct.** The engine is operated through the conversion of liquid water into steam. This is known as vaporization, so the best answer is choice **D**. Choice A is a good explanation for why water would be used in the radiator of a car, where heat is being removed from an engine so a material with a high heat capacity would prove extremely useful.

82. **Choice A is correct.** When the counterweight is at its lowest point, the cycle of the piston is complete. The counterweight is lifted again as steam is added to the core of the piston. It would be ideal if the piston were completely compressed; but because there is always some gas present in the core of the piston, full compression is not possible. This is best explained in choice **A**. In modern engines, the gas is evacuated from the chamber to help the piston descend with less resistance. Modern engines also employ multiple pistons that are out of phase, rather than use a counterweight.

83. **Choice D is correct.** Because the liquid is converted into a gas in the boiler, heat must be added to the boiler to induce evaporation. This eliminates choices A and C. The gas is then converted back into a liquid in the condenser, so heat must be removed from the condenser. A well-designed automobile has a passenger compartment heater that takes advantage of the heat released from the condenser to help heat the passenger compartment. To carry this out, a fan blows across the outside surface of the condenser, and the heat flows into the passenger compartment with the airflow. The correct answer for this question is thus choice **D**.

84. **Choice C is correct.** For the piston to rise, the internal pressure must exceed the external pressure. To build up the internal pressure, steam is added to the core of the piston through the intake valve. Pressure builds up as the moles of gas increase. This is because according to the ideal gas equation, when volume and temperature are constant, pressure increases as moles increase. The temperature is considered to be constant, because steam in the presence of water is at 100°C. Steam is added to the core of the piston by allowing steam to flow into the piston, but not flow out of the piston. This means that the intake valve should be open and the exhaust valve should be closed. The best answer is choice **C**.

85. **Choice A is correct.** An engine to converts heat into work, so an efficient engine is an engine that converts all of the heat into work. If all of the heat is converted into work, then no heat is emitted. A perfect engine is not possible. An ideal engine would run at ambient temperature, so that no heat is lost to the environment. Pick choice **A** if you know what is best for you.

Passage XIII (Questions 86 - 92)	Carnot Cycle

86. **Choice B is correct.** A Carnot engine is designed to convert heat into work. An engine takes heat in to give off work energy overall. The diagram that represents an engine is the diagram that represents a work- releasing process (one with work equal to a negative number). The vertical steps in the diagrams (b to c, d to a, e to f, and g to h) represent steps in which the volume does not change, so no work can be done in these steps (if $\Delta V = 0$, then -$P\Delta V = 0$). The trick to this question is to pick one diagram and solve it. The correct answer is either choice **B** or D, because "work flows out of the system" must be true in the statement for an engine. In the diagram in Figure 1, the step from a to b represents the expansion of the gas. When a gas expands, the process is endothermic and work energy is released. This implies that work is a negative number, because work energy is given off by the system. The change in volume (ΔV) is positive for the process, so -$P\Delta V$ must be negative. In the diagram in Figure 1, the step from c to d represents the compression of the gas. When a gas compresses, the process is exothermic and work energy is absorbed. This implies that work is a positive number, because work energy is absorbed by the system. The change in volume (ΔV) is negative for the process, so -$P\Delta V$ must be positive. The pressure is greater from a to b than it is from c to d. This means that the magnitude of the work from a to b is greater than the magnitude of work from c to d. The absolute value of the w_{a-b} > the absolute value of w_{c-d}. The overall work is the sum of both work steps. Because the negative value has a larger magnitude than the positive value, the process must be negative overall. This makes the diagram in Figure 1 an engine. This also makes choice **B** correct.

87. **Choice C is correct.** In a full cycle on the diagram for an ideal system (like the Carnot refrigerator in the diagram in Figure 2), the change in internal energy is zero. This eliminates choices A and B. For a refrigerator, work is added into the system, as heat is removed from the system. The "work in" must therefore be greater than the "work out" for the overall process to be heat absorbing. From the graph in Figure 2, going from f to g involves a positive change in volume, so a negative value for work ($w = -P\Delta V$) is calculated. From point f to point g, work energy is released, so the process is defined as "work out." From the graph, going from h to e involves a negative change in volume, so a positive value for work ($w = -P\Delta V$) is calculated. From point h to point e, work energy is absorbed, so the process is defined as "work in." The pressure is greater moving from h to e than it is moving from f to g. The magnitude for the "work in" step (h to e) is therefore greater than the magnitude for the "work out" step (f to g). This makes choice **C** the best choice.

88. **Choice D is correct.** If work for the system is positive and ΔE (the change in internal energy) is zero, then q (the heat of the system) must be negative (given that $\Delta E = q + w$). If q is negative for the system, heat was released from the system to the surroundings, meaning that q must be positive for the surroundings. The best answer is therefore choice **D**.

89. **Choice B is correct.** Because the shaft of the pump is becoming hot, it must be that air (and heat) is being compressed in the column of the shaft (assuming the heat is not due to friction). If the heat is greatest at the bottom of the shaft (where the pressure is greatest), then the heat is due to the exothermic nature of compressing gas, not friction. If the heat were due to friction, it would be uniform throughout the column of the shaft. Because the needle tip is cool, the gas must be expanding at that point. The compressed gas expands as it exits from the needle point. Because air is compressed in the shaft, choices C and D are eliminated. Because gas expands as it leaves the needle tip, choice **B** is the best answer.

90. **Choice B is correct.** From point a to point c in the diagram in Figure 1, the volume of the system has increased, so choices C and D are invalid (and thus eliminated), because the gas has expanded. As a gas expands, heat must be absorbed (expansion of a gas is endothermic). When the gas expands, work energy is given off from the system to the surroundings (when ΔV is positive, work (which equals $-P\Delta V$) must be negative). This makes choice **B** correct.

91. **Choice D is correct.** The purpose of an engine is to convert heat energy into work energy. The warmer the exhaust temperature, the more heat that is dissipated to the environment rather than being converted into useful work energy. If heat energy is wasted, the engine is not being efficient. This implies that both choice A and choice C are invalid. The more points at which energy is transferred, the more energy that is dissipated in the way of friction. If energy is dissipated as friction, it is not being used efficiently. This means that many points of energy transfer would result in decreased engine efficiency. The best answer is therefore choice **D**.

92. **Choice B is correct.** From point b to c in the diagram in Figure 1, the volume does not change, so no work can be done. Work is defined as $-P\Delta V$, so a change in volume (ΔV) of zero means that $P\Delta V$ is zero and thus no work is done. The best answer is therefore choice **B**. In choices A, C, and D, there is work being done, and that is not possible at constant volume.

(Questions 93 - 100)   **Not Based on a Descriptive Passage**

---

93. **Choice B is correct.** The First Law of Thermodynamics deals with the conservation of energy. Energy can be neither created nor destroyed, and as such, energy is neither lost nor gained in any process. The Second Law of Thermodynamics states that in any spontaneous process there is an increase in the entropy of the universe. The magnitude of the entropy change of the surroundings is always greater than or equal to the magnitude of the entropy change of the system. The Third Law states that the entropy of a perfect crystal at 0 kelvins is zero. Rutherford's experiment dealt with determining atomic structure (the location of sub-atomic particles and the nucleus), not the laws of thermodynamics, so choice D is eliminated. The Second Law of Thermodynamics, choice **B**, is the best choice.

94. **Choice C is correct.** Knowing that $w = -P\Delta V$, the work done on the system is calculated by substituting the values for P and ΔV. Because the answer choices are in units of liter·atmospheres, pressure must be converted from torr into atm. This is done as follows:

$$P = 950 \text{ torr} \left(\frac{1 \text{ atm.}}{760 \text{ torr}}\right) = 1.25 \text{ atm} \qquad \Delta V = V_{final} - V_{initial} = 2.4 \text{ L} - 0.4 \text{ L} = 2.0 \text{ L}$$

The value for work is found by substituting $w = -P\Delta V$ as follows:

$$w = -(1.25 \text{ atm})(2 \text{ L}) = -2.50 \text{ liter·atmospheres}$$

The best answer is choice **C**.

95. **Choice D is correct.** The equation you need is: $\Delta G = \Delta H - T\Delta S$. No numerical values are given for ΔH, T, or ΔS, so ΔG cannot be assigned a definite numerical answer. Since ΔH and ΔS are both given as positive, then the free energy change (ΔG) is:

$$\Delta G = (+\#) - T(+\#)$$

A large value for T would make the value of ΔG negative, while a small value for T would make the value of ΔG positive. The answer depends on T, so choose **D**. The solution to this question represents the reasoning behind Table 8.1

Case	Result
ΔS positive, ΔH negative	Favorable at all temperatures
ΔS positive, ΔH positive	Favorable at high temperatures
ΔS negative, ΔH negative	Favorable at low temperatures
ΔS negative, ΔH positive	Never favorable at any temperature

The term "spontaneous" may be used in lieu of "favorable". Spontaneous implies that the value for the free energy change (ΔG) is a negative value. The term spontaneous also implies that the reaction is favorable in the forward direction.

96. **Choice B is correct.** The only mathematical equation to know for the Carnot cycle is that the change in internal energy (ΔE) equals the sum of the heat energy (q) and the work energy (w): $\Delta E = q + w$ (which can also be written as $\Delta E = q - P\Delta V$). All of the values you need are given in easy-to-use units, so plug-and-chug to your heart's content. The mathematics should follow:

$$\Delta E = 22.2 \text{ kJ} - 24.4 \text{ kJ} = -2.2 \text{ kJ}.$$

Make sure to pick **B** to optimize your gratification quotient.

97. **Choice A is correct.** There are a few methods to solve this problem, of which three are listed. It is suggested that you adopt the method that is quickest for you. It is not a bad idea to learn multiple methods to reach a solution for all of the questions you practice with. This helps to broaden your understanding of the concepts being tested.

Method one requires taking a weighted mathematical average of the volumes and temperatures:

The final total volume of water is 128 mL. This means that 25% ($\frac{32 \text{ mL}}{128 \text{ mL}}$) of the final solution originates from the solution that starts at 36°C. This also means that 75% ($\frac{96 \text{ mL}}{128 \text{ mL}}$) of the final solution originates from the solution that starts at 64°C. The weighted average is calculated as follows:

$$0.25 \, (36°C) + 0.75 \, (64°C) = 9°C + 48°C = 57.0 \, °C.$$

This makes choice **A** the best answer.

A second approach is the intuitive approach. Intuition is often aided by drawing a diagram, as you do in physics. The sketch below shows the change in heat for the reaction and the math involved:

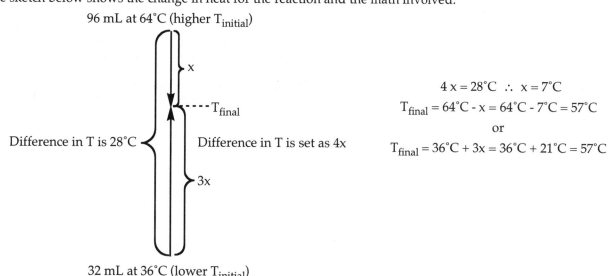

This leads to a value of 57°C again, so choice **A** results from this method as well. You could also cut the difference in half twice, getting 50°C as the midpoint and then 57°C as halfway between 50°C and 64°C.

The last approach is to equate the heat lost by the warmer solution with the heat gained by the cooler solution. If no heat is lost to the environment, then $E_{cooling} + E_{heating} = 0$.

$$E_{cooling} = -E_{heating}$$
$$mC\Delta T_{cooling} = -mC\Delta T_{heating}$$

Canceling the C from both sides and plugging in for ΔT yields:

$$m\Delta T_{cooling} = -m\Delta T_{heating} \;\rightarrow\; 96 \text{ g } (64 - T_{final}) = -32 \text{ g } (36 - T_{final}) = 32 \text{ g } (T_{final} - 36)$$

$$96 \text{ g } (64 - T_{final}) = 32 \text{ g } (T_{final} - 36) \;\rightarrow\; 3 \, (64 - T_{final}) = T_{final} - 36$$

$$192 - 3 T_{final} = T_{final} - 36 \;\therefore\; 228 = 4 T_{final} \;\therefore\; 57 = T_{final}$$

Well what do you know? The correct answer is choice **A** yet again. Each method has its unique advantages, so the best method is the one with which you feel most comfortable.

98. **Choice B is correct.** A gas is the most random phase of the three common phases of matter (solid, liquid, and gas), and a solid is the most ordered of the three common phases. Therefore, in changing from a gas into a solid, the atoms are becoming more ordered. ΔS is a measure of change in randomness for the system, and since the randomness of the system is decreasing, the value of ΔS must be a negative value. Choice **B** is the correct answer.

99. **Choice B is correct.** To expand, a gas requires the addition of heat to the system. This makes expansion of a gas an endothermic process and eliminates both choice A and choice C. Because the gas is becoming more random as it expands (it occupies a larger volume once expanded), the expansion process is entropically favorable. The best answer is choice **B**. When the system becomes more random, the change in entropy (ΔS) is positive.

100. **Choice C is correct.** All of the statements entail phase-change processes, so the following table is presented for quick reference:

Process (Phase Change)	Enthalpy Change
Melting (Solid to Liquid)	Endothermic: Small positive value
Freezing (Liquid to Solid)	Exothermic: Small negative value
Evaporation (Liquid to Gas)	Endothermic: Semi-large positive value
Condensation (Gas to Liquid)	Exothermic: Semi-large negative value
Sublimation (Solid to Gas)	Endothermic: Large positive value
Deposition (Gas to Solid)	Exothermic: Large negative value

It requires more energy to convert a liquid to a gas (vaporization) than it does to convert a solid to a liquid (fusion), because all of the intermolecular forces must be broken. Heat is absorbed during vaporization (and endothermic process). This makes statement I a valid statement. Choices B and D are eliminated. This also means that statement II is invalid. While more heat is involved in a phase change between a solid and a gas than a phase change between a liquid and a gas, the key word in statement II is "released." Energy is *absorbed* during sublimation, not released. Statement II is invalid. Heat is released when a liquid freezes into a solid, because freezing is an exothermic process and heat is released in exothermic processes. The release of heat from the system to the surroundings warms the environment. This makes statement III valid, and makes the best answer choice **C**.

Section IX

Kinetics

by Todd Bennett

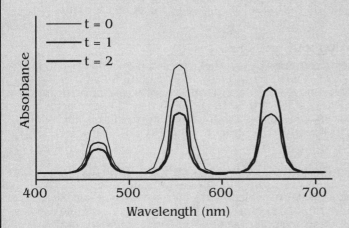

Reaction Rates

a) Observed Reaction Rate
b) Reaction Rate Experiment
c) Reaction Order
d) Rate Constant and Rate Law
e) Reaction Order Experiment
f) Typical Data and Graphs
g) Half-life

Reaction Mechanisms

a) General Mechanism Types
b) Energy Diagrams
c) Catalysis

1st order reaction

The **B**ERKELEY **R**·E·V·I·E·W®

Specializing in **MCAT** Preparation

Kinetics Section Goals

 Be able to interpret kinetic information from graphs.

The study of kinetics involves the use of graphs that show concentration versus time and graphs that show rate versus time. You must recognize typical graphs for zero-order, first-order, and second-order reactions. Many questions on the MCAT simply require that you recognize a graph and read information from it.

 Know the significance of the rate-determining step.

All kinetic data in a multi-step reaction are based on the rate-determining step. The rate-determining step of a reaction is the slowest step in the overall reaction process. The rate-determining step has the greatest activation energy (transition-state energy) of all the steps in the reaction pathway.

 Know how to determine the rate equation and rate law.

The rate equation takes into account all of the reactants that affect the observed rate of the reaction (all of the reactants in the rate-determining step). The rate law is found by setting the rate of the reaction equal to the rate constant times the reactants in the rate-determining step. For a first-order reaction, the rate law is: rate = k[Reactant]. The rate law is determined by isolating each reactant and observing how the rate changes when the concentration of that particular reactant is altered. These questions require that you analyze rate data from a table of different trials.

 Understand the correlation between temperature, activation energy, and rate.

The reaction rate is determined by the activation energy of the rate-determining step. As the temperature system is increased, there is more energy available to overcome the activation barrier. With this energy, the reaction can proceed more rapidly, because more reactants can overcome the activation barrier per unit time. The following graphs are ones that you must recognize:

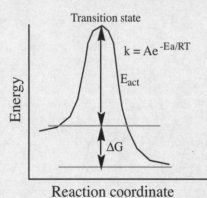 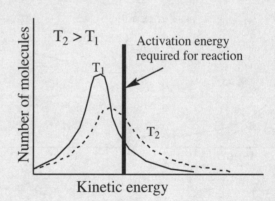

 Be able to determine quickly the concentration at any time for first-order decay.

These questions require the use of the half-life, which is defined as the period of time required for one-half of a material to decompose (or react). For a first-order reaction, the half-life is a constant value, no matter what the concentration of the reactant may be.

 Know the effect of a catalyst on the reaction rate.

A catalyst (or enzyme in biological reactions) forms a complex with the transition state of the rate-determining step in a reaction. The complex is more stable, and thus of a lower energy. In essence, a catalyst lowers the activation energy of a reaction by lowering the energy level of the transition-state complex. In doing so, the rate of the reaction is decreased. A catalyst is not consumed during the course of the reaction.

Chemical Kinetics

Kinetics is the study of how fast a reaction proceeds and the conditions that affect the speed of the reaction. Chemists observe the rate at which a product is formed or the rate at which a reactant is consumed. The disappearance of reactants is often easier to monitor, because we know their spectral data and physical properties. Products are harder to monitor, given that there are no products present when a reaction commences. A problem that often arises is deciding which kind of spectroscopic signal to use to monitor product formation: visible light, ultraviolet light, or some other electromagnetic radiation.

Because chemical reactions move simultaneously in the forward and reverse directions, chemical kinetics is concerned with the forward reaction rate, the reverse reaction rate, and the overall reaction rate. When monitoring a reaction, we observe the overall reaction rate. From the overall reaction rate, we can ascertain information about the forward and reverse reaction rates. It is also possible to monitor one component in the mixture by incorporating an isotopic label. By observing the rate of label incorporation, information about either the forward rate or the reverse rate can be obtained. Reaction rates tell us about the mechanism by which a reaction proceeds from reactants to products.

In organic chemistry, choosing between the various nucleophilic substitution mechanisms is based on kinetic data. If the concentration of the nucleophile influences the rate of the reaction, then it is assumed that the rate determining step involves the nucleophile attacking the electrophile to form the transition state that evolves into product. This is referred to as an S_N2-reaction mechanism. If changing the concentration of the nucleophile shows no effect on the rate of the reaction, then the reaction is said to follow an S_N1-reaction mechanism. Both mechanisms show a rate dependence on the electrophile concentration. The number given in the name of the mechanism refers to its reaction order.

In biochemistry, enzymatic behavior is monitored through the study of chemical kinetics. Observing the reaction rate over time reveals features of the enzyme and whether or not it is saturated. A good foundation in chemical kinetics from a general chemistry perspective makes Michaelis-Menten kinetics (studied in biochemistry) easier to understand. Conversely, if you have a strong understanding of Michaelis-Menten kinetics, then reviewing chemical kinetics in general chemistry will be much easier. We will intertwine examples of chemical kinetics from a few fields, so that we can get a more universal understanding of reaction rates and of the aspects of a chemical reaction that influence these rates.

In reviewing chemical kinetics, we will focus on experimental studies that tell us about the concentration of a component in a reaction as a function of time. By studying concentration changes over time, we can deduce information about the reaction order. Knowing the reaction order, in turn, can give us information about the reaction mechanism. If the mechanism is valid, then a reaction can be manipulated to control the rate of formation of selected products. A catalyst influences the rate of a reaction, but it does not affect the product distribution.

The last of the topics that we will address is nuclear chemistry. This section should be one of the easier sections in your review, as scientists do not understand the topic in enough detail to expect you to have a deep understanding of it. Nuclear chemistry is made easy by knowing the particles and the processes of decay and capture, and your ability to do basic math. Know the definitions of isotopes, nuclear decay, nuclear capture, nuclear particles, and half-life. This chapter starts with a basic look ate reaction rates and finishes with the concepts of decay, the half-lives of various particles, and changes the nucleus can undergo.

Reaction Rates

Observed Reaction Rate

The rate for any reaction can be measured as either the rate of disappearance of a reactant or the rate of appearance of a product. Because the ratio of a reactant to a product is not always one to one, we need a way to account for stoichiometry when studying reaction rates. As a general rule, Equation 9.1 describes the rate of reactant consumption relative to the rate of product formation for a system with no stoichiometric difference between products and reactants.

$$\frac{\Delta[\text{Products}]}{\Delta t} = -\frac{\Delta[\text{Reactants}]}{\Delta t} \qquad (9.1)$$

Given that products form as reactants are consumed, there is a negative sign in the equality shown in Equation 9.1, which is useful for determining the rate of formation of a product when the rate of consumption of a reactant is known.

Example 9.1

Given that $S_2O_3^{2-}(aq)$ in a 0.50-liter flask is consumed at the rate of 0.0080 moles per second, what is the formation rate of $S_4O_6^{2-}(aq)$?

$$2\,S_2O_3^{2-}(aq) + I_2(aq) \longrightarrow S_4O_6^{2-}(aq) + 2\,I^-(aq)$$

A. 0.0080 $\frac{M}{s}$

B. 0.0160 $\frac{M}{s}$

C. 0.0320 $\frac{M}{s}$

D. 0.0160 $\frac{s}{M}$

Solution

The product ($S_4O_6^{2-}$) appears at half the rate at which the reactant ($S_2O_3^{2-}$) disappears, because the stoichiometric relationship between the two species is 1 : 2. It is given that $S_2O_3^{2-}$ disappears at a rate of 0.008 moles/0.5 liters per second, which equals 0.0160 molar per second. This means that $S_4O_6^{2-}$ appears at a rate of 0.0080 molar per second, making choice **A** a terrific and correct choice. Choice D should have been eliminated immediately, because it has incorrect units.

Example 9.2

$O_2(g)$ appears as a reaction product at the rate of 18 torr per second. What is the rate of appearance for $SO_2(g)$ in the following reaction?

$$2\,SO_3(g) \longrightarrow 2\,SO_2(g) + O_2(g)$$

A. +36 torr·s^{-1}

B. +18 torr·s^{-1}

C. +9 torr·s^{-1}

D. -18 torr·s^{-1}

Solution

The SO_2 product appears at twice the rate at which the O_2 product appears due to the 2 : 1 stoichiometric relationship between the two products (SO_2 and O_2). This means that the SO_2 product appears at a rate of 2×18 torr·s^{-1} = 36 torr·s^{-1}. This makes choice **A** the correct answer.

The rate of a reaction is determined by the *rate-determining step* (the slowest step in the reaction mechanism). This is because the slowest step in a reaction determines the observed rate for the overall reaction. The rate is dependent only upon the concentration of the reactants involved in the rate-determining step. However, we can observe the rate from any of the reactants or products, even those that are not involved in the rate-determining step. In addition to knowing numerical relationships between formation rates and consumption rates, it is also important to be able to interpret graphical representations of reaction components. Drawn in Figure 9-1 below are two graphs, each depicting the concentration of a species as a function of time for a generic, multi-step catalyzed reaction. The shape of the graph depends on the reaction order and the rate-determining step of the mechanism, so the graphs drawn are not universal.

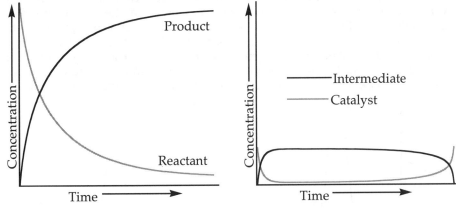

Figure 9-1

Because the curves in the graph on the left get flatter with time, the rate must be decreasing as the reaction proceeds. Products are formed during the reaction, so the product concentration starts at zero, builds rapidly at first, and then slowly levels off to a steady concentration (once the reaction reaches equilibrium). Reactants are consumed during the reaction, so the reactant concentration starts high, drops rapidly at first, and then slowly levels off to a steady concentration (once the reaction reaches equilibrium).

Catalysts present in the beginning of the reaction align to be part of the transition state during the reaction, combine with a reactant to form an intermediate, and then are regenerated at the end of a reaction. This means a catalyst starts with some concentration, drops rapidly at first, stays close to zero for most of the reaction, and then slowly increases back to its original concentration (once the reaction reaches equilibrium). Intermediates are not present in the beginning of the reaction. They are in their highest concentration during the reaction and then are in diminished quantity at the end of a reaction. This means an intermediate starts with zero concentration, increases rapidly at first, stays at a steady concentration for most of the reaction, and then slowly decreases back to zero concentration (once the reaction reaches equilibrium). When the intermediate concentration remains constant, it is known as a *steady state*. The graphs in Figure 9-1 reflect all of these conditions.

These graphs are also seen in biochemistry, where the reactant is referred to as a *substrate*, the catalyst is an *enzyme*, and the intermediate is the *enzyme-substrate complex*. Free enzyme is regenerated as the reaction reaches its endpoint and the enzyme-substrate complex eventually disappears. Other graphs from biochemistry kinetics that you may recognize include the rate of a reaction as a function of concentration and rate of reaction as a function of time in Figure 9-7.

Experimental Study of Reaction Rate

Rates are observed empirically in laboratory studies. One technique used in the lab to determine the rate of a reaction involves observing product formation or reactant consumption via ultraviolet-visible (UV-visible) spectroscopy. In cases where there is no UV-visible peak to observe, rates can be obtained using a second technique. Aliquots can be collected at uniform intervals and analyzed using gas chromatography. This requires removing some of the reaction mixture while the reaction is still proceeding, but the amount is generally so small that it has a negligible effect on the rate of the reaction. A bigger problem is that the reaction may continue to react in the syringe or pipette after it has been removed from the original flask.

To avoid this problem, the sample of solution is quenched upon removal (to prevent further reaction). Once the samples are quenched, they are analyzed by a quantitative technique, such as gas chromatography (GC) or nuclear magnetic resonance (NMR). If the concentration is analyzed at uniform intervals, it is possible to plot the data and fit a curve to the points. The graphs shown in Figure 9-2 represent data obtained from gas chromatography done on selected aliquots. The peaks can be integrated to quantify the compounds in the mixture.

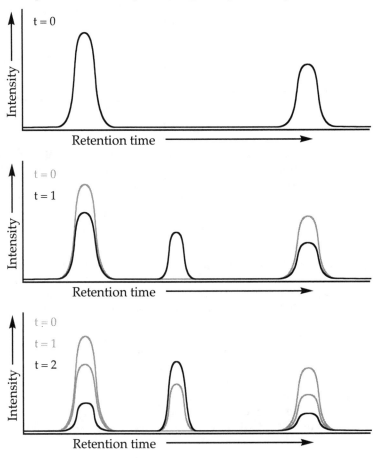

Figure 9-2

The first and last peaks (of the three) in Figure 9-2 represent reactants, because they decrease with time. The middle peak represents a product, because it grows with time. The retention time is the time it takes the sample to travel through the column. It is not important in this particular example.

UV-visible spectroscopy can be done *in vitro*, so timing and quenching are not a problem. When carrying out a reaction in a cuvette, the reaction can be placed into an UV-visible light spectrophotometer. It is best to pulse the sample with light, rather than subject the sample to continual bombardment, because the light from the detector beam adds energy to the system. An increase in the energy results in an increase in reaction rate and consequently inaccurate data. Figure 9-3 shows absorbance as a function of wavelength at different time intervals during a reaction, using a UV-visible spectrometer to collect data.

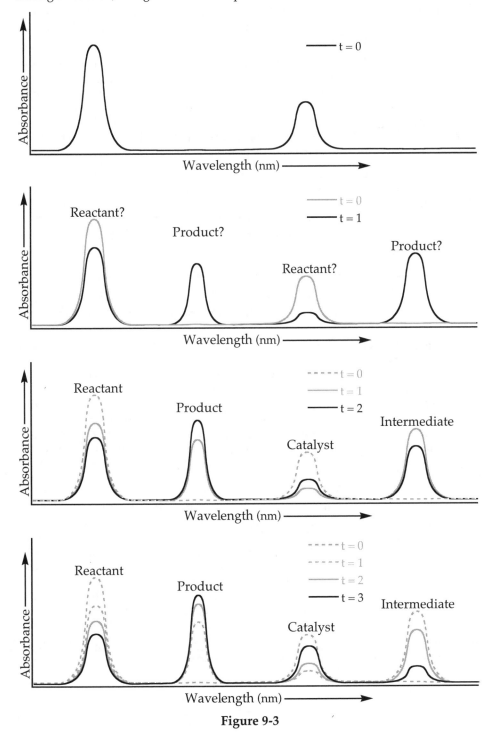

Figure 9-3

The change in height of each curve follows a pattern similar to the one in the intensity graphs in Figure 9-2. In UV-visible spectroscopy, peaks are analyzed for height, rather than area. The peaks from the UV-visible spectrometer are measured in absorbance and can be mathematically converted in concentration using Beer's law, Equation 9.2 (also listed as Equation 1.3):

$$\text{Absorbance} = \varepsilon[C]l, \tag{9.2}$$

where ε is the molar absorbtivity constant (also known as the extinction coefficient), $[C]$ is the concentration of the species, and l is the length of pathway in decimeters through which light travels through the cuvette.

It is impossible to identify each peak in Figure 9-3 until $t = 2$, which is why the peaks are labeled with question marks in the $t = 1$ entry. The biggest change in absorbance is observed between $t = 0$ and $t = 1$, and the magnitude of the change in absorbance decreases during each subsequent interval. This means that the reaction rate was fastest during the initial period, but that it slowed down as the reaction proceeded. This is typical for reactions that are not zero-order. Looking at absorbance as a function of time leads to the graphs seen in Figure 9-1.

The best peak to monitor is the peak that shows the greatest change in height (this reduces the effects of any errors). The apex of the peak should be monitored rather than the area under the curve. In measuring the height, it is assumed that the peaks are all symmetrical. In UV-visible spectroscopy, the wavelength at which the apex of the peak occurs is referred to as λ_{max} (the wavelength of maximum absorbance).

Example 9.3
Which of the following methods is the BEST way to study the rate of a chemical reaction?

A. Taking samples at regular intervals and immediately placing them into a gas chromatographer
B. Taking samples at regular intervals, immediately quenching each one, and then placing them into a gas chromatographer
C. Carrying out the reaction in a cuvette exposed to photons that continually irradiate the sample, and then analyzing the transmitted light for intensity
D. Carrying out the reaction in a cuvette exposed to photons that periodically irradiate the sample, and then analyzing the transmitted light for intensity

Solution
As mentioned in the text, it is best to analyze the sample *in vitro*, thereby avoiding problems associated with transfer. This permits an accurate recording of the time of reaction. Even with expeditious quenching of a sampling, the timing is not perfect. This eliminates choices A and B. When analyzing a sample by irradiation, care should be taken not to energize the solution more than is necessary. By continually irradiating the sample, energy is being added to the system, so it does not behave as it normally would. Reaction rates are going to be higher, due to the input of energy. From an energetics perspective, the ideal scenario is periodically to irradiate the sample at the lowest possible frequency (at the λ_{max} for the species with the lowest energy absorbance), so that minimal energy is added to the system. This is not always possible, as is the case when the peak intensity is low. The best answer is choice **D**.

Reaction Order

The order of a reaction is ascertained from the number of reagents involved in the rate-determining step. There are three fundamental reaction orders to consider: zero, first, and second. A zero-order reaction proceeds at a constant rate, independent of reactant concentration. The rate law for a zero-order reaction is rate = k. A typical case where zero-order kinetics is observed is during a catalyzed reaction, where the reaction proceeds at the turnover rate of the catalyst. Even with the addition of more reactant, the reaction rate cannot change, because the catalyst has a finite number of reactive sites. A first-order reaction depends only on one reactant (like the S_N1 reaction). The rate law for a first-order reaction is rate = k[R]. This means that the rate changes linearly as the concentration of the reactant R is changed. A second-order reaction depends on either on two different reactants (like the S_N2 reaction) or two of the same reactant. The rate law for a second-order reaction is either rate = $k[R_1][R_2]$ or rate = $k[R]^2$. In the second case, the rate changes exponentially as the concentration of the reactant R is changed.

The reaction order with respect to a specific reactant can be masked, however. For instance, in a second-order reaction, if one of the rate-influencing reactants is in significantly higher concentration than the other rate-influencing reactant, then reaction appears to be first-order, dependent on the reactant in lowest concentration. By saturating a solution with all of the reactants except for one that is involved in the rate-determining step, the reaction can become *pseudo first-order*. Something similar to this is seen in enzyme kinetics, when substrate concentration is larger than enzyme concentration. The enzyme is saturated, so the reaction obeys zero-order kinetics relative to the substrate. Additional substrate does not increase the reaction rate. The rate remains constant with the addition of substrate. The rate laws and half-life equations for three different reaction orders are listed in Table 9.1 below.

	Zero-order	First-order	Second-order
Rate law:	rate = k	rate = k[A]	rate = $k[A]^2$
Half-life:	$t_{\frac{1}{2}} = \dfrac{[A]_o}{2k}$	$t_{\frac{1}{2}} = \dfrac{\ln 2}{k} = \dfrac{0.693}{k}$	$t_{\frac{1}{2}} = \dfrac{1}{k[A]_o}$
Observation:	**Constant rate** Half-life ↓ as time ↑	Rate ↓ as time ↑ **Half-life constant**	Rate ↓ as time ↑ Half-life ↓ as time ↓

Table 9.1

Example 9.4
What is the reaction order for the following one-step reaction?

$$2\,NO_2(g) \longrightarrow 2\,NO(g) + O_2(g)$$

A. Zero-order
B. First-order
C. Second-order
D. Pseudo zero-order

Solution
Because the reaction is a one-step reaction, the rate-determining step (and the only step) involves two molecules of nitrogen dioxide colliding. The reaction depends on two reactants, making it a second-order reaction. Choice **C** is the best answer.

Example 9.5

The half-life is independent of the concentration of reactant for what order of reaction?

A. Zero-order
B. First-order
C. Second-order
D. The half-life is independent of the concentration for all reactions.

Solution

Referring to Table 9.1, we see that only with a first-order reaction is the half-life constant. This means that choice **B** is correct. It is important to be able to see new information and process it in a simple manner. Each reaction order has its unique features. For zero-order reactions, the rate is constant, so it takes less time for each subsequent half-life, because the quantity for the half-life decreases over time. For first-order reactions, the half-life is constant, which is why you often hear the phrase "half-life for a first-order decay process." Second-order reactions are known for their rapid reaction rate at first, but a drastic decrease in rate after just a short time.

Example 9.6

Given the following table equating reaction time with concentration of reactant, what is the order of reaction?

$[A_0]$	Time
1.000 M	0 sec
0.500 M	15 sec
0.250 M	45 sec
0.125 M	105 sec

A. Zero-order
B. First-order
C. Second-order
D. Third-order

Solution

The first half-life, from 1.000 M to 0.500 M, takes 15 seconds. The second half-life, from 0.500 M to 0.250 M, takes 30 seconds. The third half-life, from 0.250 M to 0.125 M, takes 60 seconds. In this case, as the concentration of reactant decreases, the value of the half-life is increasing. This means that the concentration is inversely proportional to the half-life. This is true for a second-order reaction, so choice **C** is the best answer.

In terms of mechanisms, reactions can realistically be only first-order or second-order. Other observed orders are phenomena associated with catalysts and relative concentrations. First-order reactions entail one molecule breaking apart, and are referred to as *dissociative reactions*. A dissociative reaction involves decomposition in its rate-determining step. Second-order reactions entail two molecules colliding, and are referred to as *associative reactions*. An associative reaction involves the combining of two molecules (via collision) in its rate-determining step.

Rate Constant and Rate Law

The rate constant is the term by which the concentrations of reactants in the rate-determining steps are multiplied to get the rate law. The rate law defines the rate of the reaction. Rate constants and rate laws are empirical values, obtained by observing the initial rate of a reaction under several different conditions. *Rate constants have varying and odd units!* The rate of a reaction is affected by several factors such as temperature (the reaction rate increases with increasing temperature), activation energy (the reaction rate decreases with increasing activation energy), catalysts, solvent (solvents affect the transition state stability), collision frequency, collision orientation, and the concentration of the reactants in the rate-determining step. The rate constant must account for all of these factors, except concentration of the reactants. Equation 9.3 is used to determine the rate constant.

$$k = A\, e^{-E_{act}/RT} \qquad\qquad (9.3)$$

A is the Arrhenius constant; it takes into account collision orientation and frequency. Not all collisions between reactants result in reactions. The activation energy (E_{act}) is the energy required to get through the transition state. R is the energy constant given in units of energy per mole·temperature. It is either 8.314 joules per mole·kelvins or 1.987 calories per mole·kelvins.

Example 9.7

If the rate law for the following reaction is found to be: rate $= k\, \sqrt{[Cl_2]}\, [HCCl_3]$, what are the units for rate constant (k)?

$$Cl_2(g) + CHCl_3(g) \longrightarrow HCl(g) + CCl_4(g)$$

A. $\dfrac{M^{3/2}}{s}$

B. $\dfrac{\sqrt{M}}{s}$

C. $\dfrac{1}{\sqrt{M}\cdot s}$

D. $\dfrac{1}{M^{3/2}\cdot s}$

Solution

The rate of the reaction has units of molar per second. The following equation can be used to solve for units:

Rate $= k\, \sqrt{[Cl_2]}\, [HCCl_3]$ Units: $\dfrac{M}{s} = k\sqrt{M}\,(M) = k\sqrt{M^3}$

Solving for the units of the rate constant yields: $k = \dfrac{M}{\sqrt{M^3}\cdot s} = \dfrac{1}{\sqrt{M}\cdot s}$.

It may seem counterintuitive for the rate of a reaction to depend on the square root of a concentration, but because the rate-determining step may be the second or third step of a multiple-step reaction, the rate law for the reaction may involve the concentration of intermediates. If the equation using the intermediates is manipulated in such a way that reactant concentrations replace intermediate concentrations, there are sometimes square root factors involved. The point here is that the square root is merely an artifact of the mathematical calculations, and it shouldn't upset you. The best answer is choice **C**.

Experimental Study of Reaction Order

Reaction order can be determined experimentally in one of two ways. The first method involves monitoring the concentration of a reactant over time, and then comparing the decay rate to standard reaction order data. This works well for simple cases. Zero-order reactions show a uniform decay rate for reactants, first-order reactions show a gradually diminishing decay rate for reactants, and second-order reactions show a rapidly diminishing decay rate in reactants at first that levels off to minimal decay over time. The second method determines the reaction order more precisely. In that method, the initial rate is observed as initial concentrations of reactants are systematically varied. Many rate law present data this way and ask you to obtain the order of the reaction. If the reaction rate remains constant when a reactant concentration is varied, then reaction rate does not depend on that reactant. Consider the data in Table 9.2 for a hypothetical reaction between one mole of A and one mole of B.

Trial	Initial Rate	[A]	[B]
I	3.07×10^{-3} M·s^{-1}	0.10 M	0.10 M
II	6.11×10^{-3} M·s^{-1}	0.20 M	0.10 M
III	1.23×10^{-2} M·s^{-1}	0.20 M	0.20 M

Table 9.2

To evaluate the effect of a reactant on the reaction rate, we start with the generic rate law: rate = k $[A]^a[B]^b$. Upon comparing Trial I with Trial II, we get the following results:

$$\frac{\text{Rate}_{II}}{\text{Rate}_{I}} = \frac{k\,[A]_{II}^a[B]_{II}^b}{k\,[A]_{I}^a[B]_{I}^b} \Rightarrow \frac{6.11 \times 10^{-3}\,\text{M/s}}{3.07 \times 10^{-3}\,\text{M/s}} = \frac{k\,[0.20]^a[0.10]^b}{k\,[0.10]^a[0.10]^b}$$

The ratio of the rates is approximately 2 (6.11 divided by 3.07 is roughly equal to 2) and both k and $[0.10]^b$ cancel out in the numerator and denominator. This leaves the following relationship:

$$2 = \frac{[0.20]^a}{[0.10]^a} = 2^a \therefore a = 1$$

We see that the rate doubles when [A] is doubled, so the rate depends on $[A]^1$. This means that the rate law can be modified to: rate = k $[A][B]^b$. Upon comparing Trial II with Trial III, we see that the rate doubles when [B] is doubled, so the rate depends on $[B]^1$. The rate law for the reaction is thus: rate = k[A][B]. This means that the reaction is first-order with respect to A, first-order with respect to B, and second-order overall. This technique is applicable in organic chemistry, as for example when determining the mechanism for a nucleophilic substitution reaction. The data in Table 9.3 describes the kinetics observed for a generic nucleophilic substitution reaction.

Trial	Initial Rate	[Nucleophile]	[Electrophile]
I	7.82×10^{-4} M·s^{-1}	0.10 M	0.10 M
II	1.17×10^{-3} M·s^{-1}	0.10 M	0.15 M
III	1.54×10^{-3} M·s^{-1}	0.20 M	0.20 M

Table 9.3

The numbers may not seem as simple as they were in the previous example, but the procedure is the same. Upon comparing Trial I with Trial II, we see that the rate increases by a factor of 1.5 when [Electrophile] increases by a factor of 1.5, so the rate depends on $[\text{Electrophile}]^1$. This is expected, because the rate of all nucleophilic substitution reactions depends on the electrophile concentration, whether the reaction proceeds by an S_N1-mechanism or an S_N2-mechanism. Upon comparing Trial I with Trial III, we see that the rate doubles when both [Electrophile] and [Nucleophile] are doubled. We know that there exists a relationship between reaction rate and [Electrophile] that is directly proportional, so the doubling of the reaction rate when comparing Trial I with Trial III can be attributed to the doubling of [Electrophile]. The reaction rate only doubles, so it does not depend on [Nucleophile]. The rate law is: rate = k[Electrophile], so the reaction proceeds by an S_N1-mechanism.

For Examples 9.8 through 9.12, please refer to Table 9.4 below.

Trial	Initial Rate	[X]	[Y]
I	3.57×10^{-4} M·s^{-1}	0.10 M	0.10 M
II	1.43×10^{-3} M·s^{-1}	0.10 M	0.20 M
III	3.59×10^{-4} M·s^{-1}	0.20 M	0.10 M
IV	1.44×10^{-3} M·s^{-1}	0.20 M	0.20 M

Table 9.4

Example 9.8
What is the reaction order with respect to Reactant X?

A. Zero-order
B. First-order
C. Second-order
D. Third-order

Solution
The order with respect to Reactant X is found by observing the reaction rate as [X] changes while [Y] is held constant. Comparing Trial I with Trial III (or Trial II with Trial IV) does this. Because the reaction rate doesn't change when [X] doubled and [Y] is held constant, it shows no dependence on the concentration of X. The order with respect to Reactant X is the power to which the concentration is raised, which in this case is zero. With respect to Reactant X, the reaction is zero-order. The best answer is choice **A**.

Example 9.9
Which of the following changes would MOST increase the reaction rate?

A. Doubling [X] and decreasing the temperature by 10°C
B. Doubling [X] and increasing the temperature by 10°C
C. Doubling [Y] and decreasing the temperature by 10°C
D. Doubling [Y] and increasing the temperature by 10°C

Solution
The rate does not depend on Reactant X. This eliminates choices A and B. Increasing the temperature provides more energy to the system, so that more molecules can overcome the activation barrier. This means that the reaction rate increases as temperature increases. The best answer is choice **D**.

Example 9.10
What is the overall reaction order?

A. Zero-order
B. First-order
C. Second-order
D. Third-order

Solution
The reaction rate does not depend on Reactant X, given that changes in [X] do not change the reaction rate. The order with respect to Reactant Y is found by comparing Trial I with Trial II (or Trial III with Trial IV). The rate quadruples when [Y] is doubled, so the rate depends on $[Y]^2$. The rate of the reaction depends on two moles of Y, so the reaction is second-order with respect to Y. The overall reaction depends on two molecules of Y and no moles of X, so overall, the reaction is second-order. The best answer is choice **C**.

The reaction is second-order, which means that the rate-determining step involves two molecules of Y coming together. This same question can be asked in a more convoluted manner, by asking about the mechanism and the components in the rate-determining step. Example 9.11 is seemingly different from Example 9.10, although both questions are asking about the order of the reaction and the rate law.

Example 9.11
Which of the following statements accurately describes the reaction mechanism?

A. The reaction mechanism is associative, and the rate-determining step involves one mole of Y.
B. The reaction mechanism is associative, and the rate-determining step involves two moles of Y.
C. The reaction mechanism is dissociative, and the rate-determining step involves one mole of Y.
D. The reaction mechanism is dissociative, and the rate-determining step involves two moles of Y.

Solution
The order with respect to Reactant Y is found by comparing Trial I with Trial II (or Trial III with Trial IV). The rate quadruples when [Y] is doubled and [X] is held constant, so the rate depends on $[Y]^2$. The rate law for the reaction is thus: rate = $k[Y]^2$. This means that the rate-determining step involves two moles of Y, and the reaction is second-order. Second-order reactions are associative, so the best answer is choice **B**. Although mechanisms can never be proven, from the data you can hypothesize that the reaction proceeds by a multi-step mechanism. For example, if the reaction is X + Y → P, then the mechanism must have more than one step. If the reaction is two-step, then the mechanism is probably:

$$\text{First step: } Y + Y \rightarrow Y_2 \qquad \text{rate-determining step (slowest step)}$$

$$\text{Second step: } Y_2 + X \rightarrow Y + P$$

Example 9.12

If the reaction of X with Y is monitored by visible spectroscopy, then which of the following graphs is expected for the absorbance of light by Reactant X as a function of time? The graphs are labeled with t_1, t_2, and t_3, which represent the elapsed time for the reaction, where $t_3 > t_2 > t_1$.

A.

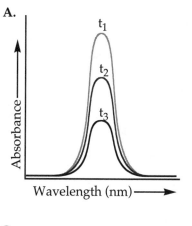

B.

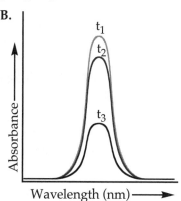

C.

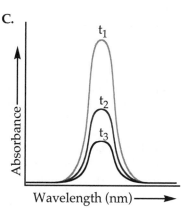

D.

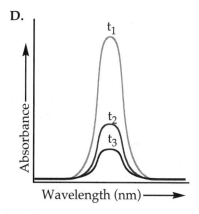

Solution

Whether we monitor Reactant X or Reactant Y, the reaction obeys second-order kinetics. Just because reactant X is not in the rate-determining step does not mean it is unreactive. It is consumed at the same rate as Reactant Y, if the two species react in a one-to-one stoichiometric fashion. For a second-order reaction, consumption of reactants (and product formation) is most rapid initially, because as the reaction proceeds, the reactant concentration diminishes, causing the rate to decrease. The greatest change in concentration should be observed between times t_1 and t_2. This eliminates choice A (which describes zero-order behavior) and choice B, which is erratic behavior. The change between times t_2 and t_3 should be substantially less than the change between times t_1 and t_2, so choice **D** is more indicative of second-order kinetics. Choice C describes first-order kinetics. This was a very tough question that required experience with rate data.

Graphs contain a great deal of information, and your ability to extract information from graphs can be of great benefit on the MCAT. Chemical kinetics entails several graphs, from which trends in reactivity can be extrapolated. Example 9.12 shows this. The information in the answer choices for Example 9.12 can be rewritten in a more traditional form of concentration as a function of time. This results in a graph typically seen in chemical kinetics.

Typical Rate Data and Graphs

Typical graphs in chemical kinetics involve reactant concentration as a function of time during the course of a chemical reaction. The rate data for zero-order, first-order, and second-order reactions have unique characteristics, because the concentration of reactant changes in a distinct way over the course of each kind of reaction, and the reactant concentration affects the rate differently for each reaction order.

Zero-order decay is recognized when the concentration of the reactants decreases in uniform increments against uniform time increments. Drawn in Figure 9-4 below are typical data in a typical graphic display for a zero-order reaction:

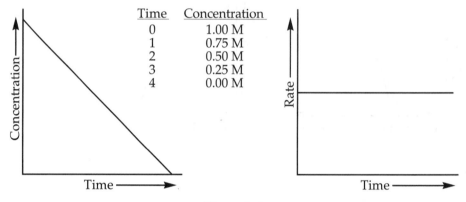

Time	Concentration
0	1.00 M
1	0.75 M
2	0.50 M
3	0.25 M
4	0.00 M

Figure 9-4

In Figure 9-4, the data in the table match the graph on the left. The concentration decreases by the same amount, 0.25 M, during each time interval. This means that the reaction rate is constant over time, as seen in the graph on the right.

First-order decay is recognized when the concentration of the reactants decreases in a logarithmic fashion against uniform time increments. It may be easier to recognize a first-order reaction by the constant half-life. Drawn in Figure 9-5 below are typical data in a typical graphic display for a first-order reaction:

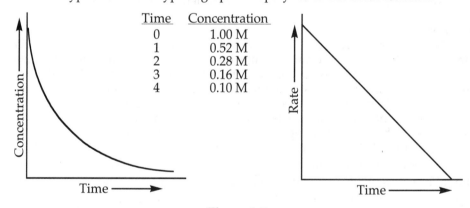

Time	Concentration
0	1.00 M
1	0.52 M
2	0.28 M
3	0.16 M
4	0.10 M

Figure 9-5

In Figure 9-5, the data in the table match the graph on the left. The concentration decreases by a gradually smaller amount, 0.48 M, then 0.24 M, then 0.12 M, during each time interval. When the time decreases in uniform increments, the concentration changes by half as much each time. This means that the reaction rate is decreasing with time, as seen in the graph on the right.

Second-order decay is recognized by the drastic drop in concentration initially followed by smaller decreases in concentration against uniform time increments. When the time decreases in uniform increments, the concentration changes by substantially decreasing amounts each time. It may be easier to recognize a second-order reaction by an increasing half-life. Drawn in Figure 9-6 below are typical data in a typical graphic display for a second-order reaction:

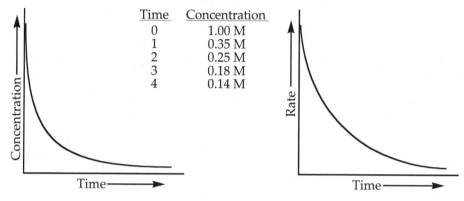

Time	Concentration
0	1.00 M
1	0.35 M
2	0.25 M
3	0.18 M
4	0.14 M

Figure 9-6

In Figure 9-6, the data in the table match the graph on the left. The concentration decreases significantly in the first interval, but the magnitude of the decrease is substantially smaller during each subsequent interval, 0.65 M, then 0.10 M, then 0.07 M. When the time decreases in uniform increments, the concentration changes by a much smaller amount much each time. This means that the reaction rate is decreasing exponentially with time, as seen in the graph on the right.

A kinetics graph from biochemistry that should look familiar involves velocity (the rate of a catalyzed reaction) as a function of substrate concentration for an enzymatic process. Because there is a finite amount of enzyme, and each enzyme has a finite number of active sites, there is a finite number of reactants that may be reacting at any given time. At high reactant concentrations, the reaction rate appears to be constant (it is equal to a value that depends on concentration of enzyme, and the turnover rate of the enzyme.) At lower reactant concentrations, the rate depends on the reactant, because the enzyme is not saturated. Figure 9-7 shows a typical graph from Michaelis-Menten enzyme kinetics:

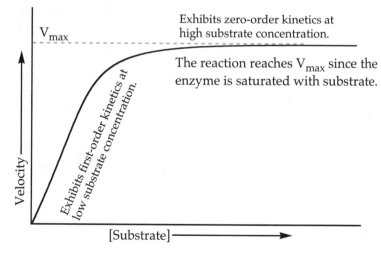

Figure 9-7

Half-Life

Half-life is defined as the period of time it takes for the concentration of a reactant to decrease to a value that is one-half of its original value. This means that after one half-life, only fifty percent of the initial value remains. The graphs in Figures 9-8, 9-9, and 9-10 show half-life dependence on concentration.

Zero-order decay involves a constant rate of decay, so the time required to carry out the first half-life (from 100% to 50%) is double that of the time required to carry out the second half-life (from 50% to 25%). As seen in Table 9.1, the half-life diminishes with concentration. Figure 9-8 presents data that show the relationship of half-life to reactant concentration for a zero-order reaction:

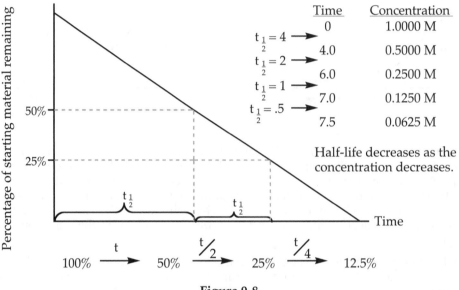

Figure 9-8

First-order decay involves a logarithmically decreasing rate of decay, but the time required to carry out the first half-life (from 100% to 50%) is equal to that of the time required to carry out the second half-life (from 50% to 25%). As seen in Example 9.5, the half-life is constant. Figure 9-9 presents data that show the relationship of half-life to reactant concentration for a first-order reaction:

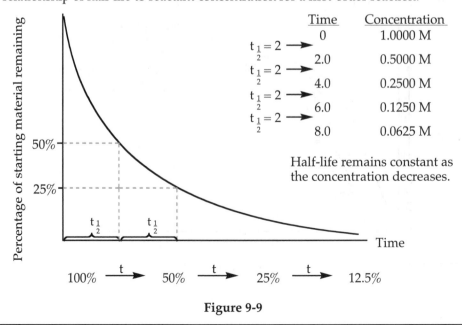

Figure 9-9

Second-order decay involves a rapidly decreasing rate of decay, so the time required to carry out the first half-life (from 100% to 50%) is half that of the time required to carry out the second half-life (from 50% to 25%). As seen in Example 9.6, the half-life increases as the reactant concentration decreases. Figure 9-10 presents data that show the relationship of half-life to reactant concentration for a second-order reaction:

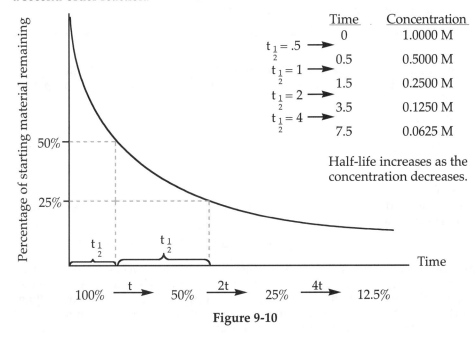

Figure 9-10

It is important that you be able to interpret data from both a graph and a table. A useful skill on the MCAT is the ability to recognize trends quickly when scanning numerical data. It is also important to recognize the effect of concentration on the half-life of a reaction. This information can be used to determine the reaction order, support a proposed reaction mechanism, or eliminate a possible reaction mechanism.

Because half-life is constant for first-order processes, most half-life questions on the MCAT involve decay (a first-order reaction). Equation 9.4 is used to calculate the concentration of a species that undergoes first-order decay at any time:

$$C_t = C_o e^{-kt} \qquad (9.4)$$

where C_t is the concentration at time t, C_o is the initial concentration, t is time, and k is the rate constant. Equation 9.4 can be manipulated to derive the half-life for a first-order reaction. The half-life is calculated using Equation 9.5.

$$C_t = C_o e^{-kt}$$

$$\frac{C_t}{C_o} = e^{-kt} \text{ and at } t = t_{1/2}, \frac{C_t}{C_o} = \frac{1}{2} \therefore \frac{1}{2} = e^{-kt_{1/2}} \Rightarrow 2 = e^{kt_{1/2}}$$

Taking the natural log of both sides yields: $\ln 2 = kt_{1/2} \therefore t_{1/2} = \dfrac{\ln 2}{k} = \dfrac{0.693}{k}$

Equation 9.5 relates the rate constant, k, and the half-life for a first-order decay process.

$$t_{1/2} = \frac{0.693}{k} \qquad (9.5)$$

Most half-life questions deal with first-order processes. Rather than using the equations to calculate values, it is often easier to cut a concentration in half several times, until the period of time is completed. For instance, after three half-lives, the amount of a material decreases from 100% to 50%, from 50% to 25%, and finally from 25% to 12.5%. This technique is far easier than doing long calculations using Equations 9.4 and 9.5. Examples 9.13 and 9.14 demonstrate how to cut the concentration in half sequentially.

Example 9.13
The concentration of some floral scent is 100 ppm. If the half-life for its decomposition is 4 minutes, how much time elapses before there is only 1 ppm in the air?

A. 20.0 minutes
B. 26.6 minutes
C. 42.2 minutes
D. 53.2 minutes

Solution
A quick method to arrive at the solution involves calculating successive half-lives. The decrease taken one-half life at a time is:

$$100 \rightarrow 50 \rightarrow 25 \rightarrow 12\tfrac{1}{2} \rightarrow 6\tfrac{1}{4} \rightarrow 3\tfrac{1}{8} \rightarrow 1\tfrac{9}{16} \rightarrow \text{less than } 1.0$$

After seven half-lives (seven arrows), the concentration reaches a value that is less than 1 ppm, so the elapsed time is just less than seven half-lives. Because the concentration after six half-lives is greater than 1 ppm, the total time is more than six-half lives. Six half-lives is 24 minutes and seven half-lives is 28 minutes, so the time is more than 24 but less than 28 minutes. The best answer is choice **B**.

Example 9.14
If a drug decomposes according to first-order kinetics, what is its concentration after one hour, if the half-life is 21 minutes?

A. 26.1% of its original concentration
B. 24.0% of its original concentration
C. 13.3% of its original concentration
D. 11.7% of its original concentration

Solution
Because the decay obeys first-order kinetics, the half-life is constant. Within one hour, given a half-life of 21 minutes, just under three half-lives will transpire. The decrease taken one half-life at a time is: 100% to 50%, then 50% to 25%, then 25% to a value slightly greater than 12.5%. The best answer is choice **C**.

$$100\% \xrightarrow{\text{21 min}} 50\% \xrightarrow{\text{21 min}} 25\% \xrightarrow[\substack{60 \text{ min}}]{\text{21 min}} \genfrac{}{}{0pt}{}{\approx 13\%}{12.5\%} \; \substack{63 \text{ min} \\ \text{total}}$$

Reaction Mechanisms

General Mechanism Types

A reaction mechanism is the stepwise pathway that a reaction is believed to take, from reactant to product and it is proposed based on energetic data, kinetic data, and structural differences between reactants and products (bonds and chirality in particular). Mechanisms account for the steps in the reactant-to-product transformation. There are one-step reactions that are said to have *concerted mechanisms*. In many cases, however, the reaction mechanism involves more than one step. To determine the mechanism for a multi-step reaction, we start by determining the components in the rate-determining step. If we know the components that affect the rate, we know the components in the slowest step of the reaction.

If the reaction is first-order, then we know that the slowest step involves one molecule breaking apart. If the reaction is second-order, then we know that the slowest step involves two molecules coming together to form a bond. When considering kinetic data to support a mechanism, the rate information applies only to the rate-determining step of the reaction. Figure 9-11 shows graphs for rate as a function of reactant concentration for some simple cases:

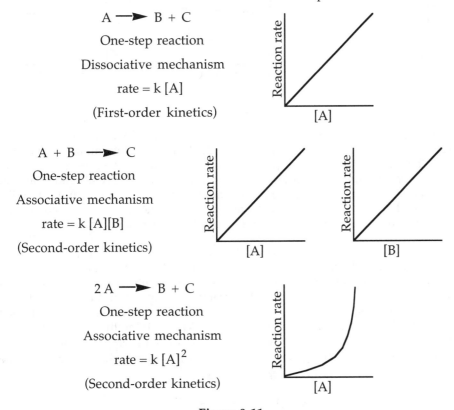

$$A \longrightarrow B + C$$

One-step reaction

Dissociative mechanism

rate = k [A]

(First-order kinetics)

$$A + B \longrightarrow C$$

One-step reaction

Associative mechanism

rate = k [A][B]

(Second-order kinetics)

$$2A \longrightarrow B + C$$

One-step reaction

Associative mechanism

rate = k $[A]^2$

(Second-order kinetics)

Figure 9-11

The first reaction in Figure 9-11 involves the dissociation of the reactant in its rate-determining step (its one and only step). The second reaction in Figure 9-11 involves the association of two different reactants in its rate-determining step. The reaction is first-order with respect to each reactant, but second-order overall. The third reaction in Figure 9-11 involves dimerization (the association of two identical reactants) in its rate-determining step. The reaction is second-order with respect to the reactant, which results in the rate as a function of reactant concentration being exponential.

Not all reactions are concerted. Reactants can form intermediates (or activated complexes), which then go on to form products. There may be individual steps in the mechanism that are independent events in the overall process. Mechanisms can be disproved or supported, but never proven. For this reason, mechanisms are best thought of as educated guesses at the reaction pathway. Figure 9-12 shows the graph for rate as a function of reactant concentration for a multi-step reaction:

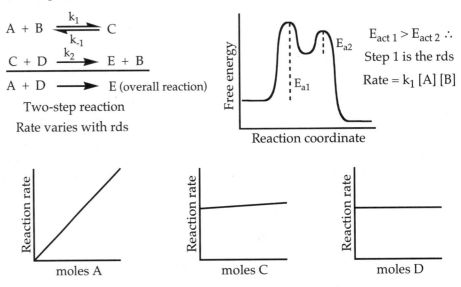

$$A + B \underset{k_{-1}}{\overset{k_1}{\rightleftharpoons}} C$$

$$\underline{C + D \xrightarrow{k_2} E + B}$$

$$A + D \longrightarrow E \text{ (overall reaction)}$$

Two-step reaction

Rate varies with rds

$E_{act\,1} > E_{act\,2}$ ∴

Step 1 is the rds

$Rate = k_1\,[A]\,[B]$

Figure 9-12

The reaction in Figure 9-12 involves the association of two reactants in both mechanistic steps. Either step could potentially be rate-determining. The step with the higher activation energy is the slower, and thus rate-determining, step. It is important that you understand the graphs to the extent that you can interpret data from them. Free energy diagrams are a common way to describe the energetics of the reaction mechanism. The energetics are used as the evidence to propose that the first step in the reaction is rate-determining.

Kinetic data are the basis for most mechanistic proposals. For instance, consider Reaction 9.1. We believe Reaction 9.1 is a one-step reaction, because the rate-determining step (and only step) involves the two nitrogen dioxide reactants colliding to form a bond. Because the reaction shows second-order kinetics, a concerted, bimolecular mechanism is proposed as the best explanation of such behavior. The rate constant for the reaction is k_1, implying that it is the forward rate constant of the first step. The subscript describes the step and the direction. For instance, if we were given a k_{-3}, we could assume that it was the rate constant for the back-reaction of the third step.

$$2\,NO_2(g) \xrightarrow{k_1} N_2O_4(g)$$

Reaction 9.1

According to the rate law, the reaction rate is equal to $k_1[NO_2]^2$ for Reaction 9.1. Observing the rate of the reaction as a function of reactant concentration can support this. This was seen in Example 9.12. Examples 9.15 and 9.16 are more specific cases where kinetic data can be used to support a proposed mechanism.

Example 9.15

The mechanism for the reaction that follows is believed to be two consecutive bimolecular reactions.

Reaction: $NO_2(g) + CO(g) \longrightarrow NO(g) + CO_2(g)$

Mechanism: $NO_2(g) + NO_2(g) \longrightarrow NO(g) + NO_3(g)$ (slow)

                   $NO_3(g) + CO(g) \longrightarrow NO_2(g) + CO_2(g)$ (fast

What is the rate law for this reaction, assuming that this reaction mechanism is correct?

A. $k(P_{NO_2})(P_{CO})$

B. $k(P_{NO_2})^2(P_{CO})$

C. $k(P_{NO_2})^2$

D. $k(P_{NO_2})$

Solution

The rate depends on the first step, because it is the slowest step in the reaction mechanism (rate-determining step). The first step of the mechanism involves two NO_2 molecules colliding together to form NO_3 and NO. The rate depends on the reactants in the rate-determining step. The rate therefore depends on two molecules of NO_2 gas. Because of this, CO (carbon monoxide) has no effect on the rate of this reaction. The addition of CO does not increase the rate of the reaction according to the mechanism provided. Choice **C** is the best answer. Observations about the rate of a reaction can be used to disprove mechanisms from an analytical standpoint. If one were to find that increasing the partial pressure of CO in the reaction mixture resulted in an increase in the rate of the reaction, then the mechanism as proposed would be invalid. Mechanisms should be able to predict the reactivity patterns of reactions before the reaction begins.

Example 9.16

For the reaction in Example 9.15, what is the expected rate law if the reaction were to occur in one step?

A. $k(P_{NO_2})(P_{CO})$

B. $k(P_{NO_2})^2(P_{CO})$

C. $k(P_{NO_2})^2$

D. $k(P_{NO_2})$

Solution

Had the reaction taken place in one step, it would have depended on the two reactants colliding with one another in the transition state. This means that the rate law of the reaction would be $k(P_{NO_2})(P_{CO})$, choice **A**. To confirm this rate law (and mechanism), it would be expected that increases in either of the two reactants would result in a linear increase in the rate of the reaction. Again, this observation could either support or disprove the proposed one-step reaction mechanism. On your exam, you may have to make some predictions about the rate of a reaction based on its proposed mechanism. The simple rule is that if the reactant is in the rate-determining step, then the rate of the reaction depends directly on the concentration of that reactant.

Energy Diagrams and Activation Energy

Activation energy is the threshold energy required for a reaction to transpire. It is the energy difference between the starting materials and the transition state (apex of the energy diagram). The higher the energy of the transition state (also referred to as the *activated complex*), the greater the activation energy, and thus the more slowly the reaction rate takes place. The highest activation energy of a multi-step reaction represents the rate-determining step in the overall reaction. There are two popular energy diagrams that you may recall. Figure 9-13 is the traditional graph (often found in organic chemistry textbooks) that relates the energy of the system to the pathway of the reaction. Energy must be absorbed by the system in order for it to ascend the energy diagram. The lower the position occupied by a species on an energy diagram, the more stable it is.

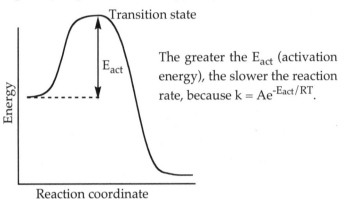

The greater the E_{act} (activation energy), the slower the reaction rate, because $k = Ae^{-E_{act}/RT}$.

Figure 9-13

Figure 9-14 is a bar graph of sorts, where the number of molecules in the system is plotted against their energy. The area under the curve represents the sum of the molecules in the system. Figure 9-14 shows that at any given time, not all molecules have the same energy within the system. These two popular graphic methods to depict activation energy are presented below:

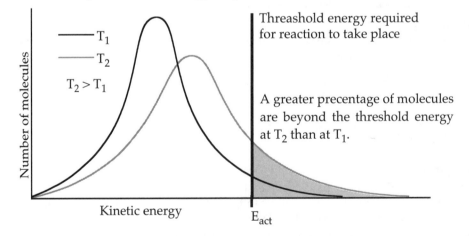

Threashold energy required for reaction to take place

A greater precentage of molecules are beyond the threshold energy at T_2 than at T_1.

Figure 9-14

At T_2, the average energy of molecules is greater than at T_1. Consequently, at T_2 more molecules have enough energy to overcome the activation barrier for the reaction. This means that more molecules react at T_2 than T_1, resulting in a faster reaction rate at higher temperatures.

Example 9.17

Using the graph below, find the value of E_{act}.

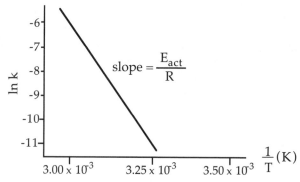

A. 1.6×10^6 J/mole
B. 1.6×10^5 J/mole
C. 1.6×10^4 J/mole
D. 1.6×10^3 J/mole

Solution

By taking natural log of the equation: $k = A\ e^{-E_{act}/RT}$, we get the following:

$$\ln k = -\frac{E_{act}}{R}\left(\frac{1}{T}\right) + \ln A$$

It looks like the equation of a line ($y = mx + b$, where m is the slope, and b is the y-intercept), so if we plot ln k as a function of T^{-1}, then the slope depends on activation energy and the y-intercept is the Arrhenius constant. By multiplying the slope of the line by - R, we get the activation energy. The slope of the line is:

$$\text{Slope} = \frac{-11 - (-6)}{3.25 \times 10^{-3} - 3.00 \times 10^{-3}} = \frac{-5}{0.25 \times 10^{-3}} = \frac{-5}{2.5 \times 10^{-4}} = \frac{-2}{10^{-4}} = -2 \times 10^4$$

Multiplying the slope by -1 and R, yields:

$$E_{act} = -(-2 \times 10^4) \times R = 2 \times 10^4 \times 8.3 = 1.6 \times 10^5, \text{ choice } \mathbf{B}.$$

Example 9.18

Which of the following does NOT always affect the rate of a reaction?

A. Changing the temperature
B. Adding a catalyst
C. Increasing the volume by adding solvent
D. Adding a reactant

Solution

The equation for rate is rate $= k$ [reactants]$_{rds}$, where rds means rate-determining step. If the reactant being added is not involved in the rate-determining step, then it does not influence the rate. This is observed in dissociative reactions (like the S_N1-reaction), where the reaction rate is determined by the dissociation of just one molecule. The best answer is choice **D**. Changing the temperature changes the rate directly. This eliminates choice A. Adding a catalyst lowers the activation energy and thus increases the reaction rate. This eliminates choice B. Increasing the volume reduces the concentrations of all reagents, including the reactants in the rate-determining step. This eliminates choice C. Increasing volume of a gas phase reaction also results in a decreased reaction rate.

Effect of Catalyst

Catalysts are added to a reaction to lower the activation energy (energy of the transition state) and consequently to increase the rate of reaction. Catalysts react with the reactants to form an activated complex of lower energy than the normal transition state for the uncatalyzed reaction. Biological catalysts are referred to as *enzymes*. An enzyme lowers the rate of a biological reaction by forming an enzyme-substrate complex. Enzymes are a little more specific than catalysts in that they also help to align the molecules into the correct orientation for reacting. Enzymes cause products to have a specific chirality. Catalysts are not consumed in the reaction. Catalysts do not make a reaction more or less favorable, because they increase the rate of the reverse reaction and the rate of the forward reaction equally.

Example 9.19
Which of the following statements is NOT true about catalysts?

A. Catalysts do not react in the reaction pathway.
B. Catalysts are not consumed in the reaction pathway.
C. Catalysts change the reaction pathway.
D. Catalysts allow the reaction to react more quickly.

Solution
The question asks for a "*NOT* true" statement. This means that you are searching for the false statement in the answer choices. Catalysts do react in the reaction pathway; otherwise, they would not lower the activation energy of a reaction. If this seems strange, think about any acid-catalyzed mechanism from organic chemistry. The acid protonates a reactant to increase its reactivity. A good example is the protonation of a carbonyl to make the OH group. Upon protonation, the carbonyl becomes more electrophilic. Once the reaction is complete, the proton comes off of the carbonyl. This makes statement **A** a false statement. To be sure about choosing **A**, remember that catalysts are regenerated at the end of a reaction, so they are not consumed in the reaction. Choice B is therefore true. Catalysts do change the reaction pathway (to one of lower energy), so choice C is true. Catalysts lower the activation energy so that reactions may proceed more quickly. This makes choice D true. The only false choice is choice **A**.

Example 9.20
In which of the following values is the concentration of a homogeneous catalyst NOT directly involved?

A. The equilibrium constant (K)
B. The rate constant (k)
C. The reaction rate
D. Both the equilibrium constant (K) and the rate constant (k).

Solution
A catalyst (homogeneous or heterogeneous) does not affect the thermodynamics of a reaction. By definition, catalysts change only the reaction rate for a given reaction. A catalyst is therefore not involved in the equilibrium constant (K). This makes choice **A** correct. A catalyst is definitely involved in the reaction rate, because it is involved in the rate constant. Choice D also contains the equilibrium constant, which makes it incorrect like choice **A**. But the MCAT asks that you to find the "best" answer, and because choice D has the rate constant in it, it is partially valid, which makes choice **A** better than choice D.

Kinetics
Passages

10 Passages

80 Questions

Suggested Kinetics Passage Schedule:

I: After reading this section and attending lecture: Passages I, III, IV, VII, & X
Grade passages immediately after completion and log your mistakes.

II: Following Task I: Passages II, V, & VI, (23 questions in 30 minutes)
Time yourself accurately, grade your answers, and review mistakes.

III: Review: Passages VIII, IX & Questions 73 - 80
Focus on reviewing the concepts. Do not worry about timing.

The BERKELEY
R·E·V·I·E·W®
Specializing in MCAT Preparation

Kinetics Study Passages

Kinetics Scoring Scale

Raw Score	MCAT Score
70 - 80	13 - 15
53 - 69	10 - 12
37 - 52	7 - 9
26 - 36	4 - 6
1 - 25	1 - 3

Passage I (Questions 1 - 7)

Reaction 1 represents a generic reaction between two reactants to form two moles of a single product.

$$A + B \longrightarrow 2\,C$$

The reaction is monitored over time using a spectrometer with a wavelength range from 200 nm to 800 nm. The three spectra in Figure 1 represent the reaction initially, the reaction after one minute, and the reaction after two minutes.

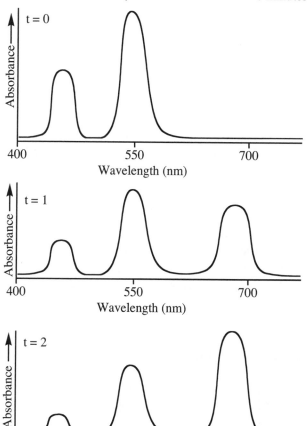

Figure 1

The absorbance for each peak can be converted into solute concentration using Equation 1:

$$Abs = \varepsilon[C]l$$

Equation 1

The term Abs refers to the absorbance of light, ε is the molar absorbtivity, [C] is the concentration in solution, and l is the path length of the cell. The peak appearing just below 700 nm is found to belong to the product, C.

1. To monitor the reaction at constant wavelength, it would be BEST to lock the setting at:

   A. 470 nm
   B. 545 nm
   C. 625 nm
   D. 695 nm

2. The peak at $\lambda_{max} = 684$ is BEST described as:

   A. a product.
   B. a reactant.
   C. a catalyst.
   D. an intermediate.

3. Which of the following statements is NOT true regarding absorbance?

   A. As the length of a cuvette increases, the absorbance increases.
   B. The concentration is directly proportional to absorbance.
   C. The absorbance always increases when the temperature increases.
   D. Molar absorbtivity constants are specific for each individual compound.

4. The rate of reaction found by monitoring the peak at 547 nm would be:

   A. $\dfrac{\Delta Abs}{\Delta t}$

   B. $-\dfrac{\Delta Abs}{\Delta t}$

   C. $\dfrac{\Delta Abs}{\Delta t \times [C]_{init}}$

   D. $-\dfrac{\Delta Abs}{\Delta t \times [C]_{init}}$

5. Which of the following statements is TRUE regarding the rate of reaction?

   A. Products appear at a constant rate throughout the reaction.
   B. Products appear at a gradually decreasing rate throughout the reaction.
   C. Products appear at a gradually increasing rate throughout the reaction.
   D. Reactants disappear at a constant rate throughout the reaction.

6. What CANNOT be determined from the experiment?

   A. The rate of disappearance of A
   B. The rate of appearance of C
   C. The concentration of B after two minutes
   D. The order of the reaction with respect to A

7. Which assumption is NOT true?

   A. $\dfrac{\Delta[A]}{\Delta t} = -\dfrac{1}{2}\dfrac{\Delta[C]}{\Delta t}$

   B. $-\dfrac{\Delta[B]}{\Delta t} = \dfrac{1}{2}\dfrac{\Delta[C]}{\Delta t}$

   C. $2\dfrac{\Delta[B]}{\Delta t} = \dfrac{\Delta[C]}{\Delta t}$

   D. $-2\dfrac{\Delta[A]}{\Delta t} = \dfrac{\Delta[C]}{\Delta t}$

Passage II (Questions 8 - 14)

The kinetics of enzymatic processes obeys the rules of Michaelis-Menten kinetics. Michaelis-Menten kinetics for enzymatic processes is based on enzymatic reactions being carried out in two steps. The first step is the rapid formation of the enzyme-substrate complex. The second step is the slow step, in which the enzyme is regenerated and the product is formed. A general reaction mechanism is shown in Figure 1.

$$E + S \underset{k_{-1}}{\overset{k_1}{\rightleftharpoons}} ES \xrightarrow{k_2} E + P$$

Figure 1

where E is the enzyme, S is the substrate, ES is the enzyme-substrate complex, and P is the product.

The first step is a rapid equilibrium, so the [ES] remains constant, unless the substrate concentration diminishes to a level where it is comparable to the enzyme concentration. At this point, the rate becomes dependent on the substrate. Figure 2 illustrates this behavior:

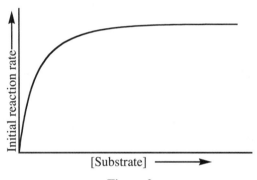

Figure 2

The reaction obeys first order kinetics until the enzyme is saturated and the enzyme-substrate concentration remains constant. The rate of the reaction obeys Equation 1, where the k_2 is the rate constant for the rate-determining step, and the [ES] is found using the steady state approximation.

$$\text{Rate} = k_2[ES] \qquad [ES] = \frac{[E][S]}{\left(\dfrac{k_{-1} + k_2}{k_1}\right) + [S]}$$

Equation 1

The relationships between the rate data can be found through simple algebraic manipulation.

8. The enzyme-substrate complex can be classified as which of the following?

    A. A product
    B. A reactant
    C. A transition state
    D. An intermediate

9. Which is NOT true about the role of an enzyme?

    A. It helps to align the reactants correctly.
    B. It lowers the energy of the transition state.
    C. It increases the reaction rate.
    D. It makes the reaction more exothermic.

10. When the catalyst is saturated, what is the reaction order with respect to substrate?

    A. Zero-order
    B. First-order
    C. Second-order
    D. Third-order

11. Given the following equation for the reaction rate, what is true when the reaction rate (v) is equal to one-half of the maximum reaction rate (v_{max})?

$$v = \frac{V_{max}[S]}{k_M + [S]}$$

    A. The reaction is first-order; $[S] = k_M$.
    B. The reaction is first-order; $V_{max} = k_M$.
    C. The reaction is zero-order; $[S] = k_M$.
    D. The reaction is zero-order; $V_{max} = k_M$.

12. Which graph BEST shows [ES] and [E] as a function of time?

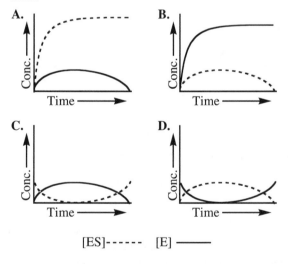

13. The rate for an enzymatically-catalyzed process that obeys the laws of Michaelis-Menten kinetics is:

    A. rate = k_1 [Enzyme]
    B. rate = k_2 [Enzyme]
    C. rate = k_1 [Enzyme·Substrate complex]
    D. rate = k_2 [Enzyme·Substrate complex]

14. Which graph accurately shows substrate concentration as a function of time for an enzymatic process that begins with the catalyst saturated with substrate?

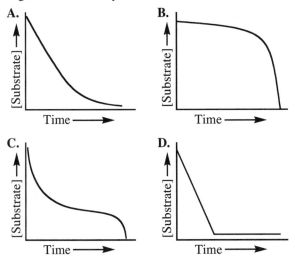

A.

B.

C.

D.

If the *rate constant*, k, is known for a standard reaction at a series of temperatures, the *Arrhenius constant*, A, and *activation energy*, E_{act}, can be determined using Equation 1:

$$\ln k = -\frac{E_{act}}{RT} + \ln A$$

Equation 1

The Arrhenius constant takes into account collision frequency and the orientation of the molecules. For instance, in an S_N2-reaction, not all collisions result in a reaction. Only the collisions oriented with the nucleophile aligned to attack the electrophile from the backside of the leaving group result in a reaction. Although the rate of a reaction can change with varying reactant concentrations, the rate constant for the reaction is constant throughout the reaction.

Reaction 1 is a one-step chemical reaction that was carried out in CCl_4 solvent (an aprotic nonpolar solvent) to determine the relationship between temperature and the rate constant (k). The gases were bubbled into two separate solutions of carbon tetrachloride to a saturation point. The two solutions were then mixed, and the reaction was observed.

$$SO_3(g) + NO(g) \rightarrow SO_2(g) + NO_2(g)$$

Reaction 1

Table 1 shows the results of six trials carried out at various temperatures on the Celsius scale.

T (°C)	$\frac{1}{T}$ (K^{-1})	k	log k
0	3.66×10^{-3}	7.87×10^{-7}	-6.10
25	3.36×10^{-3}	3.46×10^{-5}	-4.46
35	3.25×10^{-3}	1.35×10^{-4}	-3.87
45	3.14×10^{-3}	4.98×10^{-4}	-3.30
55	3.05×10^{-3}	1.50×10^{-3}	-2.82
65	2.96×10^{-3}	4.87×10^{-3}	-2.31

Table 1

The values in the chart contain slight errors, due to mechanical error within the UV-visible spectrophotometer used to measure the reactant and product concentrations. The values in this chart show a correlation between the reaction temperature and the rate constant for the reaction.

15. As temperature increases, which of the following are observed?

A. k increases; reaction rate increases.

B. k increases; reaction rate decreases.

C. k decreases; reaction rate increases.

D. k decreases; reaction rate decreases.

16. Which of the following represents log k as a function of $\frac{1}{T}$?

A.

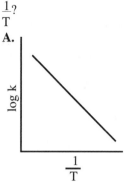

B.

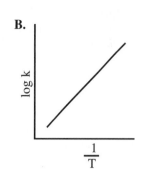

C.

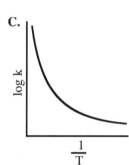

D.

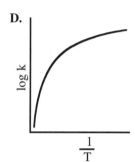

17. Which of the following rate equations applies to Reaction 1?

A. rate = $k[SO_3]$

B. rate = $k[NO]$

C. rate = $k[SO_3][NO]$

D. rate = $k[SO_3]^2$

18. When the solvent for the reaction is changed, the rate varies in a predictable manner. Which of the following variables is MOST affected by the change in solvent?

A. Activation energy

B. Temperature

C. Reactant concentration

D. The R value

19. When plotting ln k as a function of $\frac{1}{T}$, the slope of the line is equal to which of the following?

A. E_{act}

B. $- E_{act}$

C. $\frac{E_{act}}{R}$

D. $- \frac{E_{act}}{R}$

20. Why is the initial rate observed in reaction studies?

A. As a reaction proceeds, it slows. The same period in the reaction must be compared to be consistent.

B. As a reaction proceeds, its rate increases. The same period in the reaction must be compared to be consistent.

C. Only the initial rate can be accurately measured.

D. Any rate can be measured, but the initial one is most convenient.

21. To measure the rate of a reaction, which of the following CANNOT be observed?

A. The rate of appearance of product

B. The rate of disappearance of reactant

C. The change in intermediate concentration over time

D. The change in reactant and product concentration as a function of time

Passage IV (Questions 22 - 28)

Heterogeneous catalysis differs from homogeneous catalysis in the phase of the catalyst. As implied by the term "heterogeneous," the catalyst in heterogeneous catalysis is not evenly distributed through the solution. A common example involves hydrogenation of an alkene using platinum metal as a catalyst. The catalysis takes place only on the surface of the platinum, and not throughout the solution. This means that the rate of reaction varies with the surface area of the catalyst, not with its concentration.

In homogeneous catalysis, the catalyst is evenly distributed throughout the solution, and the catalysis takes place evenly throughout the solution. A common example of homogeneous catalysis is the addition of hydronium ion to solution to assist in the acid catalysis of ketal formation from a ketone. The hydronium ion is evenly distributed in solution. In homogeneous catalysis, the rate of the reaction varies with the concentration of the catalyst.

To determine the strength of a hydrogenation catalyst, the Reaction 1 was employed using four different catalysts. The turnover rate was observed and recorded for each of the catalysts. The turnover rate is defined as the rate of the reaction divided by the number of active catalytic sites. The units for turnover rate are reactions per second at the catalytic site.

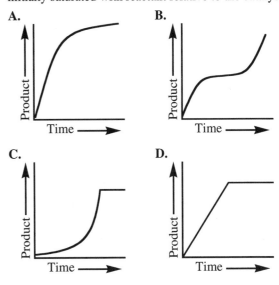

Reaction 1

Table 1 below lists the catalyst versus the turnover rate associated with each of the four catalysts:

Catalyst	Turnover rate $\left(\frac{rxn}{s}\right)$
$(Me_3P)_3RhCl$	8000
Pd/PdO_2	26,500
Pt/PtO_2	35,000
$(Me_5C_5)_2IrCO$	6500

Table 1

The experimental values are obtained from reaction rate studies using UV-visible spectroscopy. The reaction rate is divided by the surface area of each catalyst, which is best approximated by the shape of the material on which the catalysts is plated. In industrial processes, the catalysts are often applied to the surface of an inert material, such as graphite. This is done to maximize the surface area of the material, while keeping it a material large enough to filter out of solution easily at the end of the experiment.

22. Which of the following graphs BEST represents the formation of product as a function of time in a system initially saturated with reactant relative to the catalyst?

A.

B.

C.

D.

23. Which catalyst can be used in the LOWEST concentration to obtain a set rate?

A. $(Me_3P)_3RhCl$

B. Pd/PdO_2

C. Pt/PtO_2

D. $(Me_5C_5)_2IrCO$

24. For a catalyst in an industrial system, the number of active sites affects the turnover rate. What can be concluded about the maximum turnover rate of one catalytic site, if the catalyst contains three catalytic sites but the catalyst is NOT saturated with reactant?

A. The maximum turnover rate of one catalytic site is less than one-third of the observed turnover rate, assuming the three catalytic sites react equally.

B. The maximum turnover rate of one catalytic site is greater than one-third of the observed turnover rate, assuming the three catalytic sites react equally.

C. The maximum turnover rate of one catalytic site is exactly one-third of the observed turnover rate, assuming the three catalytic sites react equally.

D. The turnover rate of one catalytic site is exactly one-third of the observed turnover rate, assuming the three catalytic sites do NOT react equally.

         GO ON TO THE NEXT PAGE

25. Which of the following is NOT an example of heterogeneous catalysis?

    A. $(H_3C)_2CO + H_2$ with $Pd/PdO_2 \rightarrow (H_3C)_2CHOH$

    B. $H_3CCOCl + C_6H_6$ with $AlCl_3 \rightarrow C_6H_5COCH_3$

    C. $H_2CCH_2 + H_2$ with $Pt/PtO_2 \rightarrow H_3CCH_3$

    D. $CH_4 + CO$ with $(Me_3P)_3RhCl \rightarrow H_3CCHO$

26. What is always TRUE about a catalyst?

    A. A catalyst is always consumed in a reaction.

    B. A catalyst is always produced in a reaction.

    C. A catalyst is always regenerated during a reaction.

    D. A catalyst is always altered in a reaction.

27. If a catalytic site has a binding affinity for the product, what will be observed over time?

    A. Both the turnover rate and the overall reaction rate increase.

    B. Both the turnover rate and the overall reaction rate decrease.

    C. The turnover rate increases, while the overall reaction rate decreases.

    D. The turnover rate decreases, while the overall reaction rate increases.

28. Why is a heterogeneous catalyst applied to the surface of an inert solid for industrial reactions?

    A. To maximize the surface area

    B. To increase the concentration

    C. To make the catalyst more buoyant

    D. To make the catalyst less soluble

Passage V (Questions 29 - 35)

First-order decay processes follow a predictable pattern of decreasing concentration over time. The concentration at any given time can be calculated using Equation 1, if the initial concentration, the time, and the rate constant for decay are all known. Equation 1 applies only to a first-order decay process.

$$C_t = C_i e^{-kt}$$

Equation 1

where C_t is the concentration at time t, C_i is the initial concentration, k is the rate constant, and t is time.

The half-life for a first-order decay process is constant over the course of the decay. If the half-life is known, then the rate constant for a first-order decay process can be found, as shown in Figure 1 below:

$$C_t = C_i e^{-kt} \therefore \frac{C_t}{C_i} = e^{-kt}$$

$$\text{at } t = t_{1/2}, \frac{C_t}{C_i} = \frac{1}{2}$$

$$\frac{1}{2} = e^{-kt_{1/2}}$$

$$\ln\frac{1}{2} = -kt_{1/2}$$

$$kt_{1/2} = -\ln\frac{1}{2} = \ln 2$$

$$k = \frac{\ln 2}{t_{1/2}} = \frac{0.693}{t_{1/2}}$$

Figure 1

The half-life can also be determined from the rate constant using the same relationship. In summary, the rate constant and the half-life for a first-order decay process are inversely proportional.

29. Which of the following graphs does NOT depict first-order decay behavior?

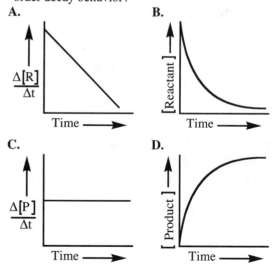

30. If k is doubled, then the half-life of a first-order decay:

    A. increases by a factor of e^2.

    B. increases by a factor of 2.

    C. decreases by a factor of 2.

    D. decreases by a factor of e^2.

31. What is TRUE about the value of half-life for a reaction?

    A. The value of the half-life is constant in first-order reaction, while it decreases with time in a zero-order reaction.

    B. The value of the half-life is constant in first-order reaction, while it increases with time in a zero-order reaction.

    C. The value of the half-life is constant in both zero- and first-order reactions.

    D. The value of the half-life decreases with time in both zero- and first-order reactions.

32. What are the units of the rate constant for a first-order reaction?

    A. sec

    B. $\dfrac{1}{\text{sec}}$

    C. [M]·sec

    D. $\dfrac{[\text{M}]}{\text{sec}}$

33. What period of time is required to reach the point in a first-order decay where only 20% of the original reactant remains?

    A. $t = \ln 5 \times k$

    B. $t = \ln \dfrac{1}{5} \times k$

    C. $t = \dfrac{k}{\ln 5}$

    D. $t = \dfrac{\ln 5}{k}$

34. What must be TRUE about a reaction that fits the graph below?

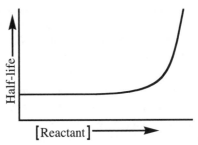

    A. The reaction is second-order at high [Reactant] and first-order at low [Reactant].

    B. The reaction is first-order at high [Reactant] and second-order at low [Reactant].

    C. The reaction is zero-order at high [Reactant] and first-order at low [Reactant].

    D. The reaction is first-order at high [Reactant] and zero-order at low [Reactant].

35. Which of these reactions has a constant half-life?

    A. One step: $X + X \rightarrow X_2$

    B. One step: $X + Y \rightarrow X - Y$

    C. Two steps: $X + Y \rightarrow Z + Q \rightarrow W + Y$

    D. One step: $X \rightarrow A + B$

GO ON TO THE NEXT PAGE

In both organic and inorganic chemistry, one of the most common mechanistic questions is, "Does the leaving group leave first, or does the nucleophile attack first?" In organic chemistry, the two reaction mechanisms are referred to as S_N1 and S_N2. In inorganic chemistry, the two reaction mechanisms are referred to as *dissociative* and *associative*. A researcher ran a nucleophilic substitution reaction four times at the same temperature, varying the concentration of reactants each time. Table 1 below lists data from each trial:

[CH$_3$SNa]	[CH$_3$CH$_2$I]	Rate (M/sec)
0.10 M	0.15 M	2.10×10^{-5}
0.10 M	0.25 M	3.52×10^{-5}
0.20 M	0.20 M	5.58×10^{-5}
0.15 M	0.30 M	6.33×10^{-5}

Table 1

$$CH_3SNa + CH_3CH_2I \rightarrow CH_3CH_2SCH_3 + NaI$$

Reaction 1

The formation of thioether was monitored using UV spectroscopy to obtain the data in table 1. The rate of the reaction is assumed to equal the rate of formation of the thioether. There were no major side products observed during the reaction. The data were repeated in subsequent trials of the experiment. The reproducibility of the data helps to substantiate the conclusions of the experiment.

36. If methanol were used in place of sodium methyl sulfide, then the reaction would show which of the following changes under identical conditions?

A. The reaction rate would increase.
B. The reaction rate would stay the same.
C. The reaction rate would decrease.
D. The reaction rate would exactly double.

37. What would the rate be, if the reaction were run with the following concentrations?

[CH$_3$SNa] = 0.25 M   [CH$_3$CH$_2$I] = 0.10 M

A. 2.10×10^{-5} [M]/sec
B. 3.52×10^{-5} [M]/sec
C. 5.58×10^{-5} [M]/sec
D. 6.33×10^{-5} [M]/sec

38. What is the reaction order of Reaction 1?

A. Zero-order
B. First-order
C. Second-order
D. Third-order

39. What would the apparent reaction order be with the following concentrations?

[CH$_3$SNa] = 1.25 M   [CH$_3$CH$_2$I] = 0.05 M

A. Zero-order
B. First-order
C. Second-order
D. Third-order

40. The following reaction is said to proceed by a dissociative mechanism. If the concentration of Co(en)$_2$NH$_3$Cl^{2+} were to double, and the concentration of NH$_3$ to triple, the new reaction rate would be changed in what way?

$$Co(en)_2NH_3Cl^{2+} + NH_3 \rightarrow Co(en)_2(NH_3)_2^{3+} + Cl^-$$

A. It would be twice as large.
B. It would be three times as large.
C. It would be four times as large.
D. It would be six times as large.

41. Which of the following does NOT increase the rate of an associative concerted reaction?

A. Increasing the temperature
B. Adding solvent
C. Adding one of the reactants
D. Using a less viscous solvent

42. What is the rate constant for the ethyl iodide substitution reaction listed in Table 1?

A. 1.40×10^{-3} [M]/sec
B. 3.15×10^{-3} [M]/sec
C. 1.40×10^{-3} 1/[M]·sec
D. 3.15×10^{-3} 1/[M]·sec

43. The reaction order of the dissociative mechanism is:

A. zero-order.
B. first-order.
C. second-order.
D. third-order.

44. Which of the following statements is INVALID with respect to the rate of an S_N1 reaction?

A. The reaction rate varies with electrophile concentration.
B. The reaction rate varies with nucleophile concentration.
C. The reaction rate varies with temperature.
D. The reaction rate varies with solvent.

Mechanisms for chemical reactions are either supported or disproven by data. For a mechanism to be accepted by the scientific community, it must be capable of predicting reactivity and of holding form, even under varying reaction conditions. Two common procedures for evaluating the validity of a mechanism are isolating an intermediate in the reaction and studying the effect on the reaction rate when varying the concentration of components. The rate depends on only the rate-determining step, so any altering of the concentrations of species involved in the rate-determining step results in a change in the reaction rate. Conversely, if the species you alter is not in the rate-determining step of the mechanism, then the rate is not affected. Reaction 1 below has been analyzed by kinetics:

$$[(NH_3)_5CoCl]^{2+} + OH^- \longrightarrow [(NH_3)_5CoOH]^{2+} + Cl^-$$

Reaction 1

Figure 1 lists the currently accepted three-step mechanism for Reaction 1:

Step I (fast):
$$[(NH_3)_5CoCl]^{2+} + OH^- \underset{k_{-1}}{\overset{k_1}{\rightleftharpoons}} [(NH_3)_4Co(NH_2)Cl]^+ + H_2O$$

Step II (slow):
$$[(NH_3)_4Co(NH_2)Cl]^+ \overset{k_2}{\longrightarrow} [(NH_3)_4CoNH_2]^{2+} + Cl^-$$

Step III (fast):
$$[(NH_3)_4CoNH_2]^{2+} + H_2O \overset{k_3}{\longrightarrow} [(NH_3)_5CoOH]^{2+}$$

Figure 1

The rate data were gathered by observing the formation of intermediates and products over time. The concentration of intermediates and products is found by monitoring the absorbance of various species using UV-visible spectroscopy. The peak for the intermediate grew initially and then remained constant until the end of the reaction, when it decreased to zero. The peaks for products also grow over time.

45. What is the rate-determining step in the proposed mechanism?

   A. Step I
   B. Step II
   C. Step III
   D. Step I and Step II are both rate-determining.

46. Addition of water to the reaction would have what effect?

   A. It would increase the reaction rate.
   B. It would have no effect on the reaction rate.
   C. It would decrease the reaction rate.
   D. It would make the reaction third-order.

47. Which kinetic relationship is predicted for Reaction 1 using steady-state approximation?

   A. $k_1 [[(NH_3)_5CoCl]^{2+}][OH^-]$
   $= (k_{-1} + k_2) [[(NH_3)_4Co(NH_2)Cl]^+] [H_2O]$

   B. $k_1 [[(NH_3)_5CoCl]^{2+}][OH^-]$
   $= (k_{-1} + k_2) [[(NH_3)_4Co(NH_2)Cl]^+]$

   C. $k_1 [[(NH_3)_5CoCl]^{2+}][OH^-]$
   $= k_{-1} [[(NH_3)_4Co(NH_2)Cl]^+] [H_2O]$
   $+ k_2 [[(NH_3)_4Co(NH_2)Cl]^+]$

   D. $k_1 [[(NH_3)_5CoCl]^{2+}][OH^-]$
   $= k_{-1} [[(NH_3)_4Co(NH_2)Cl]^+]$
   $+ k_2 [[(NH_3)_4Co(NH_2)Cl]^+] [H_2O]$

48. Which of the following statements is TRUE about the relative acidity of the cobalt compound?

   A. $pK_a \ NH_3 > pK_a \ [(NH_3)_5CoCl]^{2+}$.
   B. $pK_a \ NH_3 = pK_a \ [(NH_3)_5CoCl]^{2+}$.
   C. $pK_a \ NH_3 < pK_a \ [(NH_3)_5CoCl]^{2+}$.
   D. There is no comparison between the two.

49. Which of the following statements is TRUE with regard to the rate of Reaction 1?

   A. The rate increases as both the pH and temperature increase.
   B. The rate decreases as both the pH and temperature increase.
   C. The rate increases as the pH increases, while the rate decreases as the temperature increases.
   D. The rate decreases as the pH increases, while the rate increases as the temperature increases.

50. A catalyst does all of the following EXCEPT:

   A. affect the rate-determining step.
   B. increase the reaction rate.
   C. lower the activation energy.
   D. increase the equilibrium constant.

51. What are the units for k_{obs} in the rate equation, if rate = $k_{obs} [[(NH_3)_5CoCl]^{2+}][OH^-]$?

   A. $[M]^2 \ sec^1$
   B. $[M] \ sec^{-1}$
   C. sec^{-1}
   D. $[M]^{-1} \ sec^{-1}$

The mechanism for a reaction can be inferred from the kinetic data. The kinetic data determine the reactants that affect the rate of a reaction. The reactants in the rate-determining step can be used to predict a mechanism to match the kinetic data. If one of the reactants does not affect the rate of the reaction, then the reaction must be a multi-step reaction. A one-step reaction shows a rate dependence on all of the reactants. Reaction 1 was observed at varying initial concentrations for the reactants. The temperature was held constant for each trial.

$$2 \, SO_2(g) + O_2(g) \rightarrow 2 \, SO_3(g)$$

Reaction 1

Table 1 lists the initial reaction rate for four trials of Reaction 1, carried out at varied concentrations.

initial rate $\left(\dfrac{M}{s}\right)$	P_{SO_2} init	P_{O_2} init
2.17×10^{-2}	0.60 atm	0.40 atm
2.13×10^{-2}	0.60 atm	0.80 atm
8.66×10^{-2}	1.20 atm	0.40 atm
8.72×10^{-2}	1.20 atm	0.80 atm

Table 1

The reaction order with respect to each reactant can be determined from Table 1. Oxygen exhibits no effect on the reaction rate, so the reaction is said to be zero-order with respect to oxygen gas. The fact that oxygen is zero-order simply means that oxygen is not involved in the reaction's rate-determining step. Similar results were seen when the reaction was repeated at higher temperatures, although the reactions rates were greater. The reaction order remained the same for both SO_2 and O_2 gas as the temperature changed.

52. Which of the following accurately reflects the correlation between the initial rate and the concentration of sulfur dioxide?

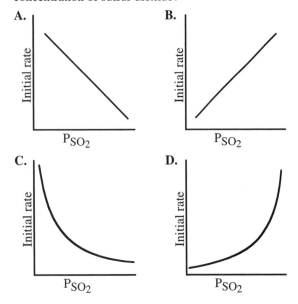

53. Addition of a catalyst to a reaction results in which of the following?

A. An increase in the forward reaction rate only
B. An increase in the amount of SO_3 formed
C. An increase in both the forward and reverse reaction rates
D. An increase in the amount of both SO_2 and O_2

54. The mechanism for the reaction is MOST likely to be which of the following?

A. Fast: $SO_2(g) + O_2(g) \rightarrow SO_3(g) + O(g)$
   Slow: $SO_2(g) + O(g) \rightarrow SO_3(g)$
B. Slow: $SO_2(g) + O_2(g) \rightarrow SO_3(g) + O(g)$
   Fast: $SO_2(g) + O(g) \rightarrow SO_3(g)$
C. Fast: $SO_2(g) + SO_2(g) \rightarrow SO_3(g) + SO(g)$
   Slow: $SO(g) + O_2(g) \rightarrow SO_3(g)$
D. Slow: $SO_2(g) + SO_2(g) \rightarrow SO_3(g) + SO(g)$
   Fast: $SO(g) + O_2(g) \rightarrow SO_3(g)$

55. What is the relative change in concentration over time between oxygen and sulfur trioxide?

A. $\dfrac{\Delta[O_2]}{\Delta t} = + 2 \dfrac{\Delta[SO_3]}{\Delta t}$
B. $\dfrac{\Delta[O_2]}{\Delta t} = - 2 \dfrac{\Delta[SO_3]}{\Delta t}$
C. $\dfrac{\Delta[O_2]}{\Delta t} = + \dfrac{1}{2} \dfrac{\Delta[SO_3]}{\Delta t}$
D. $\dfrac{\Delta[O_2]}{\Delta t} = - \dfrac{1}{2} \dfrac{\Delta[SO_3]}{\Delta t}$

56. As the reaction proceeds, what is observed for the total pressure of the system?

A. The total pressure increases at a constant rate.
B. The total pressure decreases at a constant rate.
C. The total pressure increases at a gradually decreasing rate.
D. The total pressure decreases at a gradually decreasing rate.

57. Which of the following changes does NOT increase the rate of a reaction?

   A. Increasing the temperature of the reaction
   B. Decreasing the volume of the container
   C. Adding sulfur dioxide to the mixture
   D. Adding oxygen to the mixture

58. When the same experiment was carried out at elevated temperatures, it was observed that the rate began to vary with oxygen concentration. How is this best explained?

   A. The mechanism of the reaction changed so that oxygen was now involved in the rate-determining step.
   B. The mechanism of the reaction changed, so that oxygen was no longer involved in the rate-determining step.
   C. The bond energy of oxygen is lower at higher temperatures.
   D. The bond energy of sulfur dioxide is greater at higher temperatures.

Passage IX (Questions 59 - 65)

The rate at which a metal takes on ligands depends on several factors. The strength of the coordinate covalent bond between the metal and the original ligand (leaving group) plays a major role. The frequency of collision between the new ligand and the transition metal complex also plays a role. Unique to transition metal substitution chemistry is the *chelating effect*. The chelating effect is observed when a ligand is polydentate (possesses more than one lone pair to be shared with the metal), in which case the second coordinate covalent bond forms more rapidly than the first. This is to say that once one site has been coordinated, the chance for collision of a second lone pair with the transition metal has increased over that of ligands free in solution. The net result is that it is easier for a polydentate chelating agent to form subsequent bonds to a metal than its first bond. Polydentate chelating agents have two or more lone pairs to share.

A researcher set up an experiment to study Reaction 1, in an effort to support the concept of the chelating effect. A series of hexa-coordinate metals with three sites bound by a polymer and the other three sites bound by phosphine ligands was exposed to a compound containing three amine functional groups ($H_2NCH_2CH_2NHCH_2CH_2NH_2$). The reactant has a visible absorption at $\lambda_{max} = 519$ nm. The product transition metal complex has a visible absorption at $\lambda_{max} = 465$ nm. The rate of the reaction is monitored by visible spectroscopy. Reaction 1 is drawn below:

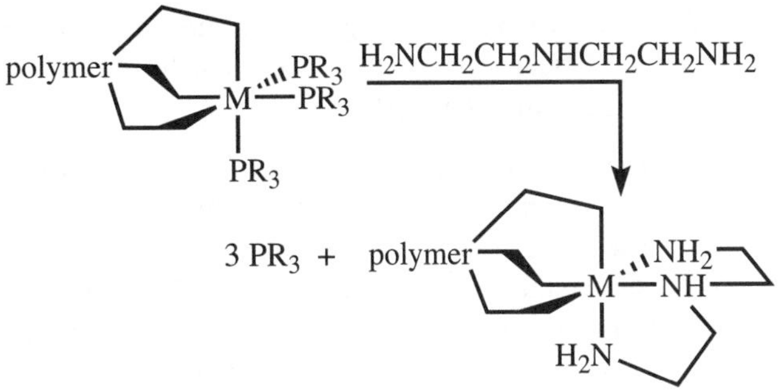

Reaction 1

The rate of the reaction can be monitored by either the disappearance of reactant or the appearance of product. A normal substitution reaction on a transition metal complex shows either first-order or second-order kinetics. In either case, the observed rate gradually decreases over time. The chelating effect predicts that the rate of formation of phosphine actually increases with time for a short period.

59. Which method is NOT effective for monitoring the reaction rate?

   A. Monitoring the appearance of polymer-$MC_4H_{13}N_3$
   B. Monitoring the disappearance of PR_3
   C. Monitoring the disappearance of $C_4H_{13}N_3$
   D. Monitoring the disappearance of polymer-$M(PR_3)_3$

60. Which of the following is TRUE for the observed reaction rate of a generic reaction?

A. The observed reaction rate increases over time during an endothermic reaction.

B. The observed reaction rate is greater, if a higher energy product is formed.

C. The observed reaction rate is greater, if a higher energy transition state is formed.

D. The observed reaction rate is greater, if a lower energy transition state is formed.

61. The exchange rate for the first phosphine is slower than that of the second phosphine and the third phosphine. This is because the:

A. second and third phosphines bind the metal more tightly, due to increased steric hindrance after the first phosphine has left.

B. second and third phosphines bind the metal more tightly, due to reduced steric hindrance after the first phosphine has left.

C. nucleophile can more easily displace the second and third phosphines, due to the chelating effect.

D. nucleophile cannot displace the second and third phosphines as easily, due to the chelating effect.

62. If in one reaction the R group of the phosphine is methyl (CH_3), what is observed when the methyl is replaced by ethyl (CH_2CH_3)?

A. The reaction rate increases with the ethyl, because steric hindrance of the leaving group has increased.

B. The reaction rate decreases with the ethyl, because steric hindrance of the leaving group has increased.

C. The reaction rate increases with the ethyl, because steric hindrance of the leaving group has decreased.

D. The reaction rate decreases with the ethyl, because steric hindrance of the leaving group has decreased.

63. The FASTEST reaction is observed with which of the following conditions?

A. A one-step reaction where a strong bond is broken and a weak bond is formed.

B. A one-step reaction where a weak bond is broken and a strong bond is formed.

C. A two-step reaction where step I requires breaking a strong bond and step II forms a strong bond.

D. A two-step reaction where step I requires breaking a strong bond and step II forms a weak bond.

64. Which of the following statements CANNOT be true about Reaction 1?

I. Adding methyl groups to the nitrogens of the triamine species reduces the reaction rate.

II. Steric hindrance forming the transition state complex increases the reaction rate.

III. Increasing the temperature lowers the energy level of the transition state.

A. I only

B. II only

C. I and II only

D. II and III only

65. Which of the following does NOT increase the reaction rate?

A. Using one bidentate ligand in lieu of two monodentate ligands

B. Adding a catalyst that weakens the leaving group bond to the transition metal

C. Adding solvent to a saturated solution

D. Increasing the temperature of the solution

Passage X (Questions 66 - 72)

The following reaction can be carried out in the gas phase. Gas phase mechanisms are very different from solution phase mechanisms, in that the solvent can be involved in the transition state in a solution phase reaction.

$$C{\equiv}O(g) + H_2O(g) \rightarrow CO_2(g) + H_2(g)$$

Reaction I

Two chemists propose mechanisms to explain the reactivity of the overall reaction. Chemist I proposes the following two-step mechanism.

Step I:

Step II:

Mechanism I

Chemist II takes issue with the mechanism proposed by Chemist I, stating that charged molecules are highly unstable in the gas phase. As an alternative, Chemist II proposes the following three-step free radical mechanism:

Step I:

Step II:

Step III:

Mechanism II

Both mechanisms have their respective strengths and weaknesses. Key features to observe include the bond dissociation energy and the stability of intermediates.

66. If the rearrangement step in Mechanism I is slower than the addition step, what is true about the reaction?

    A. The reaction is one-step, and rate = $k_1[H_2O][CO]$.

    B. The reaction is one-step, and rate = $k_2[H_2CO_2]$.

    C. The reaction is two-steps, and rate = $k_1[H_2O][CO]$.

    D. The reaction is two-steps, and rate = $k_2[H_2CO_2]$.

67. A catalyst plays what role in the reaction mechanism?

    A. It increase the value of K_{eq}.

    B. It decreases the value of ΔG.

    C. It increases the value of ΔH.

    D. It decreases the value of the activation energy.

68. Which graph accurately shows the product concentration as a function of time for a first-order reaction?

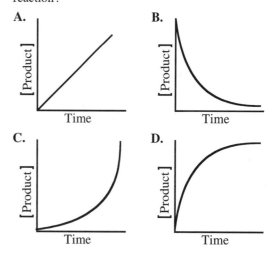

69. Mechanism II would be preferred over Mechanism I because:

    A. carbocations are stabler than free radical carbons.

    B. anions are highly stable in the gas phase.

    C. it requires less energy to break a covalent bond in a heterolytic fashion than a homolytic fashion.

    D. free radicals are stabler in the gas phase than ions.

70. Intermediates are defined as:

    A. unstable with no lifetime.

    B. unstable with a short lifetime.

    C. highly stable with no lifetime.

    D. highly stable with a short lifetime.

71. If Step II is the rate-determining step in Mechanism I, then all of the following predictions are valid EXCEPT:

    A. Labeled oxygen in CO would not be found in CO_2.

    B. Adding H_2O would increase the rate, because $[H_2CO_2]$ would increase.

    C. Removing CO would decrease the rate, because $[H_2CO_2]$ would decrease.

    D. If the temperature were held constant, the rate would decrease as the reaction proceeds.

72. With which observation would BOTH mechanisms agree?

    A. Doubling the $[H_2O]$ doubles the rate.

    B. Carrying out the reaction in ether solvent would yield the same results.

    C. As the temperature increases, the reaction rate increases.

    D. The K_{eq} is greater with a more stable intermediate.

GO ON TO THE NEXT PAGE

Questions 73 through 80 are **NOT** based on a descriptive passage.

73. As ΔG_{act} increases, which of the following statements is TRUE?

    I. A larger temperature is needed to obtain the same reaction rate.

   II. Fewer molecules have the amount of energy necessary to overcome the activation barrier.

  III. A catalyst further increases ΔG_{act}.

    A. I only
    B. II only
    C. III only
    D. I and II only

74. For a first-order reaction with k = .0693 sec^{-1}, what is the half-life, given ln 2 is 0.693?

    A. 10 seconds
    B. 1 second
    C. 0.10 seconds
    D. 0.01 seconds

75. For the hypothetical reaction listed below, the rate of disappearance of A is $0.450 \frac{M}{sec}$.

$$2 A \rightarrow B + C$$

The rate of appearance for B is which of the following?

    A. $0.225 \frac{M}{sec}$
    B. $0.450 \frac{M}{sec}$
    C. $0.900 \frac{M}{sec}$
    D. $-0.450 \frac{M}{sec}$

76. Which of the following is NOT true about an intermediate?

    A. The intermediate is in its highest concentration just after the start of the reaction.
    B. Intermediates have finite lifetimes.
    C. An intermediate is in its highest possible concentration when it is formed after the rate-determining step of the reaction.
    D. An intermediate is in its highest possible concentration when it is formed before the rate-determining step of the reaction.

77. Given the following data, what is the concentration of X at time t = 3?

Time	[X] (M)
0	1.00
1	0.56
2	0.35
4	0.25

    A. 0.33 M
    B. 0.31 M
    C. 0.30 M
    D. 0.28 M

78. Which of the following graphs BEST represents moles of B as a function of time for the following reaction?

$$2 A \rightarrow B + C$$

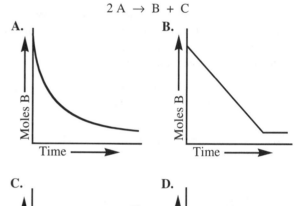

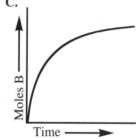
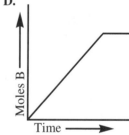

79. The rate-determining step in a two-step reaction is:

    A. always the first step.
    B. always the second step.
    C. always the fastest step.
    D. always the slowest step.

GO ON TO THE NEXT PAGE

80. The HIGHEST intermediate concentration is found with which of the following graphs?

A.

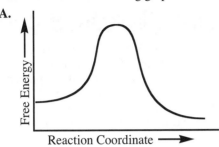

B.

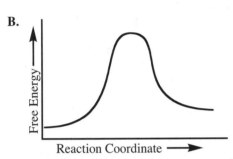

C.

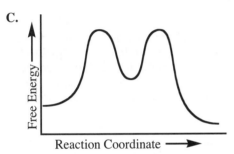

D.

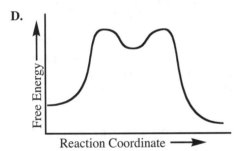

1. B	2. A	3. C	4. B	5. B
6. D	7. C	8. D	9. D	10. A
11. A	12. D	13. D	14. A	15. A
16. A	17. C	18. A	19. D	20. A
21. C	22. A	23. C	24. B	25. B
26. C	27. B	28. A	29. C	30. C
31. A	32. B	33. D	34. C	35. D
36. C	37. B	38. C	39. B	40. A
41. B	42. C	43. B	44. B	45. B
46. C	47. C	48. A	49. A	50. D
51. D	52. D	53. C	54. D	55. D
56. D	57. D	58. A	59. B	60. D
61. C	62. A	63. B	64. D	65. C
66. D	67. D	68. D	69. D	70. B
71. A	72. C	73. D	74. A	75. A
76. C	77. D	78. C	79. D	80. C

YOU ARE DONE.

Kinetics Passages Answers

1. **Choice B is correct.** At 625 nm, there is no peak throughout the experiment, so choice C should be eliminated immediately. The largest initial peak of the three remaining choices occurs at 545 nm. The peak at 695 nm at t = 2 is also large, but it is difficult to monitor product formation, because it is not possible to calibrate the machine in the beginning, given that initially there is no peak for products. It is best to monitor the largest peak associated with a reactant, because at that wavelength, there is the greatest absorbance. The greater the initial absorbance, the greater the change in absorbance. This leads to the best results when monitoring the change in absorbance. The best answer is choice **B**.

2. **Choice A is correct.** Because the peak at 684 nm is growing as the reaction proceeds, the peak is best described as belonging to a product. The best answer is therefore choice **A**. A reactant peak disappears over time, as seen with the peaks at 470 nm and 547 nm. A catalyst peak remains fairly constant throughout the course of the reaction. An intermediate peak grows and then holds steady for a while before gradually dropping off to zero at the end.

3. **Choice C is correct.** The absorbance is directly proportional to the cell length, the molar absorbtivity constant, and the concentration according to the equation. This makes choices A and B true. The molar absorbtivity constant is specific for each compound, so choice D is true. Only choice **C** can be false. The absorbance can vary with temperature as the compound and concentration vary, but not necessarily in a predictable manner. The change is not known, so the word "always" makes choice **C** invalid.

4. **Choice B is correct.** The peak at 547 nm belongs to a reactant, as is shown by its gradual decrease in concentration over the course of the reaction. The rate at which the peak at 547 nm diminishes is equal to the rate of disappearance of reactant, which is the negative of the rate of appearance of product. We define reaction rates according to the formation of product, so the reaction rate is the negative of the change in absorbance. The value for reaction rate should always be positive or zero. The concentration and absorbance are directly proportional, so their changes should be proportional. The best answer is choice **B**.

5. **Choice B is correct.** Products appear at a gradually decreasing rate, because the reaction rate slows over time until it reaches zero. The products show their biggest change in concentration initially, and the magnitude of the change decreases with the reaction time. The best answer is choice **B**. The rate slows because the reaction slowly runs out of reactant as it approaches equilibrium.

6. **Choice D is correct.** The order of the reaction cannot be determined without running the reaction at least twice. The order refers to the dependency of the rate on the reactant concentrations. The concentration of one of the reactants must be varied between two separate trials to determine its effect on the rate. All other variables must be held constant. The best choice is **D**.

7. **Choice C is correct.** The product appears at twice the rate at which the reactants disappear, because of the 1-to-2 ratio of reactants to the product in the balanced equation. This factor is important in most instances, but in this particular question, the answer can be found based solely on the negative sign. Because the product (C) appears while the reactants (A and B) disappear, the rates of change for compounds A and B relative to compound C must differ by a negative sign. A negative sign is present in every answer choice except for choice **C**, making choice **C** the best answer.

8. **Choice D is correct.** The enzyme·substrate complex is detectable by spectroscopy, meaning it has a measurable lifetime, so it cannot be a transition state. Transition states are short-lived species that cannot be detected. Choice C is eliminated. The enzyme·substrate complex is not present in the beginning or at the end of the reaction, so choices A and B can be eliminated. It is best described as an intermediate, so the best answer is choice **D**.

9. **Choice D is correct.** The enzyme is a catalyst, and like all catalysts, it lowers the activation energy (the energy of the transition state complex in the rate-determining step) and thus increases the reaction rate. This eliminates choices B and C. An enzyme is special in that it is chirally active, and thus it is responsible for aligning the reactant molecules correctly. This eliminates choice A, because it is a valid statement. Catalysts do not affect the thermodynamics of the reaction, as they are not present in the reactant or product. This means that the reaction cannot be made more exothermic by an enzyme. Thus, choice **D** is a false statement, and therefore the best answer.

10. **Choice A is correct.** Because the rate does not change upon the addition of substrate once the enzyme is saturated, the reaction obeys zero-order kinetics (which is confirmed by the fact that there is no change in rate over time). It is alluded to in the last paragraph of the passage that the reaction has lost its first-order behavior by becoming zero-order. It is best if you were to select choice **A**. Zero-order reactions have constant reaction rates, which according to Michaelis-Menten terminology is known as V_{max}.

11. **Choice A is correct.** This is a classic Michaelis-Menten kinetics question, which is best solved through mathematical substitution and manipulation. The calculation is as follows:

$$V = \frac{V_{max}}{2} = \frac{V_{max}[S]}{k_M + [S]} \quad \text{Canceling out } V_{max} \text{ gives: } \quad \frac{1}{2} = \frac{[S]}{k_M + [S]} \Rightarrow k_M + [S] = 2[S] \Rightarrow k_M = [S]$$

The reaction is first-order, because the enzyme is not saturated when the reaction rate is one-half of V_{max}, so the reaction rate depends on the substrate concentration ([S]). The math shows that $k_M = [S]$, making choice **A** the best answer choice.

12. **Choice D is correct.** The enzyme·substrate complex is an intermediate. Therefore, it should not be seen in the beginning and at the end of the reaction. It should be present only during the course of the reaction. This eliminates choices A and C. The enzyme starts and finishes with the same quantity; but because it is converted to the enzyme·substrate complex during the reaction, its concentration dwindles to zero in the middle of the reaction. Choice **D** describes this best. From the graphs, it can be seen that the intermediate is in a steady-state concentration only during the middle of a reaction. This is why the steady-state approximation only applies during the middle of a reaction, once equilibrium between the intermediate and reactants has been established.

13. **Choice D is correct.** The relevant information is given directly in the passage, so your answer should be the obvious choice of answer **D**. If you chose not to read the passage, then you should at least know that the reaction when the enzyme is saturated has its second step as its slowest, (and thus rate-determining) step.

14. **Choice A is correct.** Because the catalyst is initially saturated, the reaction proceeds according to zero-order kinetics, which can be viewed as uniform decay at a constant rate. This is seen with all four answer choices. The reaction evolves slowly from zero-order to first-order, meaning that no sharp changes should be observed. This eliminates choice D. Choice C should be eliminated, because the erratic rate behavior shown at the end of the reaction would not be observed. Choice B should be eliminated, because the reaction rate should be constant, and then gradually slowly down, not speed up. The graph that best shows zero-order kinetics slowly evolving into first-order kinetics is choice **A**.

Passage III (Questions 15 - 21)   Reaction Rates from Graphs

15. **Choice A is correct.** From the equation, as T increases, the value for $\frac{E_{act}}{RT}$ decreases. This means that the value of $-\frac{E_{act}}{RT}$ increases. Because $-\frac{E_{act}}{RT}$ is directly proportional to ln k, ln k must also increase, as does k. The ultimate conclusion is that k increases with T. The reaction rate also increases with T, so answer **A** is correct.

16. **Choice A is correct.** Equation 1, the rate equation, is the equation of a line where y is ln k and x is T^{-1}. This eliminates choices C and D. As log k increases (as you read down the chart), the value of T^{-1} increases. This makes graph **A** correct.

17. **Choice C is correct.** It is stated in the passage that the reaction is a one-step reaction, so the rate depends on both reactants. The reaction is second-order when there are two reactants and the mechanism is concerted. The correct answer is choice **C**, rate = $k[SO_3][NO]$.

18. **Choice A is correct.** The temperature and R constant are independent of any other factors. This eliminates choices B and D. The concentration of all solutes (including the reactants) is affected by changing the solvent, but only by the quantity of solvent added, not the type of solvent. In one liter of solution, the concentration is the same, independent of the solvent. This means that changing solvent may not necessarily change the concentration of reactants. The question emphasizes a change in the type of solvent, not a change in the amount of solvent (concentration). This makes choice **A** the best answer. The activation energy is affected, because the solvent can solvate the transition states and thus stabilize or destabilize the transition state. Changing the stability of the transition state changes the activation energy, so changing the solvent affects the reaction rate. If you need a tangible example to support this notion, consider nucleophilic substitution reactions. A polar/protic solvent favors an S_N1-reaction while a polar/aprotic solvent favors an S_N2-reaction.

19. **Choice D is correct.** Viewing Equation 1 as the equation for a line, ln k is the y-term and T^{-1} can be considered to be the x-term. The slope is $-\dfrac{E_{act}}{R}$ and the y-intercept is ln A. The question asks for the slope, so choice **D** is the best answer.

20. **Choice A is correct.** The reaction rate depends on the concentration of the reactant, so the reaction rate decreases as the reaction proceeds, because the reactant concentration decreases over the course of the reaction. The fact that the rate decreases eliminates choice B. In reality, the rate at any given time can be measured accurately, but precisely the same time interval in the course of the reaction must be measured in each trial for the values to be comparable. In practicality, the rate is determined after the concentration has been measured for the duration of a reaction. The rate at any point in the reaction is thus easy to measure. This eliminates choice C. The initial rate is chosen primarily because that time can most accurately be repeated in subsequent trials, which assures that the time of the reaction is the same in each comparative trial. This makes choice **A** the best choice.

21. **Choice C is correct.** The rate of a reaction is defined as the rate of appearance of product and/or the rate of disappearance of reactant. This means that either the rate of appearance of product or the rate of disappearance of reactant can be monitored to determine the reaction rate. This eliminates choices A and B. The intermediate concentration should remain fairly constant in a multi-step reaction; but in a one-step reaction, there is no intermediate formed. This means that choice **C** is an invalid statement and thus the correct answer selection. Choice D is eliminated, because by definition, the rate of a reaction is the change in reactant and product concentration as a function of time.

<hr>

Passage IV   (Questions 22 - 28)   **Catalyst Turnover Rate**

22. **Choice A is correct.** If the catalyst is the limiting reagent in the rate-determining step, then the catalyst regulates the rate of the reaction. The reaction can go only as fast as free sites on the catalyst open up. This means that the reaction proceeds at a constant rate (the rate at which the catalyst can reopen catalytic sites after binding a reactant molecule) until the reactant gets depleted. The product forms at a constant rate until the reaction reaches a point where the catalyst is no longer a limiting reagent. At this point, it follows standard kinetics by gradually slowing to a stop. The graph that shows this best is choice **A**. Choice D shows a change in rate that is too abrupt. The reaction gradually slows, rather than abruptly stopping. Choice C shows a reaction that gradually speeds up, then abruptly stops. There is no common scenario that would produce such results. Choice B is just tossed in there to complete the four choice per question requirement, and should be eliminated immediately.

23. **Choice C is correct.** The catalyst that can be used in the *lowest* concentration is the one with the greatest turnover rate. The passage does not discuss the lifetime of a catalyst, so only the rate of reaction need be considered. Table 1 lists the turnover rate of the four choices. The fastest turnover rate is 35,000 reactions per second, so the catalyst that can be used in lowest concentration and still have a fast reaction rate is Pt/PtO_2. The best answer is choice **C**. The rate of a catalyzed reaction depends on catalyst concentration and turnover rate.

24. **Choice B is correct.** If all three catalytic sites react equally, then it can be assumed that each site has a turnover rate of one-third that of the observed turnover rate for the catalyst. Because the catalyst is not saturated, the observed turnover rate is less than the maximum turnover rate for the catalyst. Combining these relationships yields the following:

Maximum site rate $= \dfrac{1}{3}$ Maximum catalyst turnover rate $> \dfrac{1}{3}$ Observed catalyst turnover rate = Observed site rate

This assumes that the maximum turnover rate per catalytic site is equal to or less than one-third of the maximum turnover rate for the catalyst. Choice A can be eliminated, because the maximum turnover rate of one catalytic site is greater than, not less than, one-third of the observed turnover rate. Because the maximum turnover rate per catalytic site is therefore greater than one-third of the observed turnover rate for the catalyst when it is not saturated, the best answer is choice **B**. The maximum turnover rate of one site equals one-third of the observed turnover rate only when the catalyst is saturated. Because the catalyst is *not* saturated, choice C can be eliminated. If the sites do not react equally, then no solid conclusion can be drawn. This eliminates choice D. Pick choice **B**.

25. **Choice B is correct.** A heterogeneous catalyst does not evenly distribute itself in solution. This is most commonly observed when the catalyst is in the solid phase and the reaction is either a gas phase or solution phase reaction. Aluminum trichloride is a Lewis acid that dissolves into solution evenly to react throughout the solution with the acid chloride. The three metal catalysts listed as other choices (Pd/PdO_2, Pt/PtO_2, and $(Me_3P)_3RhCl$) are from Table 1 of heterogeneous catalysts, so they are all examples of heterogeneous catalysts. The best choice is answer **B**.

26. **Choice C is correct.** A catalyst by definition is neither consumed nor produced in a reaction, so choices A and B are eliminated. A catalyst is regenerated in the reaction, which means that the correct choice is answer **C**. A catalyst is not altered in a reaction, unless it undergoes an undesirable reaction that renders it useless. The word "always" appearing the answer choice should get your attention, but because it is present in all of the answer choices, we can disregard any concerns.

27. **Choice B is correct.** If the product has a binding affinity for a catalytic site, then it does not release from the catalytic site as easily. This means that the product competes with the reactant for the catalytic site. Less free catalyst is available for the reactant as more of the product is formed. Because increasingly more product is formed as the reaction proceeds, the catalytic turnover rate slows as the reaction proceeds. This means that both the reaction rate and the turnover rate slow as the reaction proceeds. That makes choice **B** correct. This is known as *feedback inhibition*.

28. **Choice A is correct.** The turnover rate for a heterogeneous catalyst in the solid phase depends on its surface area. The more surface area, the more active sites available to reactant. To maximize the surface area, a solid catalyst can be powdered. An alternative to powdering the catalyst is to apply a thin coating of the catalyst to the surface of an inert solid. As mentioned in the passage, carbon is often chosen as the inert solid, because metals can be reduced onto the surface of carbon through electroplating. Choose **A** as the best answer to this question. The other advantage to plating a metal catalyst onto the surface of an inert solid is the ease with which the catalyst can be removed (filtered) from solution once the reaction is complete. A large chunk of solid can be removed from solution rather easily.

Passage V (Questions 29 - 35)   Half-Life Calculation and First-Order Decay

29. **Choice C is correct.** For a first-order reaction, the rate does in fact decrease with time, so choice A accurately depicts a first-order reaction. For a first-order reaction, the half-life remains constant, so the decay of reactant and formation of products is greatest initially, and slowly the rate tapers off. The concentration is based on an exponential relationship, so the graphs of both the disappearance of reactant and formation of product appears as they do in choices B and D. In choice **C**, the graph shows a steady rate throughout the process, which is true for zero-order reactions, but not for first-order reactions. The best answer is choice **C**.

30. **Choice C is correct.** Because the product of the half-life and rate constant ($t_{1/2} \times k$) is ln 2 (a constant), the half-life and rate constant are inversely proportional to one another. This implies that if the rate constant is doubled, the half-life is cut in half. The best answer is choice **C**.

31. **Choice A is correct.** One notable feature of a first-order reaction is that the half-life remains constant throughout the reaction. This eliminates choice D. The rate for a zero-order reaction is constant, so it takes more time to go from 100% reactant to 50% reactant than it does to go from 50% reactant to 25% reactant. This means that for a zero-order reaction, the half-life is decreasing with time. The best answer is choice **A**.

32. **Choice B is correct.** Because the product of the rate constant and the half-life is a constant, the units of the rate constant must cancel the unit of half-life. The unit of half-life is simply time, so the units of the rate constant must be inverse time (sec^{-1}). The best answer is choice **B**.

33. **Choice D is correct.** Twenty percent is one-fifth, so in the derivation in the passage, simply substitute one-fifth for one-half. The math is shown below, which leads you to select choice **D**.

$$\frac{C_t}{C_i} = e^{-kt} \therefore e^{-kt} = \frac{1}{5} \quad \text{which means that:} \quad \ln\frac{1}{5} = -kt \therefore -\ln\frac{1}{5} = kt \therefore \ln 5 = kt \quad \text{so} \quad t = \frac{\ln 5}{k}$$

34. **Choice C is correct.** At low reactant concentration, the half-life of the reaction is constant, so the reaction must be first-order at low concentrations. At higher concentrations, the half-life increases as the reactant concentration increases. A zero-order reaction has a constant rate, so the first fifty percent of reactants takes longer to decay than the next twenty-five percent (the second half-life) and so on. For a zero-order reaction, as the concentration of reactant increases, so does half-life. The graph shows zero-order behavior at higher reactant concentrations. The best answer is choice **C**. You may recall from enzyme kinetics that at high substrate concentration, the reaction is zero-order (saturated), but at lower substrate concentrations, the reaction becomes first-order.

35. **Choice D is correct.** A constant half-life is associated with a first-order reaction. A first-order reaction depends on just one reactant in its rate-determining step. In choices A and B, there is one step, but they each have two reactants, so both of them are second-order. In choice C, there are two steps, but both steps involve two reactants, so no matter which step is rate-determining, the reaction is second-order. In choice **D**, there is one step and just one reactant, so the reaction is first-order.

36.   **Choice C is correct.** Because the overall reaction is second-order, there must be a first-order rate dependence on the nucleophile. Methanol is not as good a nucleophile as the methyl sulfide, so the reaction rate should decrease with methanol. To support this idea, methyl sulfide is a stronger base than methanol, so methyl sulfide is a stronger lone pair donor than methanol. This makes choice **C** the best answer.

37.   **Choice B is correct.** The reaction is second-order, so rate = k $[CH_3SNa][CH_3CH_2I]$. The concentration values given in this problem correspond to the values given in the second row of the chart within the passage, except in the reverse order (which does not matter in this case, since the reaction is first-order with respect to both substrates). Rate = k $[0.25][0.10] = 3.52 \times 10^{-5}$, so answer **B** is the right choice.

38.   **Choice C is correct.** It is stated in the passage that the reaction is a substitution reaction, which depends on either one or two reactants. This makes it either an S_N1 reaction, and thus a first-order reaction, or an S_N2 reaction, and thus a second-order reaction. To determine the dependence on both reactants, hold the concentration of one of the reactants constant, and observe how the rate changes with an increase in the concentration of the other reactant. Comparing the data for the first two trials, $[CH_3CH_2I]$ is increased by a factor of five-thirds, while $[CH_3SNa]$ remains constant. The rate between the first two trials also increases by a factor of five-thirds. This implies that the reaction is first-order with respect to CH_3CH_2I. There are no two trials to compare where $[CH_3CH_2I]$ stays constant. This is where intuition comes into play. From Trial 1 to Trial 4, $[CH_3CH_2I]$ increases by a factor of two, while $[CH_3SNa]$ increases by a factor of 1.5. If the reaction depends only on $[CH_3CH_2I]$, then the rate will increase by a factor of two, while if the reaction depends on both, the rate will triple. The rate does in fact triple, so the reaction rate depends on both reactants. The reaction is second-order, meaning it is an S_N2 reaction. Choose **C**.

39.   **Choice B is correct.** According to Table 1, the reaction is second-order; but since $[CH_3SNa]$ is much larger than $[CH_3CH_2I]$, we can disregard the reactant in high concentration $([CH_3SNa])$ in the rate equation. The normal rate law for a second-order reaction is rate = k $[CH_3SNa][CH_3CH_2I]$; but because $[CH_3CH_2I] \ll [CH_3SNa]$, the rate law is given as rate = $k_{obs} [CH_3CH_2I]$, because throughout the duration of the reaction, the $[CH_3SNa]$ stays relatively constant so it does not act as a variable. It becomes engulfed by k_{obs}. Thus, even though the reaction is truly second-order, it appears to be first-order due to the vast difference in concentrations. This is referred to as *pseudo first-order*. The best answer is **B**.

40.   **Choice A is correct.** Since the reaction mechanism is dissociative, the rate of the reaction can be only as fast as the reactant that dissociates. This also means that the rate of the reaction depends on the concentration of the species that dissociates. In this case, $Co(en)_2NH_3Cl^{2+}$ is the only reactant in the rate-determining step, so doubling its concentration will in turn double the reaction rate. The new reaction rate is twice as large as the reaction rate was before doubling the reactant concentration. The nucleophile NH_3 has no direct effect on the rate. Choose **A** for success and correctness.

41.   **Choice B is correct.** Increasing the temperature of a system increases the reaction rate. This is true because more reactant molecules have enough energy to overcome the activation barrier ay a higher temperature than a lower temperature. Choice A is thus eliminated. Adding solvent lowers the concentrations of all species in solution, including the two reactants in the rate determining step. Adding solvent decreases the reaction rate, so choice **B** does not increase the reaction rate. The best answer is choice **B**. Adding a reactant in the rate-determining step increases the reaction rate. The reaction is concerted (one-step), so all reactants are involved in the rate determining step. This means that addition of one reactant increases the reaction rate, so choice C is eliminated. Using a less viscous solvent in a one-step reaction allows the molecules to move through solution faster, and thus collide more frequently. An increase in collision frequency causes an increase in reaction rate, so choice D is eliminated.

42.   **Choice C is correct.** According to the data in Table 1, the reaction order for the ethyl iodide substitution reaction is second-order, so the rate is proportional to the product of reactant concentrations. This makes the rate law for the reaction equal to k $[CH_3SNa][CH_3CH_2I]$. We can solve for the rate constant by substituting any row of data points from Table 1 into the equation. Choosing the first row of data points yields: $2.10 \times 10^{-5} = k [0.15][0.10]$, and solving for k yields:

$$k = \frac{2.10 \times 10^{-5} \, M\!/\!s}{0.015 \, M^2} = 1.40 \times 10^{-3} \, [M]^{-1}s^{-1}, \text{ choice } \mathbf{C}.$$

43. **Choice B is correct.** A dissociative reaction mechanism is synonymous with the S_N1 reaction mechanism, which is known to be a first-order reaction. In inorganic chemistry, a dissociative mechanism means a ligand dissociates (leaves) first, before another one attaches to the central metal. Choice **B** is the best answer.

44. **Choice B is correct.** The rate of an S_N1 reaction depends exclusively on the electrophile concentration, since the electrophile must dissociate (the leaving group must leave) before a nucleophile can attack. The dissociation reaction of the electrophile is the rate-determining step, so answer choice **B** is not a valid statement. The nucleophile has no influence on the rate of an S_N1 reaction. The rest of the choices are valid with respect to the rate of an S_N1 reaction.

45. **Choice B is correct.** As stated in the passage, the slowest step of the three steps is Step II. A reaction can proceed only as fast as the slowest step in the mechanism, so the rate-determining step must be Step II. Choice **B** is the best answer.

46. **Choice C is correct.** Adding water to the reaction mixture would push the Step I reaction backwards, generating more reactants ($[(NH_3)_5CoCl]^{2+}$ and OH^-) and consuming the intermediate product ($[(NH_3)_4Co(NH_2)Cl]^+$). The rate-determining step, Step II, depends on the concentration of the product from Step I $[(NH_3)_4Co(NH_2)Cl]^+$. Thus, a decrease in products from Step I will slow down the rate-determining step, thereby decreasing the overall reaction rate. The best answer is choice **C**. Choose **C** for sensations of correctness and satisfaction.

47. **Choice C is correct.** The steady state approximation says that after an initial period of time, balance within the reaction takes place, and the concentration of any intermediates stay relatively constant (in a steady state). This means that the rate at which the intermediate is produced is equal to the rate at which it is consumed. The intermediate in this case is $[(NH_3)_4Co(NH_2)Cl]^+$, which is held constant by being in the rate-determining step. It is formed by the forward reaction in Step I and consumed by both the reverse reaction of Step I and the forward reaction of Step II. Water is involved only in the reverse reaction of Step I, so water must appear only with k_{-1}. This eliminates all choices except **C**, which is the correct choice. In choice **C**, the rate law for the reaction that forms the intermediate is set equal to the sum of the rate law for the reverse reaction of Step I and the forward reaction of Step II.

48. **Choice A is correct.** Because of the bulky metal group attached to NH_3, the lone pair is withdrawn from the nitrogen, which increases the acidity of the protons bonded to nitrogen. This is verified by Step I, where the hydroxide anion (OH^-) deprotonates a proton from the NH_3 that is attached to the cobalt. Hydroxide anion is not strong enough to deprotonate ammonia normally, so the cobalt complex must have increased the acidity of ammonia. Increased acidity results in the lowering of the pK_a, so choose **A** for best result. The metal acts like a Lewis acid, and the ammonia acts like a Lewis base.

49. **Choice A is correct.** As pH is increased, the $[OH^-]$ is increased, so the equilibrium of Step I is pushed to the product side, resulting an increase in $[[(NH_3)_4Co(NH_2)Cl]^+]$. As $[[(NH_3)_4Co(NH_2)Cl]^+]$ increases, the rate of the reaction increases. So, as the pH increases, it can be concluded that the rate of the reaction increases. A temperature increase always affects the reaction rate, so pick **A**.

50. **Choice D is correct.** A catalyst does not increase the equilibrium constant (the yield). A catalyst increases only the ease and rate at which the reaction proceeds to the products. That is, it lowers the activation energy, which speeds up the rate-determining step, which increases the reaction rate. Choice **D** is not characteristic of a catalyst.

51. **Choice D is correct.** The units for rate are molar per second, and the units for concentration are molar. Solving for the units of k_{obs} gives us $M^{-1}s^{-1}$, which makes choice **D** the best answer.

$$k_{obs} = \frac{rate}{product\ of\ concentrations} = \frac{M/sec}{M^2} = \frac{1/sec}{M} = \frac{1}{M \cdot sec}$$

52. **Choice D is correct.** Table 1 shows that when the partial pressure (and thus the concentration) of sulfur dioxide is doubled, and the partial pressure of oxygen remains constant, then the rate of the reaction is quadrupled. This means that there is an exponential relationship between the initial rate and sulfur dioxide. This is best shown in choice **D**.

53. **Choice C is correct.** A catalyst lowers the activation energy for a reaction. According to the principle of microscopic reversibility, the same pathway that is taken for the forward reaction is also taken for the reverse reaction. This means that a catalyst lowers the activation energy for both the forward and the reverse reactions by the same amount. Consequently, the forward and reverse reaction rates are both lowered, making choice **C** the best answer.

54. **Choice D is correct.** Because the reaction rate does not depend on oxygen gas, O_2 cannot be involved in the rate-determining (slowest) step of the reaction mechanism. This eliminates choices B and C. Because the rate depends on the square of the partial pressure of sulfur dioxide, SO_2 must be in the rate-determining (slowest) step twice. The slowest step must involve two molecules of SO_2. This eliminates choice A, making the best choice **D**.

55. **Choice D is correct.** For every oxygen molecule lost, two sulfur trioxide molecules are gained. This means that the equality between the two rates must contain both a negative sign and a factor of 2. Choices A and C are both eliminated because they both lack a negative sign in the equality. The magnitude of the rate of consumption of oxygen is one-half that of the magnitude of the rate of formation of sulfur trioxide, so choice **D** is the best answer.

56. **Choice D is correct.** Because three gas molecules lie on the reactant side of the equation and only two gas molecules lie on the product side of the equation, the total pressure of the system decreases as the reaction proceeds forward. The reaction is fastest initially, so the pressure shows the greatest reduction in the early stages of the reaction. As the reaction slows, so does the rate at which the total pressure of the system decreases. The total pressure decreases, but at a gradually decreasing rate, until it comes to rest. Choice **D** is the best answer.

57. **Choice D is correct.** The rate of the reaction increases when the temperature increases, so choice A is valid and thus eliminated. Decreasing the volume of the container increases the concentration of the reactants, so the rate increases. Choice B is valid and thus eliminated. Because sulfur dioxide shows a dependency on the rate of the reaction, choice C is valid and thus eliminated. As shown in Table 1, there is no effect on the rate when oxygen is added. Choice **D** is the best answer.

58. **Choice A is correct.** The only way that the rate could depend on oxygen would be if the rate-determining step involved oxygen. At the temperature of the original experiment, oxygen was not involved in the rate-determining step. Adding a catalyst sometimes lowers one step of a reaction enough so that it is no longer the rate-determining step. In this case, the increased temperature gives rise to an altogether different mechanism, where oxygen is now involved in the rate determining step. This is sometimes seen with thermodynamic versus kinetic control reaction mechanisms, where a change in the system temperature changes the mechanism by which the reaction proceeds. The best answer is choice **A**.

Passage IX (Questions 59 - 65)   Chelating Effect

59. **Choice B is correct.** To monitor the rate of a reaction, one must monitor either the appearance of product or disappearance of reactant. The products are polymer-$MC_4H_{13}N_3$ and PR_3, so the reaction can be monitored by the appearance of either one. Choice **B** suggests monitoring by the disappearance of PR_3, which would *not* work. The reactants are $C_4H_{13}N_3$ and polymer-$M(PR_3)_3$, so it is correct to monitor the reaction by their disappearance. Choice **B** is the best answer.

60. **Choice D is correct.** An endothermic reaction absorbs heat, so that over time, the reaction cools the solution. As the solution cools, the reaction rate decreases, resulting in a lower observed reaction rate. This eliminates choice A. A higher energy product is associated with an endothermic reaction (or less exothermic reaction), so the rate decreases, because the heat energy in the system decreases. Choice B is eliminated. A higher energy transition state requires more activation energy, so the rate decreases. This eliminates choice C. The correct answer must be choice **D** because of the lower activation energy associated with the lower energy transition state.

61. **Choice C is correct.** The ligand replacing the phosphines is a tridentate ligand. Therefore, after the new ligand attaches, the second and third lone pairs of the tridentate ligand can more easily bind the metal and displace the phosphine. This is known as the chelating effect and makes choice **C** the best answer choice. The chelating effect is greatest in associative (S_N2-like) mechanisms where there is a rate dependence on the nucleophile. The chelating effect is weakest in dissociative (S_N1-like) mechanisms where there is no rate dependence on the nucleophile.

62. **Choice A is correct.** The ethyl substituent is larger than the methyl substituent, so the triethyl phosphine is bulkier than the trimethyl phosphine. This makes the triethyl phosphine a better leaving group. The rate of the reaction increases with the ethyl substituents, making choice **A** the best answer. Whether the reaction mechanism is associative or dissociative, the leaving group affects the reaction rate.

63. **Choice B is correct.** Any time that a strong bond must be broken it slows the reaction rate. A one-step reaction is faster than a two-step reaction as a general (but not absolute) rule. The lowest activation energy is associated with the breaking of a weak bond. The best answer is choice **B**.

64. **Choice D is correct.** By adding methyl groups onto the nitrogens of the amine, the steric hindrance in the transition state increases and thus the reaction rate decreases. This makes statement I a true statement. The fact that steric hindrance in the transition state reduces the reaction rate makes statement II false (*not* true). Changing the temperature affects only the free energy in the system and does not affect the energy levels of any transition states. This makes statement III false (*not* true). The correct answer is therefore choice **D**.

65. **Choice C is correct.** Using one bidentate ligand instead of two monodentate ligands increases the reaction rate, because of the chelating effect. It is easier for the second lone pair of a bidentate ligand to bind the central metal than it is for a second ligand to attach to the metal. Choice A is thus eliminated. Adding a catalyst that weakens the leaving group's bond to the transition metal lowers the transition state energy and thus increases the reaction rate. Choice B is therefore eliminated. Adding solvent lowers the concentration of all species in solution, so the concentration of any species in the rate-determining step is reduced. The rate of the reaction decreases (or remains the same, if it remains saturated), so choice **C** is the choice that does *not* increase the reaction rate. Increasing the temperature of a reaction always increases the reaction rate. Choose **C** for best results.

Passage X (Questions 66 - 72)   **Proposed Mechanisms**

66. **Choice D is correct.** Regardless of which step is the rate-determining step in the reaction, according to Mechanism I, the reaction is a two-step reaction, so choices A and B are eliminated. On top of that, the question discusses two reaction steps (rearrangement and addition), so it cannot be a one-step mechanism. Because the second step is the rate-determining step, the rate law for the reaction is k_2 times the reactant in step two (H_2CO_2). Choice **D** is the best answer.

67. **Choice D is correct.** A catalyst does not affect the thermodynamic values of a reaction; it affects only the reaction rate and the activation energy. Choices A, B, and C are all thermodynamic values, while choice **D** involves a kinetic value. This eliminates choices A, B, and C, while making choice **D** the only possible answer. A lower activation energy leads to a greater rate of reaction. This makes choice **D** the best answer.

68. **Choice D is correct.** Choice A would represent product formation, if the reaction proceeds at a constant rate; but a constant reaction rate describes a zero-order reaction, not a first-order reaction, so choice A is eliminated. Choice B describes the consumption of reactant in a first-order reaction, so it is eliminated. Choice C does not describe any obvious typical graph associated with kinetics in chemistry. It shows exponential growth, but such things are more associated with population genetics than chemical kinetics. Choice C is eliminated. In choice **D**, the product concentration is building with time, but the rate at which it builds (slope of the tangent) is gradually decreasing, indicating that the reaction is slowing as it proceeds. A gradually diminishing reaction rate is observed with a first-order reaction, so the best answer is choice **D**.

69. **Choice D is correct.** In the gas phase, free radical carbons are more stable than carbocations, so choice A is a false statement. If choice A were a true statement, it would support Mechanism I over Mechanism II (not Mechanism II over Mechanism I), so choice A should be eliminated. Ions in general are not stable in the gas phase, so anions (being a sub-group of ions) are not stable, making choice B a false statement. Choice C requires previous knowledge to be eliminated. More energy is required to break a bond in a heterolytic fashion (resulting in ions) than to break a bond in a homolytic fashion (resulting in free radicals). Choice C should be eliminated. If you didn't know this, then move on to choice **D**. Chemist II states that charged molecules are highly unstable in the gas phase, so choice **D** must be valid, because free radicals are more stable in the gas phase than ions are.

70. **Choice B is correct.** Intermediates are unstable relative to the products and reactants. This eliminates choices C and D. A transition state is defined as unstable with no measurable lifetime, so choice A can be eliminated. An intermediate is said to have a short lifetime, so choice **B** is the best answer.

71. **Choice A is correct.** Labeled oxygen in the reactant (CO) can still be found in the CO_2, because carbon dioxide is the only reactant that contains oxygen, so all oxygen atoms in the reactants (labeled or not) will be found in carbon dioxide. This means that choice **A** is invalid. Adding H_2O causes more intermediate to form, so the reaction rate increases with the increasing intermediate concentration. This makes choice B a valid statement. Removing CO causes less intermediate to form, so the reaction rate decreases with the decreasing intermediate concentration. This makes choice C a valid statement. As the reactant concentration decreases, the rate must decrease, because there are fewer collisions between reactant molecules as the concentration decreases. This makes choice D a valid statement. Choice **A** is the best answer.

72. **Choice C is correct.** Doubling the [H_2O] may or may not change the reaction rate, depending on whether water is involved in the rate-determining step. Choice A is probably eliminated. Carrying the reaction out in a different solvent (or in this case, using a solvent), definitely changes the reaction, meaning that one mechanism may be preferred over the other. This eliminates choice B. Because the rate constant varies directly with temperature, it is always true that as the temperature is increased, the reaction rate increases. Choice **C** is thus the best answer. The stability of the intermediate affects the reaction rate, but should have no bearing on the K_{eq} for the overall reaction. This eliminates choice D. The K_{eq} for a reaction depends on the stability of the product and reactants.

Questions 73 - 80   Not Based on a Descriptive Passage

73. **Choice D is correct.** Be careful not to use thermodynamics when looking at kinetics in this case. $\Delta G° = -RT \ln K$ and a reaction is favorable if ΔG is negative, according to thermodynamics. This is ΔG_{act}, however, and that is the activation energy. As the activation barrier becomes greater, fewer molecules can overcome the activation barrier, and more energy (heat) is needed to obtain the same reaction rate. Statements I and II are both correct. A catalyst lowers the energy needed to form the transition state, which reduces the value of ΔG_{act}. It does not increase the value of ΔG_{act}, so statement III is eliminated. Choice **D** is consequently the best answer.

74. **Choice A is correct.** For a first-order reaction, the half-life is found as follows:

$$t_{1/2} = \frac{\ln 2}{k}$$

They gave us that the value of $\ln 2$ is 0.693 and k is 0.0693 sec^{-1}, so this is just a plug-in mathematical problem.

$$t_{1/2} = \frac{0.693}{0.0693 \text{ s}^{-1}} = 10 \text{ seconds}$$

The best answer is choice **A**.

75. **Choice A is correct.** Using the equation for the reaction, it is easiest to follow changes in concentration for each component in the reaction.

$$\begin{array}{ccccc} 2\text{ A} & \rightarrow & \text{B} & + & \text{C} \\ -0.450 & & +0.225 & & +0.225 \end{array}$$

The rate of disappearance of A is twice the rate of appearance of B and C, so the rate of appearance of B must be half of the rate of disappearance of A, which is 0.225 molar per second. Choice **A** is the best answer.

76. **Choice C is correct.** The intermediate is in its highest concentration just after the start of the reaction, because it is formed from the reactant but is not yet used up to form the product. As the reaction proceeds toward completion, the intermediate is depleted. Choice A is valid. Intermediates are defined as species that have finite lifetimes and exist only during the course of the reaction. If the lifetime is too small to be measured, then the species is referred to as a *transition state*. Choice B is therefore valid. An intermediate builds up when it collects before the rate-determining step. This makes choice D valid and choice **C** invalid, which means the latter is the best choice. Select answer choice **C** for correctness rewards.

77. **Choice D is correct.** To solve this problem, you must see the trend in the data. The rate of decomposition is greatest initially, and it slows drastically with time. The data describe a second-order process, where 0.25 is the concentration after 4 minutes. Because the half-life constantly doubles, the first half-life is 1 minute 20 seconds and the second half-life is 2 minutes 40 seconds. The trend shows that significantly more X decomposes between 2 minutes and 3 minutes than decomposes during the period between 3 minutes and 4 minutes. This means that the [X] at the 3-minute mark is less than the midway point between 2 minutes and 4 minutes. The correct answer must be less than 0.30 M, making choice **D** the best answer.

78. **Choice C is correct.** B is a product, so the [B] is initially zero. This eliminates the graphs in choices A and B. Equilibrium is represented by a flat slope, but it is reached gradually and is not the sharp point indicated in the graph in choice D. The graph in choice **C** is the best representation of the reaction.

79. **Choice D is correct.** The rate-determining step of a reaction is always the slowest step in the reaction. The slowest step in a two-step reaction can be either the first or second step. The best answer is choice **D**.

80. **Choice C is correct.** Choices A and B can be eliminated, because there is no intermediate (both reactions are one-step). The deeper nadir (low point) between the two transition states is associated with the greater concentration of the intermediate. This makes choice **C** the best answer.

Section X

Electrochemistry

by Todd Bennett

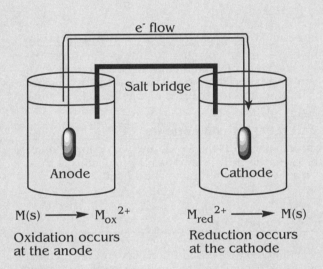

e⁻ flow

Salt bridge

Anode

Cathode

$M(s) \longrightarrow M_{ox}^{2+}$

Oxidation occurs
at the anode

$M_{red}^{2+} \longrightarrow M(s)$

Reduction occurs
at the cathode

Redox Reactions
a) Determining Oxidation States
b) Oxidation and Reduction
c) Balancing Redox Reactions
   i. by the Bridge Method
   ii. by the Half-Cells Method
d) Variations on Balancing

Voltage and Energy
a) Energetics
b) Half-Reaction Potentials (EMF)
c) Cell Potentials
c) Free Energy Change

Electrochemical Cells
a) Definitions and Terminology
b) Galvanic Cell
c) Electrolytic Cell
d) Concentration Effects on Voltage
e) Nernst Equation

Redox Applications
a) Batteries
b) Electrical Devices
c) Chemical Applications
d) Electrolysis
e) Electroplating
f) Galvanizing

The BERKELEY R·E·V·I·E·W®

Specializing in MCAT Preparation

Electrochemistry Section Goals

 Know the definitions of terms used in oxidation-reduction chemistry.

In oxidation-reduction chemistry, there are two half-reactions which together form the overall electron-transfer reaction. The species losing electrons is being oxidized and is referred to as the *reducing agent*. The species gaining electrons is being reduced and is referred to as the *oxidizing agent*.

 Be able to balance a redox equation in neutral aqueous solution, acid, or base.

You must be able to identify the oxidation states of atoms within the molecules, determine which atom has gained electrons and which atom has lost electrons, and then set the stoichiometric coefficients so that the same number of electrons lost by one reactant equals the number of electrons gained by the other reactant. This balances the electrons in the reaction. The atoms and charges must also balance, and this is often accomplished by adding either hydroxide anions or hydronium cations along with water to the reaction.

 Be able to calculate the voltage for redox reactions, given the half-cell potentials.

The voltage for a redox reaction is the sum of the half-reaction voltages. You do not multiply the voltage by any factor to balance electrons, because voltage is measured in terms of a set number of electrons. For the free energy, the number of electrons becomes important, because the free energy is expressed in terms of moles, not electrons. The equation for the free energy is: $\Delta G° = -nFE°$.

 Be able to draw an electrochemical cell and label its components.

In an electrochemical cell, oxidation (loss of electrons) occurs at the anode and reduction (gain of electrons) occurs at the cathode. This means that electron flow (the opposite of current) is from anode to cathode. The counter-flow of anions is from cathode solution to anode solution, through a membrane or salt bridge.

 Be able to identify a galvanic cell and an electrolytic cell.

A galvanic cell is characterized by a favorable redox reaction that releases energy. An electrolytic cell is characterized by an unfavorable redox reaction that requires the addition of energy. A galvanic cell has a solid wire or a voltmeter in the wire, while an electrolytic cell has a battery (applied voltage) in the wire.

 Understand the principle behind the Nernst equation.

The Nernst equation demonstrates that voltage depends not only on the standard reaction, but also on the concentrations of the products and reactants. As is true of all reactions, an electrochemical reaction becomes increasingly less favorable until it reaches an equilibrium state, where in the reaction shows no net change in concentration. At equilibrium, no energy is exchanged, so the reaction is complete and the cell is no longer functional. The Nernst equation calculates the voltage of a cell under any conditions, taking into account this concentration dependence.

 Be able to determine the quantity of metal formed during electroplating.

Metal cations plate out on the surface of the cathode (electron-rich electrode) when a current is applied to a cell. This process is known as *electroplating*, a special case of electrolysis. The voltage applied when electroplating must be great enough to force an unfavorable reaction to proceed.

 Understand how a battery functions.

Batteries are essentially reversible cells that discharge voltage when they are acting in a galvanic fashion, and that absorb energy when they are acting in an electrolytic fashion. A battery can be made of many electrochemical cells in series with a selectively-permeable membrane for ion exchange.

 Understand the similarities between circuits and electrochemical cells.

In physics we discuss voltage and current, while in chemistry these are referred to as *electrochemical potential* and *electron flow*, respectively. You should recognize these synonyms and know how chemical properties of the reactants affect its physical values (e.g., electron affinity and reduction potential).

Electrochemistry

Electrochemistry addresses chemical reactions that involve electron transfer. Electrochemistry is found in general chemistry (i.e., electrochemical cells), biology (i.e., anabolism and catabolism), organic chemistry (i.e., gain and loss of oxygen atoms by carbon), and physics (i.e., voltage generated by batteries). Because of the abundance and breadth of electrochemical applications, it is one of the key topics to fully understand before sitting for your MCAT. We shall start with a general chemistry perspective by identifying changes in oxidation states and accounting for electrons to help us answer oxidation-reduction questions. The number of electrons lost by the molecules being oxidized equals the number of electrons being gained by the molecules being reduced. The reactant being oxidized experiences an increase in oxidation state and the reactant being reduced experiences a decrease in oxidation state.

When electrons are exchanged in an oxidation-reduction reaction, large quantities of energy are involved. Of the different types of chemical reactions (including oxidation-reduction, composition, decomposition, substitution, acid-base, and precipitation), oxidation-reduction reactions generate the greatest change in free energy and enthalpy. As a consequence of the large amount of energy involved in oxidation-reduction reactions, they are used as the chemical source of energy for many everyday devices. Most fuels and power sources stem from oxidation-reduction reactions. Common examples include hydrocarbon fuels for combustion engines, and oxidation-reduction reactions involving transition metals used in batteries. While chemists keep track of the energy associated with an oxidation-reduction reaction, physicists and engineers develop devices to harness this energy. We need to make sure that our rules and concepts can be used to answer both chemistry and physics questions.

To harness the energy of electron transfer in chemical reactions, electrochemical cells are designed to separate the oxidation half-reaction from the reduction half-reaction. Electrons are transferred through a wire from the molecule releasing the electrons (located in the anode) to the molecule gaining the electrons (located in the cathode). The energy associated with electron flow can be converted into mechanical work, heat, light, and translational energy for particles. The role of a chemist in all of this is to design an energy source that efficiently generates electron flow. This is done through galvanic cells and batteries. We will address the difference between a galvanic cell and a battery later in this section. To understand electrochemical cells, you must be able to identify the direction of the electron flow and determine the energy and voltage associated with the process. Electromotive force determines the cell voltage, which can be converted into an amount of energy that is proportional to the number of electrons involved in the overall oxidation-reduction reaction.

Electrochemistry also entails reactions that naturally occur in an oxygen rich environment. Oxygen in the air oxidizes (rusts away) most metals with which it comes in contact. Natural oxidation is facilitated in the presence of moisture or a conducting solvent. We shall consider simple biological examples. We will also consider chemistry concepts such as galvanizing. Galvanizing is a protective process that involves plating a more reactive metal onto a less reactive metal, so that this more reactive species (the sacrificial metal) is the one oxidized by air, rather than the material being protected. Repairs to oxidized metals can be made using electroplating, which lays a coat of a conducting material onto its surface. This works only if the material can conduct electricity. Oxidation-reduction chemistry can also be used to form pure liquids and gases. This procedure is referred to as electrolysis, and we will address it briefly. Electrochemistry, in summary, covers a ton of applications.

Redox Reactions

Determining Oxidation States

Each atom within a molecule shares at least one electron with each neighboring atom to which it is bonded. Oxidation states of an atom result from electronic bookkeeping. Oxidation states are based on an all-or-nothing approach to electron-sharing. Bonding electrons are viewed as being completely associated with the more electronegative atom. Within a bond, the more electronegative atom is considered to take all of the electrons, while the less electronegative atom is considered to get none of the bonding electrons. Determining the oxidation state of an atom within a molecule requires comparing the electronegativity of the atom of interest with the electronegativity of all atoms to which it is bonded. The oxidation state is a sum of these bonding values. Drawn in Figure 10-1 below are the oxidation states for a series of molecules.

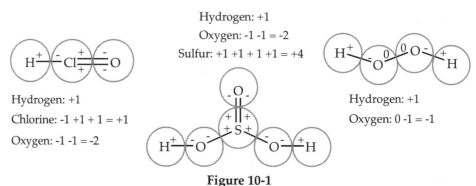

Figure 10-1

Oxygen usually has an oxidation state of -2 (except in molecular oxygen, when it's 0 and peroxides, when it's -1) and hydrogen usually has an oxidation state of +1 (except in hydrides, when it's -1 and molecular hydrogen, when it's 0). For example, in H_3PO_3, H is +1 and O is -2. In order for H_3PO_3 to be neutral, the sum of the oxidation states must be zero, so the oxidation state of P must be +3. In addition, know that alkali metals (group I metals) usually have an oxidation state of +1, alkaline earth metals (group II metals) usually have an oxidation state of +2, and halogens usually have an oxidation state of -1 (except in oxyacids and molecular halogens). Let's consider $SOCl_2$. The oxidation state of sulfur in $SOCl_2$ is +4 because oxygen is -2 and chlorines are -1 each. For the molecule to be neutral, the oxidation state of sulfur must be +4. The sum of the oxidation states of the atoms within a molecule must equal the charge of the molecule.

Example 10.1

In which of the following compounds is the oxidation state of phosphorus the GREATEST?

A. P_4O_6
B. P_4
C. PH_3
D. $POCl_3$

Solution

Using the idea that hydrogen carries an oxidation state of +1, chlorine -1, and oxygen -2, the oxidation state of phosphorus can be found in each compound. In P_4O_6, the oxidation state is +3. In P_4 (and every pure element), the oxidation state is 0. In PH_3, the oxidation state is -3. Finally, in $POCl_3$, the oxidation state is +5. This makes the oxidation state of phosphorus highest in $POCl_3$, choice **D**.

Oxidation-reduction reactions involve the transfer of electrons from the reducing agent (reductant) to the oxidizing agent (oxidant). The consequence of electron transfer in a chemical reaction is a change in the oxidation states of at least two atoms. If the oxidation state increases due to the loss of electrons, then that process is oxidation. If the oxidation state decreases due to the gain of electrons, then that process is reduction. In every redox reaction, there must be both oxidation and reduction. To help remember the definitions, use the mnemonic **"Leo the red cat say 'GER'."** This tells us **l**oss of **e**lectrons is **o**xidation, **g**ain of **e**lectrons is **r**eduction, and **red**uction occurs at the **cat**hode. Listed below are some common electrochemistry terms you must know.

Oxidation: A loss of electrons by an atom, resulting in an increase in oxidation state.

Reduction: A gain of electrons by an atom, resulting in a decrease in oxidation state.

Oxidizing agent: The reactant doing the oxidizing, getting reduced in the process.

Reducing agent: The reactant doing the reducing, getting oxidized in the process.

A few useful things to know about oxidizing agents and reducing agents are:

Oxidation (LEO)	Reduction (GER)	Reducing Agent	Oxidizing Agent
Loss of electrons	Gain of electrons	Gets oxidized/Cause reduction	Gets reduced/Cause oxidation
Ox State increases	Ox State decreases	Rich in H/Poor in O/e⁻ rich	Rich in O/Poor in H/e⁻ poor
Gain of Bonds to O	Gain of Bonds to H	Metal in low oxidation state	Metal in high oxidation state
Loss of Bonds to H	Loss of Bonds to O	$LiAlH_4$, $NaBH_4$, Pd/H_2	CrO_3/H_2SO_4, $KMnO_4/OH^-$
Catabolism	Anabolism	N_2H_4/OH^-, NADH, $FADH_2$	RCO_3H, O_3, NAD^+, FAD

Example 10.2
Which of the reactions below represents oxidation-reduction?

I: $HBr(g) + Al(s) \rightarrow H_2(g) + AlBr_3(s)$

II: $HClO_4(aq) + Ti(OH)_2(aq) \rightarrow HClO(aq) + TiO_2(s) + 2 H_2O(l)$

III: $Na_2CO_3(aq) + HCl(aq) \rightarrow H_2O(l) + CO_2(g) + NaCl(aq)$

A. I only
B. II only
C. I and II only
D. I and III only

Solution
In Reaction I, the oxidation state of hydrogen changes from +1 (in HBr) to 0 (in H_2), so hydrogen is reduced. Aluminum changes from 0 (in Al) to +3 (in $AlBr_3$), so aluminum is oxidized. This makes Reaction I an oxidation-reduction reaction. In Reaction II, the oxidation state of chlorine changes from +7 (in $HClO_4$) to +1 (in HClO), so chlorine is reduced. Titanium changes from +2 (in $Ti(OH)_2$) to +4 (in TiO_2) so titanium is oxidized. This makes Reaction II an oxidation-reduction reaction. This makes choice **C** correct. Reaction III is an acid-base reaction in which no oxidation states change. Protons are transferred, but not electrons.

Example 10.3
Which compound is the oxidant (oxidizing agent) in the reaction below?

$HCl(aq) + KMnO_4(aq) + FeCl_2(aq) \rightarrow MnCl_2(aq) + FeCl_3(aq) + H_2O(l) + KCl(aq)$

A. $HCl(aq)$
B. $KMnO_4(aq)$
C. $FeCl_2(aq)$
D. $MnCl_2(aq)$

Solution

Oxidizing and reducing agents are reactants, so choice D, $MnCl_2$, is eliminated immediately. Oxidizing agents (oxidants) get reduced, thus causing oxidation. Thus, we are looking for the reactant that has an element that finishes with a lower oxidation state. Mn in $KMnO_4$ has an oxidation state of +7. Once reduced, Mn (in $MnCl_2$) has an oxidation state of +2. Manganese is reduced from +7 to +2 in the reaction. The reactant containing Mn is the oxidizing agent. This makes choice B, $KMnO_4$, the best answer. In the reaction, Fe is oxidized from +2 to +3, making $FeCl_2$ (the iron containing reactant) the reducing agent.

Biological Oxidation-Reduction

Oxidation-reduction reactions are quite common in organic chemistry and biochemistry. During you MCAT studies, it is inefficient to try to memorize several biochemical pathways and organic chemistry reactions. The test writers are typically good about feeding you details in the passage. What will help greatly in your preparation is seeing the common themes within each of the various types of reactions. From an organic chemistry and biochemistry perspective, oxidation is often the gain of bonds to oxygen and/or the loss of bonds to hydrogen. For instance, dehydrogenation (loss of H_2) is an oxidative process. From an organic chemistry and biochemistry perspective, reduction is often the loss of bonds to oxygen and/or the gain of bonds to hydrogen. For instance, conversion from a ketone into a secondary alcohol (loss of a bond to O) is a reductive process.

Generally speaking, organic and biological oxidizing agents are rich in oxygen and poor in hydrogen (i.e., Na_2CrO_4, $KMnO_4$, NAD^+, and FAD) and reducing agents are poor in oxygen and rich in hydrogen (i.e., $NaBH_4$, $LiAlH_4$, NADH, and $FADH_2$). It might also prove useful to note that like in organic chemistry where a certain reagent can carry out a specific reaction, biochemical reagents show a similar repeated reactivity. As a general rule, NADH reduces carbonyls while FADH2 reduces alkene double bonds. Such knowledge can make several biochemical pathways easier to process. Consider glycolysis for instance. Simply put, it's the breakdown of a six-carbon molecule with a carbonyl group into two three-carbon molecules. Because it's a breakdown (catabolic process, therefore oxidation), it requires an oxidizing agent. Oxidizing agents are poor in H, so it requires either NAD^+ or FAD. Because it involves a carbonyl and not an alkene double bond, it requires NAD^+ and not FAD. Figure 10-2 demonstrates this approach to glycolysis.

1 6-Carbon carbonyl compound $\xrightarrow{\text{Breakdown}}$ 2 3-Carbon carbonyl compounds

1) Involves Breakdown (C6 → C3), so it is **Oxidative/Catabolic**
2) Gets oxidized, so it needs an oxidizing agent (**Compound poor in H**)
3) Involves a carbonyl, so it **requires NAD^+** (NAD for C=O and FAD for C=C)

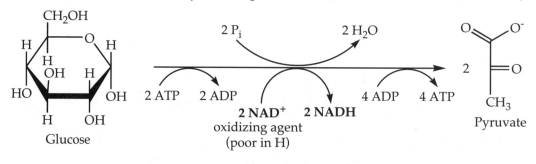

Figure 10-2

Balancing Redox Reactions (Balancing Electrons, Charges, and Atoms)

Balancing redox reactions may be accomplished using either the bridge method or the half-cell method. The bridge method involves connecting atoms that have changed oxidation states and determining the number of electrons that have been exchanged. The half-cell method involves breaking the reaction into two sub-reactions: oxidation and reduction. In either method, you start by determining the oxidation states of atoms within the reactant and product molecules, you balance the reaction electronically by having equal numbers of electrons involved in the oxidation and reduction half-reactions, and you balance the charges and atoms last. Balancing oxidation-reduction reactions entails following a basic recipe. The recipe, shown below, is true for the half-cell and the bridge methods.

First: Determine the oxidation states of the atoms.

Second: Identify how many electrons are involved in the oxidation half-reaction and how many electrons are involved in the reduction half-reaction.

Third: Balance the electrons (by cross-multiplying the half-reactions).

Fourth: Balance the charges on each side of the equation by adding H^+ to the side with either excessive negative charge or insufficient positive charge (or OH^- to the side with either excessive positive charge or insufficient negative charge).

Fifth: Balance the atoms by adding water to the appropriate side of the reaction.

Bridge Method (Connect-the-Reactants Method)

Balancing by the bridge method entails connecting the oxidizing agent to its reduced product and the reducing agent to its oxidized product, thereby creating a so-called *bridge*. The electron count in each bridge must be the same. To accomplish this, the bridges are cross-multiplied as shown below:

Consider the following reaction: $V(s) + Zr^{2+} \rightarrow V^{3+} + Zr(s)$

First: The oxidation state of $V(s)$ is 0, while the oxidation state of vanadium in V^{3+} is +3. The oxidation state of zirconium in Zr^{2+} is +2, while the oxidation state of $Zr(s)$ is 0.

Second: Identify how many electrons are involved in the oxidation half-reaction and how many electrons are involved in the reduction half-reaction. Connect like reactants and products by a bridge.

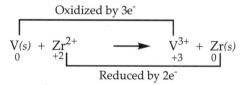

Third: To balance the electrons, cross-multiply the two bridge half-reactions. The oxidation half-reaction is multiplied by **2** and the reduction half-reaction is multiplied by **3**.

Following the three steps yields the following balanced reaction.

$$2 V(s) + 3 Zr^{2+} \rightarrow 2 V^{3+} + 3 Zr(s)$$

This particular example was straight-forward, and likely could have been done by inspection. More challenging cases involve the balancing of charges and atoms, which is accomplished by adding either hydroxide or hydronium, depending on the pH, and then water.

Consider the balancing of the following reaction in a basic solution:

$$VO_3^-(aq) + Ti(OH)_2(aq) \rightarrow VO(s) + Ti(OH)_4(aq)$$

First: The oxidation state of vanadium in VO_3^- is +5. The oxidation state of vanadium in VO is +2. The oxidation state of titanium in $Ti(OH)_2$ is +2. The oxidation state of titanium in $Ti(OH)_4$ is +4.

Second: Identify how many electrons are involved in the oxidation half-reaction and how many electrons are involved in the reduction half-reaction. Connect like reactants and products by a bridge.

Reduced by 3e⁻
$\overset{+5}{V}O_3^-(aq) + \overset{+2}{Ti}(OH)_2(aq) \longrightarrow \overset{+2}{V}O(s) + \overset{+4}{Ti}(OH)_4(aq)$
Oxidized by 2e⁻

Third: To balance the electrons, cross-multiply the two bridge half-reactions. The oxidation half-reaction is multiplied by 3 and the reduction half-reaction is multiplied by 2.

$2 \times 3e^-$
$2\,VO_3^-(aq) + 3\,Ti(OH)_2(aq) \longrightarrow 2\,VO(s) + 3\,Ti(OH)_4(aq)$
$3 \times 2e^-$

Fourth: The net charge on the left side of the equation is 2 (-1) = -2, while the net charge on the right side of the equation is 0. Because the reaction is carried out in base, hydroxide is added to balance charges. To balance the charges, 2 OH- are added to the right side, making the net charge on each side of the equation -2. This yields the following:

$$2\,VO_3^-(aq) + 3\,Ti(OH)_2(aq) \rightarrow 2\,VO(as) + 3\,Ti(OH)_4(aq) + 2\,OH^-(aq)$$

Fifth: To balance atoms, count the H atoms on both sides. There is an excess of 8 H atoms (14 - 6 = 8) on the right side of the equation so 4 H2O are added to the left side of the equation to balance the hydrogen atoms. This leaves the following overall balanced equation:

$$4\,H_2O(l) + 2\,VO_3^-(aq) + 3\,Ti(OH)_2(aq) \rightarrow 2\,VO(s) + 3\,Ti(OH)_4(aq) + 2\,OH^-(aq)$$

Example 10.4
In acidic solution, what is the balanced form of the following reaction?

$$BiO_3^-(aq) + Mn^{2+}(aq) \rightarrow Bi^{3+}(aq) + MnO_4^-(aq)$$

A. $8\,H^+(aq) + 3\,BiO_3^-(aq) + 2\,Mn^{2+}(aq) \rightarrow 5\,Bi^{3+}(aq) + 2\,MnO_4^-(aq) + 4\,H_2O(l)$

B. $14\,H^+(aq) + 5\,BiO_3^-(aq) + 2\,Mn^{2+}(aq) \rightarrow 5\,Bi^{3+}(aq) + 2\,MnO_4^-(aq) + 7\,H_2O(l)$

C. $12\,H^+(aq) + 5\,BiO_3^-(aq) + 2\,Mn^{2+}(aq) \rightarrow 5\,Bi^{3+}(aq) + 2\,MnO_4^-(aq) + 6\,H_2O(l)$

D. $14\,H^+(aq) + 3\,BiO_3^-(aq) + 2\,Mn^{2+}(aq) \rightarrow 3\,Bi^{3+}(aq) + 2\,MnO_4^-(aq) + 7\,H_2O(l)$

Solution
First, the electrons must be balanced. The oxidation state of Bi changes from +5 to +3 (Bi is reduced by 2 electrons) while the oxidation state of Mn changes from +2 to +7 (Mn is oxidized by 5 electrons). To balance the electrons, the bismuth compounds must be multiplied by 5 and the manganese compounds must be multiplied by 2. This eliminates choices A and D. Charge must also balance. In choice **B**, the reactant side charge is +14 -5 +4 = +13 and the product side charge is +15 -2 = +13. The charges balance in choice **B**, making it the best answer.

Half-Cell Method (Separate the Half-Reactions Method)

Balancing by the half-cell method entails separating, and independently balancing the half-reaction of the oxidizing agent to its reduced product and the half-reaction of the reducing agent to its oxidized product. The electron count in each half-reaction must be equal. To accomplish this, the half-reactions are cross-multiplied. This method is shown below:

Consider the balancing of the following reaction in a basic solution:

$$MnO_4^-(aq) + Zn(s) \rightarrow MnO_2(s) + Zn(OH)_4^{2-}(aq)$$

First: The oxidation state of manganese in MnO_4^- is +7, while in MnO_2, the oxidation state of manganese is +4. The oxidation state of zinc in Zn is O, while in $Zn(OH)_4^{2-}$ the oxidation state of zinc is +2. Using this information, the half-cell reactions can be drawn:

Second: Identify how many electrons are involved in the oxidation half-reaction and how many electrons are involved in the reduction half-reaction.

Reduction half-reaction: $MnO_4^- + 3\,e^- \rightarrow MnO_2$

Oxidation half-reaction: $Zn \rightarrow Zn(OH)_4^{2-} + 2\,e^-$

Third: To balance the electrons at six for each half-cell reaction, the reduction half-reaction must be multiplied by 2 and the oxidation half-reaction must be multiplied by 3.

Reduction: $\mathbf{2}\,(MnO_4^- + 3\,e^- \rightarrow MnO_2)$

Oxidation: $\mathbf{3}\,(Zn \rightarrow Zn(OH)_4^{2-} + 2\,e^-)$

This leads to the electronically balanced half-reaction equations:

Reduction: $2\,MnO_4^- + \mathbf{6}\,e^- \rightarrow 2\,MnO_2$

Oxidation: $3\,Zn \rightarrow 3\,Zn(OH)_4^{2-} + \mathbf{6}\,e^-$

Fourth: For the reduction half-reaction, the net charge on the left side of the equation is -8, while the net charge on the right side of the equation is 0. For the oxidation half-reaction, the net charge on the left side of the equation is 0, while the net charge on the right side of the equation is -12. Because the reaction is carried out in base, hydroxide is added to balance charges. To balance the charges, 8 OH- are added to the right side in reduction half-reaction and 12 OH- are added to the left side in oxidation half-reaction. Net charge does not have to equal zero on both sides of a reaction, it just has to be equal on both sides. This yields the following half-reactions:

Reduction: $2\,MnO_4^- + 6\,e^- \rightarrow 2\,MnO_2 + \mathbf{8}\,OH^-$

Oxidation: $3\,Zn + \mathbf{12}\,OH^- \rightarrow 3\,Zn(OH)_4^{2-} + 6\,e^-$

Fifth: To balance atoms in the reaction, count the H atoms. There is an excess of 8 H atoms on the right side of the reduction half-reaction, so 4 H_2O are added to the left side to make the hydrogens balance. The atoms are already balanced in the oxidation half-reaction.

Reduction: $\mathbf{4}\,H_2O + 2\,MnO_4^- + 6\,e^- \rightarrow 2\,MnO_2 + 8\,OH^-$

Oxidation: $3\,Zn + 12\,OH^- \rightarrow 3\,Zn(OH)_4^{2-} + 6\,e^-$

The two half-reactions are added to complete our balancing process, yielding the final balanced reaction:

$$4\,H_2O(l) + 4\,OH^-(aq) + 2\,MnO_4^-(aq) + 3\,Zn(s) \rightarrow 2\,MnO_2(s) + 3\,Zn(OH)_4^{2-}(aq)$$

Potentially Difficult Species (Compounds with Multiple Redox Sites)
Balancing redox reactions is easy when you follow the procedure just outlined in the previous section. However, there are a few pitfalls of which you should be aware. They involve compounds with multiple atoms undergoing oxidation or reduction. Reaction 10.1 and Reaction 10.2 are examples of reduction half-reactions with multiple atoms within a molecule being reduced.

$$Cr_2O_7{}^{2-} + 6\,e^- \rightarrow Cr_2O_3 \qquad\qquad H_2O_2 + 2\,e^- \rightarrow 2\,OH^-$$

$$\textbf{Reaction 10.1} \qquad\qquad\qquad\qquad \textbf{Reaction 10.2}$$

Example 10.5
What are the coefficients after the following reaction is balanced in base?

$$H_2O_2(aq) + VO^{2+}(aq) \rightarrow VO_2{}^+(aq) + OH^-(aq)$$

A. $1\,H_2O_2(aq) + 2\,VO^{2+}(aq) \rightarrow 2\,VO_2{}^+(aq) + 2\,OH^-(aq) + 2\,H_2O(l)$
B. $1\,H_2O_2(aq) + 2\,VO^{2+}(aq) + 2\,OH^-(aq) \rightarrow 2\,VO_2{}^+(aq) + 2\,H_2O(l)$
C. $2\,H_2O_2(aq) + 2\,VO^{2+}(aq) \rightarrow 2\,VO_2{}^+(aq) + 2\,OH^-(aq) + 2\,H_2O(l)$
D. $2\,H_2O_2(aq) + 2\,VO^{2+}(aq) + 2\,OH^-(aq) \rightarrow 2\,VO_2{}^+(aq) + 2\,H_2O(l)$

Solution
The oxidation state of oxygen in H_2O_2 is -1, while in OH^-, the oxidation state of oxygen is -2. The oxidation state of vanadium in VO^{2+} is +4, while in $VO_2{}^+$ the oxidation state of vanadium is +5. Two oxygen atoms per peroxide molecule are reduced, so the peroxide reduction half-reaction requires two electrons (as shown below). The vanadium oxidation half-reaction releases one electron.

$$H_2O_2 + 2\,e^- \rightarrow 2\,OH^-$$

Upon cross-multiplying the half-reactions, the ratio of peroxide to vanadium oxide dication (VO^{2+}) is 1 : 2, eliminating choices C and D. Although it seems that hydroxide should be on the product side of the reaction, the charges, oxygen atoms, and hydrogen atoms do not balance in choice A. This eliminates choice A. Choice **B** is correct, because hydroxide is added to the reactant side to balance charges. This cancels out the hydroxide formed upon the reduction of peroxide.

Example 10.6
What is the ratio of silver species to aluminum species in the following reaction?

$$AgOH(aq) + Al(s) \rightarrow Ag(s) + AlO_2{}^-(aq)$$

A. $3 : 1$
B. $1 : 3$
C. $3 : 2$
D. $2 : 3$

Solution
In this example, the silver atom is being reduced by one electron and the aluminum atom is being oxidized by three electrons. This means that balancing yields a ratio of three silver species (AgOH) to one aluminum species (Al). The ratio of the silver species to aluminum species is 3 : 1, choice **A**.

You may have experienced Example 10.6 first hand (or more appropriately, "first tooth"), if you have ever bitten into a piece of aluminum foil with a tooth containing an old silver filling. This experience is rather jolting.

Voltage and Energy

Energetics

Electrochemistry involves the transfer of energy in oxidation-reduction reactions. Energy is released in the form of electrical flow. The driving force is a voltage (Joules per Coulomb). Current is the result of a potential difference (voltage) between two points that have an electrically conducting medium between them. This is definitely the case when biting on foil with a silver filling. The task of interest becomes converting this less than pleasurable jolt into a productive form of energy (such as heat, light, or mechanical work). The first step involves determining the voltage that is generated by an oxidation-reduction reaction.

Electrons flow from the species with the lower electron affinity to the species with the greater electron affinity. However, we do not calculate the energetics of the reaction based on electron affinity difference, we use electromotive force (*emf*). Electromotive force is a voltage, and exhaustive tables have been produced that list the *emf* values associated with hundreds of half-reactions.

Half-Reaction Potentials (Standard *emf* Values Relative to Hydrogen)

The energetics of half-cells are measured relative to the reduction of hydronium into hydrogen. **The reduction of two protons (H^+) to form hydrogen gas (H_2) is defined as the reference standard, and assigned an *emf* of zero volts.** Any compound that can be reduced more favorably than a proton has a positive reduction potential. Likewise, any compound for which reduction is less favorable than a proton has a negative reduction potential. Oxidation values are relative to the oxidation of hydrogen gas, $H_2(g)$. Any compound that can be oxidized more favorably than a hydrogen gas has a positive oxidation potential. Likewise, any compound for which oxidation is less favorable than hydrogen gas has a negative oxidation potential. Table 10.1 is an abbreviated list of some of common reduction half-reactions and their corresponding *emf* value.

Half Reaction	$E°$ (V)	Half Reaction	$E°$ (V)	Half Reaction	$E°$ (V)
$Au^{3+} + 3e^- \rightarrow Au$	1.50	$2\,H^+ + 2e^- \rightarrow H_2$	0.00	$Mn^{2+} + 2e^- \rightarrow Mn$	-1.18
$Cl_2 + 2e^- \rightarrow 2\,Cl^-$	1.36	$Ni^{2+} + 2e^- \rightarrow Ni$	-0.23	$Al^{3+} + 3e^- \rightarrow Al$	-1.66
$Pd^{2+} + 2e^- \rightarrow Pd$	0.99	$Fe^{2+} + 2e^- \rightarrow Fe$	-0.44	$Mg^{2+} + 2e^- \rightarrow Mg$	-2.37
$Ag^+ + 1e^- \rightarrow Ag$	0.80	$Cr^{3+} + 3e^- \rightarrow Cr$	-0.73	$Na^+ + 1e^- \rightarrow Na$	-2.71
$Cu^{2+} + 2e^- \rightarrow Cu$	0.34	$Zn^{2+} + 2e^- \rightarrow Zn$	-0.76	$K^+ + 1e^- \rightarrow K$	-2.92

Table 10.1

Example 10.7

Which of the following species is the strongest reducing agent?

A. Cl_2
B. Cu
C. Mg^{2+}
D. Zn

Solution

Reducing agents get oxidized, so we need to reverse the reactions in Table 10.1. This eliminates choices A and C, because Cl_2 and Mg^{2+} cannot oxidize further. Between Zn and Cu, the more favorable oxidation (reverse reaction from Table 10.1) is found with zinc (0.76 > -0.34). Choice **D** is the best answer.

Most tables list reduction half-reactions, rather than oxidation half-reactions. Reduction half-reactions with larger (more positive or less negative) *emf* values, are more favorable than reduction half-reaction with smaller *emf* values. Table 10.1 can be used to determine relative strength of an oxidizing agent. Of the reactants listed in Table 10.1, Au^{3+} is the strongest oxidizing agent, because it is the species that undergoes most favorable reduction half-reaction. Conversely, of the products listed in Table 10.1, K is the strongest reducing agent, because it is the species that undergoes most favorable oxidation half-reaction. Reactions in Table 10.1 can be reversed to show oxidation half-reactions. When the half-reaction is reversed, the sign of *emf* changes, but the magnitude does not.

There is a pattern within the table. Generally speaking, *precious metals* do not readily oxidize, which is what makes them so ideal for currency. As such, the cations of precious metals such as gold, silver, platinum, palladium, and to a small extent copper have relatively high reduction potentials. On the other end of the spectrum are the alkali and alkaline earth metals, which have relatively low ionization energies, so they are easily oxidized. As such, the cations of alkali and alkaline earth metals such as sodium, potassium, and magnesium have very negative reduction potentials. Viewing redox questions using a periodic trend perspective can sometimes make a question easier. For instance, lithium metal is a better reducing agent than calcium metal, because alkali metals are more easily oxidized than alkaline earth metals given their lower ionization energies. Lastly there are the transition metals that tend to make up the bulk of the reduction table. They have no predictable periodic trends, so there is no clear pattern with their reduction potentials.

Example 10.8
Which of the following species is the strongest oxidizing agent?

A. Ca^{2+}

B. Li^+

C. Pt^{2+}

D. Zr^{2+}

Solution
Oxidizing agents get reduced, so we need to determine which species will most readily gain electrons. None of the reactions are listed in Table 10.1, so we must depend on periodic trends and intuition. Choice A, Ca^{2+}, is an alkaline earth metal, so it is stable as a +2 cation. As such, Ca^{2+} does not have a strong drive to gain electrons, so it will not be a strong oxidizing agent. Choice A is eliminated. Choice B, Li^+, is an alkali metal, so it is stable as a +1 cation. As such, Li^+ does not have a strong drive to gain electrons, so it will not be a strong oxidizing agent. Choice B is eliminated. Choice C, Pt^{2+}, is a valuable metal, so it is highly probable that it is unstable as a cation and prefers to be in its metallic state. As such, Pt^{2+} likely has a strong drive to gain electrons, so it is a strong oxidizing agent. Choice **C** is the best answer so far. Choice D, Zr^{2+}, is a transition metal, so it's hard to know how it will react. You may notice that the currency metals are later in the transition metal block of the periodic table, so zirconium being on the left side is probably willing to give up electrons and become a cation. It's not ideal reasoning, but choice D is not the best answer. Choice **C** is the best answer.

Cell Potential (Voltage Associated with Redox Reactions Pairs)

The cell potential for an oxidation-reduction reaction is a sum of the oxidation half-reaction potential and the reduction half-reaction potential. This is shown as Equation 10.1 below:

$$\varepsilon_{reaction} = \varepsilon_{reduction} + \varepsilon_{oxidation} \qquad \textbf{(10.1)}$$

The values for ε are listed in terms of voltage, which is independent of the number of electrons in the reaction. Voltage is defined as joules per coulomb, so the number of electrons in a reaction is not pertinent, given that a coulomb of charge is the same amount, no matter how many electrons are exchanged in a reaction. This is to say that a coulomb represents a fixed number of electrons. Whether a coulomb of charge is gathered one electron at a time or three electrons at a time, there is a fixed amount of energy per coulomb. The *emf* value for the oxidation-reduction reaction from Example 10.6 is determined by a standard procedure, as shown below:

$$AgOH(aq) + Al(s) \rightarrow Ag(s) + AlO_2^-(aq)$$

The half-cell reactions are:

$$Al(s) \rightarrow Al^{3+}(aq) + 3\,e^- \qquad\qquad Ag^+(aq) + 1\,e^- \rightarrow Ag(s)$$

From Table 10.1, the $\varepsilon°$ for two corresponding reduction half-reactions:

$$Al^{3+}(aq) + 3\,e^- \rightarrow Al(s) \quad \varepsilon_{red} = -1.66V \qquad Ag^+(aq) + 1\,e^- \rightarrow Ag(s) \quad \varepsilon_{red} = 0.80V$$

The Al half-reaction must be reversed to fit the overall reaction, because Al is oxidized in the reaction. When reversing the Al half-reaction, the emf sign is reversed too. However, it should be noted, when you multiply a reaction by an integer, you **do not multiply** the *emf* by an integer. Reduction potential is an intensive property that does not change with conditions. This means that voltage does not depend on the number of electrons in the reaction. The following value is determined for the silver-aluminum oxidation-reduction reaction:

Oxidation:	$Al(s) \rightarrow Al^{3+}(aq) + 3\,e^-$	1.66 V
Reduction:	$3\,Ag^+(aq) + 3\,e^- \rightarrow 3\,Ag(s)$	0.80 V
Overall:	$3\,Ag^+(aq) + Al(s) \rightarrow 3\,Ag(s) + Al^{3+}(aq)$	2.46 V

Emf values need not be memorized, but in general, the greater the electron affinity, the greater the reduction potential. Likewise, a lower the ionization energy corresponds to a greater the oxidation potential.

Example 10.9
What is the emf for the following oxidation-reduction reaction?

$$Cl_2(g) + Cu(s) \rightarrow 2\,Cl^-(aq) + Cu^{2+}(aq)$$

A. 2.38 V
B. 1.70 V
C. 1.02 V
D. 0.68 V

Solution
The redox half-reactions are: $Cl_2(g) + 2e^- \rightarrow 2\,Cl^-(aq)$ and $Cu(s) \rightarrow Cu^{2+}(aq) + 2e^-$. According to Table 10.1, the *emf* for the reduction of chlorine gas is + 1.36V and the *emf* for the oxidation of copper metal is - 0.34V. This means that the overall reaction voltage is 1.36 - 0.34 = 1.02 V. Choice **C** is the best answer.

Free Energy Change (Conversion from Voltage to Energy)

In the same manner that energy is exchanged when bonds are broken and formed, energy is exchanged when an electron is transferred from one atom to another. However, unlike electromotive force (cell potentials), the energy associated with an electrochemical cell depends on the number of electrons. Free energy is considered in units of joules per mole of electrons. The energy per mole of electrons can be determined from the cell voltage. Equation 10.2 is the equation for free energy in an electrochemical cell:

$$\Delta G_{reaction} = -nF\varepsilon_{cell} \qquad (10.2)$$

where F = 96,500 C per mole and n = electrons per reaction

A positive electromotive force (cell voltage) is associated with a favorable oxidation-reduction reaction, while a negative free energy change (ΔG) is associated with a favorable oxidation-reduction reaction.

Example 10.10

How much work can be done by a 1.60 V cell where there is one electron in the oxidation half reaction and from which 1.00 mole of electrons flow?

A. 0.772×10^5 J
B. 1.286×10^5 J
C. 1.554×10^5 J
D. 1.882×10^5 J

Solution

The units for work are Joules (Newton·meters). By keeping units in mind, calculations can be made far easier. This is even truer in physics than chemistry, where there are more units. Work is a form of energy, so the equation to use in solving this question is:

$$w = nF\varepsilon$$

The sign is ignored, because all of the answer choices are positive numbers. Substituting into the equation yields the following:

$$w = 1 \text{ mole electrons} \times 96,500\ ^C/_{\text{mole electrons}} \times 1.60\ ^J/_C = (96,500 \times 1.60)\ J$$

This multiplies out to be just less than 1.6×10^5 Joules, which makes choice **C** the best answer. The important conceptual message here is that energy is proportional to both cell voltage and the number of electrons involved in the oxidation-reduction reaction.

Electrochemical Cells

Definitions and Terminology

Electrochemical cells convert energy produced in a chemical reaction and electric flow (current). This is accomplished by separating the oxidation half-reaction from the reduction half-reaction, and connecting the two half-reactions by using a conducting wire. Rather than generate heat energy, the reaction generates electrical flow that travels from the reducing agent to the oxidizing agent. Electrical flow is a form of energy, just as heat, light, and mechanical work are forms of energy.

There are some standard terms that hold true for all electrochemical cells. These terms can be a source of confusion, because, physicists, biochemists, and chemists focus on different aspects of electrical devices and components such as the anode and cathode, so each scientist defines the terms slightly differently. A primary goal of this section is to develop a generic set of definitions that can be used in electric circuits, electrochemistry, and electrophoresis. The following terms are fundamentally defined to hold true for all electrical circuits, electric fields, and electrochemical cells.

Oxidation occurs at the anode, therefore, electrons flow away from the anode.

Reduction occurs at the cathode, therefore, electrons flow towards the cathode.

Cells are cyclic, therefore, ions must flow to balance the charge difference caused by electron flow.

Anions migrate towards the anode and cations migrate towards the cathode through electric fields.

Physicists often concern themselves with the flow of charge through a wire (current or electron flow), so they assign charges to the anode and cathode of a discharging battery according to the type of flow that the poles of the battery induce. Electrons flow from the anode to the cathode, so a physicist reaches the conclusion that the anode of a battery carries a negative charge (repelling the electrons) and the cathode of a battery carries a positive charge (attracting the electrons). Conventional usage among physicists denotes the cathode of a battery by a positive sign, and the anode by a negative sign.

Biochemists focus on the flow of ions through electrical fields (gel electrophoresis occurs between the charged plates of a capacitor). They assign charges to the anode and cathode of a charged capacitor according to the type of ions they attract. Anions migrate to the anode because of the anode's positive charge build-up (the anode has lost electrons). A biochemist concludes that the anode of a capacitor carries a positive charge (attracting anionic molecules). Cations migrate towards the cathode, because of the cathode's negative charge build-up (the cathode has gained electrons). A biochemist concludes that the cathode of a capacitor carries a negative charge (attracting cationic molecules).

Physicists and biochemists define the anode and cathode differently, because they are looking at different circuit elements (*discharging* battery versus a *charging* capacitor). Both perspectives are valid. They each are specific for their topic of interest. In electrochemical cells, we have both electron flow and ion migration, so we need a more general set of rules. To achieve that, we start by presenting the cathode and anode according to a multi-discipline perspective.

Cathodes have a positive core and accumulate negative charge on their surface, as current flows. Anodes have a negative core and accumulate positive charge on their surface, as current flows.

          Exclusive MCAT Preparation

Figure 10-3 shows the circuit notation for a battery and capacitor from this universal perspective.

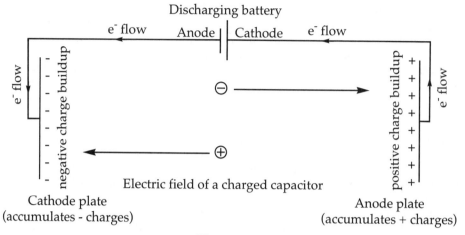

Figure 10-3

Figure 10-3 shows the flow of electrons through a wire, the migration of ions through a field, the poles of a battery, and the plates of a charging capacitor. All of the terms are addressed, so any observations in Figure 10-3 are universal for all electrical devices. The universal rules for electrical circuits, electric fields and electrochemical cells are thus:

1. Electrons flow from the anode to the cathode

2. Cations migrate through electric fields to the cathode

3. Anions migrate through electric fields to the anode

The physical make-up of an electrochemical cell allows for the transfer of electrons from the reductant (material being oxidized) to the oxidant (material being reduced). This is accomplished by placing the oxidation half-reaction in the anode and the reduction half-reaction in the cathode. Figure 10-4 shows a generic electrochemical cell, where the reactions and components are defined.

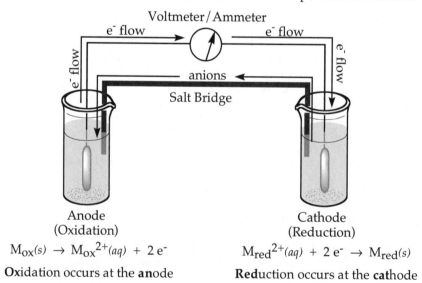

Figure 10-4

The salt bridge (or porous membrane in some cells) allows for the flow of ions (specifically anions). Salt bridges are not made of salt. They contain an aqueous solution, held in by a membrane, through which ions can diffuse from one half-cell into the other half-cell. Anions flow in the direction opposite to the direction of the electron flow, in order to balance out the distribution of charge associated with moved electrons. The salt bridge completes the loop. Without a salt bridge, or some form of anion transfer, the circuit is incomplete and the cell could not produce energy. Components of a cell carry out specific tasks. For instance, reduction occurs at the cathode and oxidation occurs at the anode. In electrochemical cells where both electrodes involve a reaction with a cation and metal, cathodes plate out (cations in solution are converted into a metal coating on the surface of the electrode) and anodes dissolve (the metal coating on the surface of the electrode is converted into cations which dissociate into solution).

In addition to cell layout, there is also standard *line notation* for cells. It is a standard representation that test writers can use instead of drawing out the electrochemical cell. When reading left to right, it goes from anode to cathode, and reactant to product within each half-reaction electrode. It follows the format shown in Figure 10-5:

$$M_{oxidation}(s) \mid yM\ M_{oxidation}^{2+}(aq) \mid\mid zM\ M_{reduction}^{2+}(aq) \mid M_{reduction}(s)$$
Reactant in anode | Product in anode || Reactant in cathode | Product in cathode

Figure 10-5

The oxidation half-reaction in Figure 10-5 is $M_{oxidation}(s) \rightarrow M_{oxidation}^{2+}(aq)$, and the reduction half-reaction is $M_{reduction}^{2+}(aq) \rightarrow M_{reduction}(s)$. The molarity of the cation in each cell is given with the individual cell, which in Figure 10-5 are represented by the letters y and z.

Example 10.11

A cell is composed of Zn metal in 0.10 M $Zn^{2+}(aq)$ solution in one half-cell and Cu metal in 0.10 M $Cu^{2+}(aq)$ solution in the other half-cell. A wire connects the metal plates, and by a salt bridge connects the solutions in the standard cell manner. After a given amount of time, it is expected that:

A. zinc metal dissolves away.
B. copper metal dissolves away.
C. both zinc metal and copper metal dissolve away.
D. zinc cation precipitates out as zinc metal.

Solution
The first task is to determine which metal is being oxidized and which cation is being reduced. This requires using the Table 10.1. The reduction half-cell potential for $Cu^{2+}(aq) \rightarrow Cu(s)$ is 0.34 V and the reduction half-cell potential for $Zn(s) \rightarrow Zn^{2+}(aq)$ is -0.76 V. For a positive cell potential, zinc must be oxidized and copper cation must be reduced. Because zinc is being oxidized, zinc metal dissolves away. This makes choice **A** the best answer.

There are two types of electrochemical cells we shall consider. They are *galvanic* (a spontaneous cell with $\varepsilon° > 0$) and *electrolytic* (a non-spontaneous cell with $\varepsilon° < 0$ and an applied voltage present to power the cell). Galvanic cells release energy in the form of electrical flow. Electrolytic cells are used for the storage of electrical potential, as is seen when recharging a battery. Electrolytic cells are also used in electrolysis (used to purify gases) and electroplating (used to purify metals and coat conducting surfaces). Because the voltage can be controlled, the rate of plating (dependent on the current) can be controlled.

Galvanic Cell (Voltaic Cell)

Galvanic cells discharge voltage, which means that they harness the energy of a favorable oxidation-reduction reaction. The oxidation-reduction reaction of a galvanic cell has a negative ΔG and a positive *emf*. By convention in chemistry, galvanic cells are drawn with the anode on the left and the cathode on the right. Electrons flow naturally from left to right (anode to cathode) through a wire connecting the two electrodes, because the reaction is favorable. A salt bridge must be present to allow spectator anions to migrate from the cathode solution to the anode solution. The spectator anion is often chloride or nitrate, because of their high solubility and lack of base properties. Drawn in Figure 10-6 below is a galvanic cell comprised of a zinc anode and copper cathode with a salt bridge.

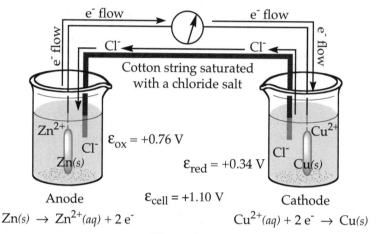

Figure 10-6

Over the life of the cell, the anode dissolves away and the cathode plates out. Higher quality electrochemical cells use a membrane that selects for anion flow.

The voltage for a cell is calculated by summing the reduction half-cell potential and the oxidation half-cell potential, as shown in Equation 10.1. To increase the voltage for a galvanic cell, the concentrations of the ions in the cathode solution can be increased or the concentration of the ions in the anode solution can be decreased. The more a reaction can proceed in the forward direction, the greater its voltage. A change in cation concentration changes voltage only slightly. To increase voltage significantly, multiple cells are aligned in series. This is why multiple batteries are hooked up in line in many battery-operated devices.

Example 10.12

How many of the galvanic cells shown in Figure 10-6 are required to generate a battery with a potential of approximately 5.5 volts?

A. 5 cells connected in parallel
B. 6 cells connected in parallel
C. 5 cells connected in series
D. 6 cells connected in series

Solution

According to Table 10.1, the reduction half-reaction potentials for zinc dication and copper dication are - 0.76V and + 0.34V respectively. The cell voltage for the galvanic cell shown in Figure 10-5 is 0.34 - (- 0.76) = 1.10 volts. To have an overall voltage of 5.5 V, you would need five times the standard cell voltage. This means that five cells are needed, so choices B and D are eliminated. Voltages add in series, so the five galvanic cells would need to be aligned in series. Choice A is eliminated and choice **C** is the best answer.

Electrolytic Cell

Like all electrochemical cells, an electrolytic cell involves two half-cells that are separated to allow for electrons to flow from the site of oxidation to the site of reduction. However, an electrolytic cell is based on a chemical reaction going in the thermodynamically unfavorable direction. Energy must be added to the electrolytic cell to accomplish this. This means that electrolytic cells must be connected to a voltage source. The sequence of circuits in Figure 10-7 shows two batteries opposing one another, which is analogous to an electrolytic cell. If two batteries oppose one another in series, then the electron flow direction is determined by the relative magnitudes of the voltage sources. The greater voltage source dictates the direction of electron flow. This is the reason why a voltage source is added to an electrolytic cell to oppose the natural flow of electricity from the chemical reaction.

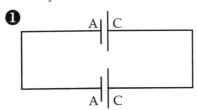

Without the voltages, the direction of the electron flow is uncertain.

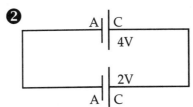

The larger voltage dictates the direction of the electron flow.

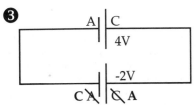

The poles of the lower battery are reversed by he forced electron flow.

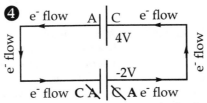

Electrons flow in a counterclockwise direction, charging the lower battery.

Figure 10-7

In an electrolytic cell, the applied voltage must exceed the natural voltage in order to force the reaction to proceed in the reverse direction. An electrolytic cell is the reverse of a galvanic cell, with electrodes being reversed because of the applied voltage. If the applied voltage is not high enough, then the reaction does not proceed in the reverse direction, and no charge is stored. Figure 10-8 shows the same half-reactions (except now they are reversed) as seen in Figure 10-6.

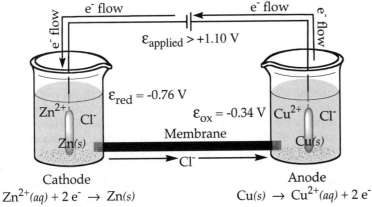

Cathode	Anode
$Zn^{2+}(aq) + 2\,e^- \rightarrow Zn(s)$	$Cu(s) \rightarrow Cu^{2+}(aq) + 2\,e^-$
Zn^{2+} is **red**uced at the **cat**hode where it plates out as $Zn(s)$	$Cu(s)$ is **ox**idized at the **an**ode where it dissolves away as Cu^{2+}

Figure 10-8

Concentration Effects on Cell Voltage

Galvanic cells eventually die out, so reactant and product concentrations must affect cell voltage. There are three ways to address this: first by observation of a battery-operated device (a flashlight is a good example), second by using Le Châtelier's Principle, and finally by a more rigorous mathematic calculation (using the Nernst equation). If one observes the light emitted by a flashlight over time, the intensity is constant for several hours before the light dims and then rapidly diminishes to zero over a few minutes. Figure 10-9 shows light intensity (a direct measure of cell voltage) as a function of time.

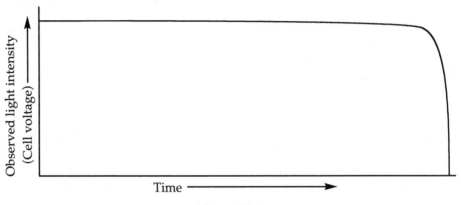

Figure 10-9

A good explanation for this observation is provided by Le Châtelier's principle. As more reactant is added to a reaction, the reaction becomes more favorable, so it produces more energy. Likewise, as more product is added to a reaction, the reaction becomes less favorable, so it produces less energy. Over the course of a reaction, reactants are converted into products, so the reaction becomes gradually less favorable until it reaches equilibrium, where it stops. Once at equilibrium, the reaction can give off no more energy. As a galvanic cell runs, reactants (cathode cations) are consumed and products (anode cations) are formed. This lowers the favorability, the energy, and the voltage of the cell. To maximize cell voltage, the reactants must be maximized and the products must be minimized. In fact, no products are needed to get the reaction to start.

Example 10.13

Which of the following cells has the GREATEST voltage?

A. $Zn(s) \mid 0.10 \text{ M } Zn^{2+}(aq) \mid\mid 1.00 \text{ M } Cu^{2+}(aq) \mid Cu(s)$

B. $Zn(s) \mid 1.00 \text{ M } Zn^{2+}(aq) \mid\mid 0.10 \text{ M } Cu^{2+}(aq) \mid Cu(s)$

C. $Ni(s) \mid 0.10 \text{ M } Ni^{2+}(aq) \mid\mid 1.00 \text{ M } Ag^{+}(aq) \mid Ag(s)$

D. $Ni(s) \mid 1.00 \text{ M } Ni^{2+}(aq) \mid\mid 0.10 \text{ M } Ag^{+}(aq) \mid Ag(s)$

Solution

To answer this question, we must by first use Table 10.1 to get *emf* values for the standard half reactions and then consider ion concentrations to determine if the actual voltage is higher or lower than the standard voltage. The zinc oxidation half-reaction produces +0.76 V and the copper reduction half-reaction produces +0.34 V. A standard zinc/copper cell produces +1.10 V. The nickel oxidation half-reaction produces +0.23 V and the silver reduction half-reaction produces +0.80 V. A standard nickel/silver cell produces +1.03 V. This eliminates choices C and D. To decide between choices **A** and B, we must consider the ion concentration. The greater voltage is found in the cell with most reactants and least products. A cell richer in reactant cations than product cations will have a cell voltage slightly greater than the standard voltage.

In the zinc/copper galvanic cell, Cu^{2+} is a reactant (it's being reduced) and Zn^{2+} is a product (it's being formed from the oxidation of zinc metal). The cell with the greatest voltage is the cell with more copper cation and less zinc cation. This is choice **A**. As a point of interest, because concentration affects the voltage, *emf* tables are measured starting at standard conditions of 25°C, 1 atm, and 1.00 M concentration of ions. And because temperature affects the equilibrium, it affects the voltage. That's why when flashlight batteries appear to have died, they work again for a short time after the flashlight is switched off for a brief interval to cool down. As the batteries cool, the reaction is no longer at equilibrium, because equilibrium changes with temperature.

Electrochemical potential can be generated when an anode and cathode contain the same species, but at different concentrations. This is what is known as a *concentration cell*. Concentration cells have no common application in chemistry, but the effect of concentration is observed as a cell loses reactant and gains product. Using the Nernst equation, it is possible to calculate the effect of concentration on the voltage of an electrochemical cell. This is observed with action potentials in physiology, but we will not address that here. The key fact is that as a cell runs down, voltage drops because reactants are depleted.

Nernst Equation

The effect of half-cell concentrations on voltage can be quantified according to the relationship between the reaction quotient (Q_{rx}) and the equilibrium constant (K_{eq}). For an oxidation-reduction reaction with K_{eq} greater than 1.0, if there are more reactants than products, then the cell voltage is greater than the standard cell voltage. If there are fewer reactants than products, the cell voltage is less than the standard cell voltage. In a general sense, the following estimate is valid:

$$Zn(s) \mid 0.10 \text{ M } Zn^{2+}(aq) \mid\mid 1.00 \text{ M } Cu^{2+}(aq) \mid Cu(s)$$
cell voltage is: 1.10 V + a little bit

$$Zn(s) \mid 1.00 \text{ M } Zn^{2+}(aq) \mid\mid 0.10 \text{ M } Cu^{2+}(aq) \mid Cu(s)$$
cell voltage is: 1.10 V - a little bit

The Nernst equation can be used to determine the exact value of the quantity represented by "a little bit" in the relationships above. The Nernst equation is derived from standard thermodynamic principles. The energy of any reaction, including electrochemical reactions, is the energy released as the reaction proceeds from its starting point to equilibrium. You should recall from thermodynamics that $\Delta G°$ is $RT \ln K_{eq}$ (the energy of reaction starting at standard conditions) and Q_{rx} is the reaction quotient at initial conditions. This means that the following relationship holds true.

$$Energy_{\text{initial-to-equilibrium}} = Energy_{\text{initial-to-standard}} + Energy_{\text{standard-to-equilibrium}}$$

This equation translates in a free energy relationship as:

$$\Delta G_{overall} = \Delta G° + RT \ln Q_{rx}$$

Substituting $-nF\varepsilon_{cell}$ for $\Delta G_{overall}$ and $-nF\varepsilon°$ for $\Delta G°$ in the equation yields:

$$-nF\varepsilon_{cell} = -nF\varepsilon° + RT \ln Q_{rx}$$

Upon dividing both sides of the equation by $-nF$, we get, Equation 10.3:

$$\varepsilon_{cell} = \varepsilon° - \frac{RT}{nF} \ln Q_{rx}$$

(10.3)

Converting from natural log to base-10 log is done by multiplying by 2.3, which converts Equation 10.3, the Nernst equation, into Equation 10.4:

$$\varepsilon_{cell} = \varepsilon° - 2.3\frac{RT}{nF}\log Q_{rx}$$

(10.4)

By substituting 8.314 for R, 298 for standard T, and 96,500 for F, we get a working equation, Equation 10.5:

$$\varepsilon_{cell} = \varepsilon° - \frac{0.059}{n}\log Q_{rx}$$

(10.5)

Equations 10.4 and 10.5 are derivations of the Nernst equation, which puts a quantitative value on the effects of concentration on cell voltage. The equation looks intimidating, but the likelihood of using in a detailed calculation on the MCAT is minimal. Conceptually, however, it is useful for determining relative voltages of different electrochemical cells. For instance, in the two zinc/copper examples in answer choices A and B in Example 10.13, Q is 10 in choice A and Q is 0.1 in choice B. There are two electrons in the reaction, log 10 is equal to 1.0 and log 0.1 is equal to -1.0. This means that the voltage of the cell in choice A is 1.10 + 0.03 = 1.13 V and the voltage of the cell in choice B is 1.10 - 0.03 = 1.07 V. Because 0.03 is small compared to the standard *emf* for the cell, the conceptual method using equilibrium principles is more than adequate for arriving at an answer. The small magnitude of the difference in voltage as concentration goes from 1.00 M to 0.10 M also explains why cell voltage remains relatively constant during the lifetime of a galvanic cell. While ion concentration affects the voltage, it does not significantly affect the voltage until the ratio of products to reactants is either extremely high or extremely low. The Nernst term for concentration is on the millivolt scale, making it useful in cell physiology, but not in general chemistry.

Example 10.14
What is the voltage an electrochemical cell with an anode of zinc metal in 0.01 M $Zn(NO_3)_2(aq)$ and a cathode of silver metal in 1.00 M $AgNO_3(aq)$?

A. 2.42 V
B. 2.30 V
C. 1.62 V
D. 1.50 V

Solution
First, we must identify the half-reactions.

Oxidation: $Zn(s) \rightarrow Zn^{2+} + 2\,e^-$ Reduction: $Ag^+ + 1\,e^- \rightarrow Ag(s)$

The standard cell potential for the reaction is found using values from 10.1 and substituting into Equation 10.1:

$$\varepsilon° = 0.80\text{ V} - (-0.76\text{ V}) = 1.56\text{ V}$$

The actual cell voltage is slightly higher than 1.56, because there is a higher cation concentration in the cathode than in the anode. We can safely choose choice **C** at this point. The exact value is found using Equation 10.5:

$$\varepsilon_{cell} = \varepsilon° - \frac{0.059}{n}\log\frac{[Zn^{2+}{}_{anode}]}{[Ag^+{}_{cathode}]^2} = 1.56\text{ V} - \frac{0.059}{2}\log\frac{0.01}{1^2}$$

$$\varepsilon_{cell} = 1.56 - 0.03\,(\log 0.01)\text{ V} = 1.56 + 0.06\text{ V} = 1.62\text{ V}$$

Choice **C** is the best answer.

Redox Applications

Batteries

Batteries are essentially a galvanic cell or a group of galvanic cells in series. Batteries convert electrical potential energy into direct current. By using a reversible oxidation-reduction reaction, a battery can act as either a galvanic cell or an electrolytic cell. As the battery discharges current (releases voltage), it is acting as a galvanic cell. By applying an opposing voltage to a battery, it can be recharged. As the battery absorbs current (recharges voltage), it is acting as an electrolytic cell. Batteries have a membrane that is highly selective, so that only spectator ions can pass. By keeping the two electrodes (half-reactions) separate, it is possible to discharge and recharge a battery for eternity. Eventually, entropy and chemical side-reactions will deteriorate the battery; but until that time, it can be used as a reliable power source. The lead car battery found in most cars can be discharged and recharged roughly 2000 to 3000 times.

Example 10.15

What is the cell potential of the following reaction used in a typical car battery?

Overall reaction:

$$Pb(s) + PbO_2(aq) + H_2SO_4(aq) \rightarrow PbSO_4(aq) + 2 H_2O(l)$$

Half-reactions:

$$PbO_2(aq) + 3 H^+(aq) + HSO_4^-(aq) + 2 e^- \rightarrow PbSO_4(aq) + 2 H_2O(l) \qquad \varepsilon_{cell} = 1.69 \text{ V}$$

$$PbSO_4(aq) + H^+(aq) + 2 e^- \rightarrow Pb(s) + HSO_4^-(aq) \qquad \varepsilon_{cell} = -0.35 \text{ V}$$

A. 1.02 V
B. 1.34 V
C. 2.04 V
D. 4.08 V

Solution

The second half-cell reaction must be reversed, so that when it is added to the first half-reaction, the sum is the overall reaction. This means that the *emf* must also be reversed. The cell potential for the battery is 1.69 - (-0.35) = 2.04 Volts, choice **C**. To achieve 12 volts total (as most standard car batteries provide), six cells must be aligned in series. This explains why there are six cells in water-based batteries to which you must add distilled water, if you have such a battery.

The dry cell batteries with which we are most familiar (used to power flashlights, portable radios, and other devices) are alkaline based. They typically employ the oxidation of zinc metal coupled with the reduction of manganese dioxide (MnO_2). A graphite rod serves as the conducting material through which electrons are transferred. A paste made of MnO_2 in NH_4Cl surrounds the graphite rod in the interior of the battery. This paste is in turn surrounded by insulated zinc which is connected a cap at the end of the battery. If the battery is placed into a circuit, then the cap is connected to the graphite rod, resulting in the transfer of electrons from the zinc to the manganese dioxide, through the circuit. Graphite is a good conductor because of its conjugation, but it has an internal resistance of roughly 15 Ω. As a result, batteries heat up when they are in use. The *emf* is not significantly affected, but the equilibrium of the reaction is.

Electrical Devices (Conversion of Electrical Flow into Work or Energy)

Some common devices are designed to convert electrical flow into other forms of energy, such as light, heat, and mechanical work. Knowing the basic schematics of how such devices operate will help you on the MCAT. Listed below are some typical examples of the conversion of electrical flow into other energy forms.

Fluorescent Tubes

Fluorescent tubes work by creating a potential difference between two plates (i.e., one plate builds up a positive charge by losing electrons as the other plate builds up a negative charge by gaining electrons). A gaseous ion between the plates is accelerated towards the oppositely charged plate (and away from the like-charged plate). Acceleration increases the kinetic energy of the particle until it collides with another gas particle. Some of the ion's kinetic energy is transferred to the other particle, which absorbs this energy by exciting an electron. When this excited electron relaxes back to its ground state, a photon is emitted from the gas particle in the tube. The energy of each photon is random, although the average energy of an emitted photon depends on the density of the gas, the length of the tube, and the plate charges. The inside surface of the tube is coated with either a fluorescing or phosphorescing agent to convert ultraviolet radiation into visible light.

Fluorescent tubes use alternating current. If direct current were used, then each plate would retain their same charge. As such, the ion in the tube would accelerate in one direction until striking the oppositely-charged plate. After reaching the plate, the ion would no longer move. The tube would be finished, and thus only a short flash of light would be produced. In order for the tube to function, the ion must move back and forth, which occurs as the plates reverse charges because of the alternating current. This means that fluorescent tubes actually produce pulsing light, much like a strobe lamp. The frequency is too fast for the human eye to detect, so the bulbs appear to produce continuous light. For this to work, the frequency of the pulsing light cannot be a harmonic of the eye's processing frequency, otherwise we'd see every second or third flash.

Example 10.16
Why would it be dangerous to use fluorescent lighting in sawmills?

A. Because the tubes emit light at frequency that could deteriorates lubricants.
B. Because the tubes emit light that could decompose wood.
C. Because the tubes emit light that could be in phase with the saw blade.
D. Because the tubes emit light that could initiate combustion.

Solution
The fluorescent bulb emits light that is periodic. Under certain circumstances, the spinning saw blade in a sawmill could appear to be in phase with the light. It could be perfectly in phase with the light, or it could be that the symmetry of the blade is such that a tooth appears to be in the same spot during each flash. The result would be an optical illusion that would make the spinning saw blade appear to be stationary. Generally speaking, spinning saw blades that appear stationary to the eye can be dangerous to the touch. Choice **C** is the best answer.

Heating Coils

Conventional heaters function by having a coiled wire through which current passes. A fan blows air across the surface of the hot coils, removing heat energy from the coils via convection. Electrical flow is converted into heat by the resistance in the wire. Each coil is thin, so resistance is high. Coils are employed to maximize surface area. Heat is transferred only at an interface between mediums, so more surface area allows for more heat transfer.

Incandescent Light Bulbs

Incandescent bulbs convert electrical flow into light by passing current through a resistor in a vacuum. The thermal energy builds up in the resistor, but it cannot be dissipated through convection or conduction in a vacuum (due to the absence of a medium). The only way to release energy to the environment is through radiation of light causing the hot bulb filament to glow. The bulb emits electromagnetic radiation of many frequencies.

Incandescent bulbs are spherical to maintain their structural stability. It is nearly a vacuum inside the bulb, so the spherical shape prevents the atmospheric pressure from crushing the bulb. Gas-filled bulbs are typically more tubular than evacuated incandescent bulbs. An added benefit is the inert nature of a vacuum, which protects the filament from oxidation. If preventing oxidation were the only consideration when designing the bulb, then some incandescent bulbs might be filled with an inert gas, such as nitrogen or a noble gas. This is not the case. If an incandescent bulb were filled with an inert gas, then the increase in temperature would cause the gas to build up pressure inside the bulb, which could rupture the bulb.

Example 10.17

Why is the filament thin and made of tungsten?

A. It is thin to maximize resistance, and tungsten is used because its low thermal coefficient of expansion.

B. It is thin to maximize resistance, and tungsten is used because its high heat of fusion.

C. It is thin to maximize resistance, and tungsten is used because its low ionization energy.

D. It is thin to minimize resistance, and tungsten is used because its high sublimation point.

Solution

A thin filament maximizes resistance, and thus removes more energy from the current ($P = I^2R$). This eliminates choice D. Tungsten is chosen because it has the highest melting point of any conducting metal. The temperature of the filament is extremely high, so a filament with a high melting point must be used to avoid having the filament melt and break the circuit. A high melting point is associated with a large enthalpy of fusion, so choice **B** is the best answer. A material with a low melting point would be found in a fuse. A fuse is designed to break when current exceeds a certain value, which is why metals used to make fuses generally have a low melting point.

Electric Motors

Electric motors function by means of a magnetic field induced by electrical flow. When current flows through a loop, a magnetic field with specific orientation is generated. By allowing the induced field to interact with an external, stationary magnetic field, a torque can be exerted upon the loop (depending on the orientation of the fields). The loop rotates to align with the existing stationary magnetic field (rotating up to a maximum of 180°). When the current is reversed, the induced magnetic field reverses, and thus opposes the external, stationary magnetic field. Torque is again generated, so the loop rotates another 180° to realign. By repeating this process (using alternating current through the loop), the loop spins, generating mechanical work that can turn the axis of a motor. The loop may actually be a series of loops comprising a solenoid.

Chemical Applications (Common Usage of Redox Reactions)

In addition to being responsible for most of the energy used to power household devices and heavy equipment, redox chemistry is also useful industrially for the purification of materials, the production of catalytic surfaces, and cosmetic applications in automobile accessories and jewelry plating. The surface of any material that can conduct electricity can be the site of an electrochemical reaction. This means that the different processes involve different reactants and different materials for the electrodes. Given that the MCAT test writers often present applications of physical science concepts, the important message is not that you understand each application in detail, but that you can answer electrochemistry questions based on the reactions and processes they give you in the passage.

Electrolysis

Electrolysis involves the application of a voltage (addition of electrical energy) to carry out an overall unfavorable process. This is what an electrolytic cell does as well. The goal of electrolysis is not to store charge, however, but to generate less favorable compounds. It is commonly used to obtain pure samples of gases (such as oxygen and chlorine) and reduced metals that naturally found in an oxidized state under ambient conditions (such as sodium and calcium). Shown below is Reaction 10.3, the electrolysis reaction of water to form oxygen gas and hydrogen gas and Reaction 10.4, the electrolysis reaction of hydrochloric acid to form hydrogen gas and chlorine gas.

$$2 \, H_2O(l) \rightarrow 2 \, H_2(g) + 1 \, O_2(g)$$

Reaction 10.3

$$2 \, HCl(aq) \rightarrow 1 \, H_2(g) + 1 \, Cl_2(g)$$

Reaction 10.4

Because hydrogen ion is reduced in both Reaction 10.3 and Reaction 10.4, it forms on the cathode (reduction occurs at the cathode), and the bubbles of hydrogen gas can be collected as they rise from the cathode. Chlorine gas and oxygen gas can also be collected, but from the anode. Generally, the anode and cathode plates in an electrolysis apparatus are made of an inert material that can conduct electricity. Materials commonly used include carbon (in its graphite allotrope) and platinum. Figure 10-10 below is the basic schematic of an electrolysis apparatus as applied to Reaction 10.3.

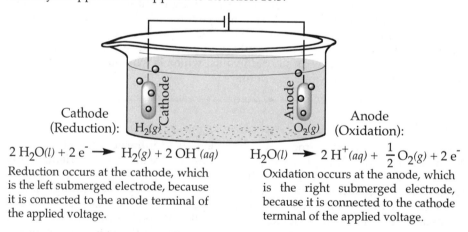

Cathode
(Reduction):

$$2 \, H_2O(l) + 2 \, e^- \rightarrow H_2(g) + 2 \, OH^-(aq)$$

Reduction occurs at the cathode, which is the left submerged electrode, because it is connected to the anode terminal of the applied voltage.

Anode
(Oxidation):

$$H_2O(l) \rightarrow 2 \, H^+(aq) + \frac{1}{2} O_2(g) + 2 \, e^-$$

Oxidation occurs at the anode, which is the right submerged electrode, because it is connected to the cathode terminal of the applied voltage.

Figure 10-10

To carry out an electrolysis reaction, the applied voltage must be great enough to overcome the negative voltage of the unfavorable redox reaction. If an excessively large voltage is applied to the cell, then other unfavorable reactions can take place, resulting in multiple products being formed. The ideal scenario is to apply a voltage that is slightly in excess of the absolute value of the voltage for the unfavorable oxidation-reduction reaction. Because the half-reactions both have water as the reactant, they need not be separated into half-cells.

Example 10.18
When a voltage is applied to the following reaction in the electrochemical cell below, what is true of the gases that form on each electrode and the solution?

$$2 H_2O(l) + 2 Cl^-(aq) \rightarrow 1 H_2(g) + 1 Cl_2(g) + 2 OH^-(aq)$$

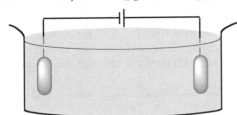

A. $H_2(g)$ bubbles form on the left electrode, $Cl_2(g)$ bubbles form on the right electrode, and the pH of the solution gradually increases.
B. $H_2(g)$ bubbles form on the right electrode, $Cl_2(g)$ bubbles form on the left electrode, and the pH of the solution gradually increases.
C. $H_2(g)$ bubbles form on the left electrode, $Cl_2(g)$ bubbles form on the right electrode, and the pH of the solution gradually decreases.
D. $H_2(g)$ bubbles form on the right electrode, $Cl_2(g)$ bubbles form on the left electrode, and the pH of the solution gradually decreases.

Solution
Because the applied voltage is drawn the way it is, then according to convention, electrons are considered to be flowing from the right to left. As a result, reduction takes place on the left electrode, and oxidation takes place on the right electrode. $H_2(g)$ results from reduction, so it forms at the cathode (left electrode). Hydrogen gas forms bubbles on the left electrode, and chlorine gas forms bubbles on the right electrode. This eliminates choices B and D. Because hydroxide anion is formed as a by-product, the solution becomes basic over time, causing the solution pH to increase. This makes the best answer choice **A**.

Electroplating
Electroplating is the process of reducing ions in solution onto the surface of a conducting material. Reduction occurs at the cathode, so the cathode gains a thin film of the reduced metal on its surface. Practical applications of this include gold-plated jewelry, chrome-plated car parts, and platinum-plated carbon matrices used in catalytic processes. Electroplating can be used to convert your copper necklace into a beautiful gold necklace (vastly increasing your desirability at the local discotheque). The copper necklace is placed at the electrode poll in the cathode cell, which is filled with a solution of gold cations. Gold is reduced and consequently plates out onto the surface of the copper.

Electroplating requires a voltage source so that the current (and thus rate of plating) can be controlled. Electroplating is used to maximize the surface area of a catalytic metal, such as platinum and palladium. Catalytic metals are often plated onto the surface of graphite, so that all of the molecules of the precious metal are on the surface, and involved in catalysis. This maximizes the utility (surface area) and makes recovery easier (a large solid can be filtered more easily than a small solid). Because the carbon matrix of graphite contains extensive conjugation, graphite conducts electricity, making it a material that can be used as an electrode. You may recall from organic chemistry that hydrogenation of an alkene employed platinum metal on a carbon support, Pt(C).

Galvanizing

Metals exposed to the environment will oxidize over time. This is especially true when they are exposed to salt water, because salt water conducts electricity better than fresh water and air. To prevent against this, a metal can be galvanized. Galvanizing involves the addition of a more reactive metal (known as the *sacrificial metal*) to be preferentially oxidized over the metal being preserved. Consider a steel-hulled boat for instance. The boat rests in salt water for most of its life, so it oxidizes at a rapid pace. To lengthen the boat's lifetime, a metal that is easier to oxidize than iron (the major component of steel) is added, thereby galvanizing the steel. A thin, reactive metal plate is added to the surface of the steel hull to prevent the iron in steel from rusting away. Because ions conducts electricity, the galvanizing plate can be placed anywhere on the hull, as long as it's in direct contact with the iron and not submerged in the water.

Example 10.19
Which of the following metals can be used to galvanize steel?

A. Iron
B. Nickel
C. Potassium
D. Zinc

Solution
When galvanizing steel, the goal is to protect iron. The metal added must be more reactive than iron, which has an oxidation potential of +0.44 V according to Table 10.1. Iron is the component in steel that needs to be protected, so iron cannot be added to protect iron from oxidation. Choice A is eliminated. Nickel is not reactive enough, with an oxidation potential of +0.23 V, so choice B is eliminated. Potassium is too reactive with an oxidation potential of +2.92 V. Potassium would explode in water, and while this would in fact minimize the oxidation of iron in steel, as a general rule, exploding boats are not as effective as non-exploding boats! This eliminates choice C. Zinc is slightly more susceptible to oxidation than iron, with an oxidation potential of +0.76 V, so zinc is a good galvanizing material. Choice **D** is the best answer.

Electrochemistry
Passages

14 Passages

100 Questions

Suggested Electrochemistry Passage Schedule:

I: After reading this section and attending lecture: Passages II - III & XII - XIII
Grade passages immediately after completion and log your mistakes.

II: Following Task I: Passages I, IV, VII, VIII, & XI (34 questions in 44 minutes)
Time yourself accurately, grade your answers, and review mistakes.

III: Review: Passages V -VI, IX - X, XIV & Questions 94 - 100
Focus on reviewing the concepts. Do not worry about timing.

The BERKELEY
R·E·V·I·E·W®
Specializing in MCAT Preparation

Electrochemistry Study Passages

Electrochemistry Scoring Scale

Raw Score	MCAT Score
84 - 100	13 - 15
66 - 83	10 - 12
47 - 65	7 - 9
34 - 46	4 - 6
1 - 33	1 - 3

Many oxidation-reduction reactions take place in water. Water provides the medium through which electrons may transfer. The presence of ions enhances the conductivity of water. Reactions 1 through 4 are some oxidation-reduction reactions that take place in water, which acts as a reactant:

$$Br_2(l) + H_2O(l) \rightarrow HOBr(aq) + HBr(aq)$$
Reaction 1

$$Cl_2(g) + H_2O(l) \rightarrow HOCl(aq) + HCl(aq)$$
Reaction 2

$$K(s) + H_2O(l) \rightarrow KOH(aq) + \frac{1}{2}H_2(g)$$
Reaction 3

$$Na(s) + H_2O(l) \rightarrow NaOH(aq) + \frac{1}{2}H_2(g)$$
Reaction 4

In Reactions 1 and 2, water is ionized and not oxidized or reduced. Hydroxide and hydronium counteract the charges on the halides. In Reactions 3 and 4, the hydrogen of water is being reduced to form hydrogen gas. A correlation can be drawn between ionization energy of the species and the electromotive potential associated with oxidation of the species. The lower the ionization energy, the more favorable the oxidation. The first ionization energy for each of the non-aqueous reactants is listed in Table 1.

Compound	Ionization Energy $\left(\frac{kJ}{mole}\right)$
$Br_2(l)$	987.2
$Cl_2(g)$	1251
$K(s)$	418.7
$Na(s)$	495.9

Table 1

The same relative reactivity of the species observed in water can be observed in other solvents, but not with the same absolute energy values as those found in water solvent.

1. Which of the following processes does NOT involve the loss of an electron?

   A. Oxidation
   B. Ionization
   C. Conversion of oxidation state from -1 to 0
   D. Electron affinity

2. Which of the following reactions is the MOST favorable (has the MOST positive value for E°)?

   A. $2 K(s) + Br_2(l) \rightarrow 2 KBr(aq)$
   B. $2 Na(s) + Br_2(l) \rightarrow 2 NaBr(aq)$
   C. $2 K(s) + Cl_2(g) \rightarrow 2 KCl(aq)$
   D. $2 Na(s) + Cl_2(g) \rightarrow 2 NaCl(aq)$

3. What is the oxidation state of chlorine in both HOCl and HCl?

   A. +1 in HCl and +1 in HOCl
   B. +1 in HCl and -1 in HOCl
   C. -1 in HCl and +1 in HOCl
   D. -1 in HCl and -1 in HOCl

4. What is the ionization energy of Rb metal?

   A. The value is greater than 1000 $kJ/mole$.
   B. The value is less than 1000, but greater than 495.9 $kJ/mole$.
   C. The value is less than 495.9, but greater than 418.7 $kJ/mole$.
   D. The value is less than 418.7 $kJ/mole$. $kJ/mole$

5. What forms when lithium metal is added to water?

   A. No reaction is observed.
   B. Lithium hydroxide (LiOH) and lithium hydride (LiH) form.
   C. Only lithium hydroxide (LiOH) forms.
   D. Only lithium hydride (LiH) forms.

6. In the reaction of potassium metal in water, what are the oxidizing and reducing agents?

   A. The oxidizing agent is K (potassium), and the reducing agent is H_2 (hydrogen gas).
   B. The oxidizing agent is H_2 (hydrogen gas), and the reducing agent is K (potassium).
   C. The oxidizing agent is K (potassium), and the reducing agent is H_2O (water).
   D. The oxidizing agent is H_2O (water), and the reducing agent is K (potassium).

7. Which of the following statements must be TRUE about redox chemistry in water?

   I. Metals are more easily oxidized than nonmetals.
   II. Metals in water form metal oxides and metal hydroxides.
   III. Nonmetals in water form metal oxides and metal hydroxides.

   A. I only
   B. II only
   C. I and II only
   D. II and III only

Passage II (Questions 8 - 14)

A pH meter is an instrument that uses two electrodes to measure the potential difference between a solution of unknown pH and a standard solution of known pH. Because the potential difference between the solutions is dependent upon the [H^+], it is possible to determine the pH from the voltage of the cell. A typical standard cell employed in the electrode of a pH meter is the calomel half-cell, which is shown as Reaction 1 below:

$$Hg_2Cl_2(s) + 2 e^- \rightarrow 2 Hg(l) + 2 Cl^-(aq)$$

Reaction 1

The standard $E°_{cell}$ for the calomel half-cell is 0.285 V. Combining this with the Nernst equation provides the equation used to calculate pH, Equation 1.

$$E_{observed} = E°_{cell} - 0.0592 \log [H^+]$$

Equation 1

Using Equation 1, it is possible to calculate the pH of a solution from the observed voltage of the cell, because the electrode of the pH meter contains the calomel cell. Under standard conditions, $E°_{cell}$ is 0.285 V. When in contact with the calomel half-cell through a porous membrane, the unknown solution experiences a potential difference. The electrode probe of a pH meter is shown in Figure 1.

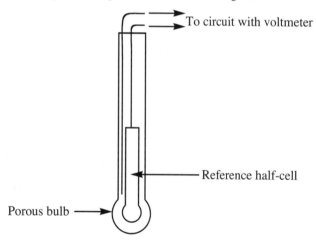

Figure 1

Getting an accurate reading of the pH requires that the bulb be neutralized and dried before it is placed into an unknown solution. To preserve the lifetime of the electrodes, they are stored in saturated chloride solutions. Cells must be refilled at least three times a year to prevent crystallization of the salt caused by the evaporation of water.

8. Which of the following would be observed after base is added to a solution monitored by a pH meter?

A. Both $E_{observed}$ and pH would increase.
B. $E_{observed}$ would increase and pH would decrease.
C. $E_{observed}$ would decrease and pH would increase.
D. Both $E_{observed}$ and pH would decrease.

9. To reduce the reading on a pH meter, which of the following can be added to a solution?

A. HCl(aq)
B. NH3(aq)
C. NaOH(aq)
D. KCl(aq)

10. A pH meter would yield what reading in a 0.010 M HCl solution?

A. .01
B. 1
C. 2
D. 7

11. The $E°_{cell}$ would not be 0.285 V, if:

A. a stronger acid was replaced by a weaker acid in the solution.
B. the resistance in the wires connecting the cell to the voltmeter was increased.
C. Ag^+ was used rather than Hg_2^{2+}.
D. the bulb had fewer pores.

12. In the calomel half-cell, which of the following is TRUE?

A. Chlorine in $Hg_2Cl_2(s)$ is reduced.
B. Chlorine in $Hg_2Cl_2(s)$ is oxidized.
C. Mercury in $Hg_2Cl_2(s)$ is reduced.
D. Mercury in $Hg_2Cl_2(s)$ is oxidized.

13. What is the pH of a solution that shows $E_{observed}$ = 0.699 V?

A. 0.7
B. 1.0
C. 4.1
D. 7.0

14. Which of the following does NOT affect the pH of the solution?

A. A change in temperature
B. A change in the volume of water solvent
C. A change in the type of solvent
D. A change in the position of the electrode in solution.

GO ON TO THE NEXT PAGE

Passage III (Questions 15 - 20)

Metals can be purified using metallurgy. They are often isolated as a pure salt (through precipitation), and the salt can be purified by electrolysis or an oxidation-reduction reaction (single displacement). Listed below are industrial methods for purifying gold, zinc, mercury, silicon, and phosphorus.

Gold: Impure samples of gold ores are treated with aqueous cyanide anion in the presence of O_2 gas. Other contaminants in the ore are filtered out. The gold cyanide complex is then reduced using zinc metal, leaving pure gold behind.

Rx I: $4 \, Au(s) + 8 \, CN^-(aq) + O_2(g) + H_2O(l) \rightarrow$
$$4 \, Au(CN)_2^-(aq) + 4 \, OH^-(aq)$$

Rx II: $Zn(s) + 2 \, Au(CN)_2^-(aq) \rightarrow Zn(CN)_4^{2-} + 2 \, Au(s)$

Zinc: Zinc sulfide can be mined and then purified by exposure to a hot stream of oxygen gas. The zinc oxide that forms can be treated with finely powdered carbon at 700°C to generate carbon monoxide and pure zinc metal.

Rx I: $2 \, ZnS(s) + 3 \, O_2(g) \rightarrow 2 \, ZnO(s) + 2 \, SO_2(g)$

Rx II: $ZnO(s) + C(s) \rightarrow Zn(s) + CO(g)$

Mercury: Like zinc, mercury sulfide can be mined and then purified by exposure to a hot stream of oxygen gas. The mercury oxide that forms can be heated to drive off O_2 gas.

Rx I: $2 \, HgS(s) + 3 \, O_2(g) \rightarrow 2 \, HgO(s) + 2 \, SO_2(g)$

Rx II: $2 \, HgO(s) + heat \rightarrow 2 \, Hg(s) + O_2(g)$

Silicon: Silicon oxide (known as *sand*) can be treated with finely powdered carbon at 1350°C to yield carbon monoxide and pure silicon (a liquid at that temperature).

Rx I: $SiO_2(l) + 2 \, C(s) \rightarrow Si(l) + 2 \, CO(g)$ (1350°C)

Phosphorus: Calcium phosphate (found in tooth enamel) can be treated with sand (SiO_2) and finely powdered charcoal to yield calcium silicate, carbon monoxide, and pure phosphorus (occurring naturally in the tetra-atomic state).

Rx I: $2 \, Ca_3(PO_4)_2(s) + 10 \, C(s) + 6 \, SiO_2(s) \rightarrow$
$$6 \, CaSiO_3(s) + 10 \, CO(g) + P_4(s)$$

The two-step processes require purification between the two reactions. This is done by filtering the product mixture through molecular sieves to remove any impurities that are too large to fit through the pore, or too small to be caught, depending on the sieve design. Solid oxides are assumed to be pure.

15. What is the role of CN^- in the first reaction in the purification of gold?

 A. The cyanide serves as a reducing agent.
 B. The cyanide serves as an oxidizing agent.
 C. The cyanide serves as a Lewis acid.
 D. The cyanide serves as a Lewis base.

16. What is the oxidation state of gold in $Au(CN)_2^-$?

 A. +3
 B. +1
 C. -1
 D. -3

17. In the purification of zinc metal, which of the following statements must be true?

 I. Sulfur is reduced in the overall process.
 II. Zinc is reduced in the overall process.
 III. Oxygen gas is the oxidizing agent.

 A. II only
 B. III only
 C. I and II only
 D. II and III only

18. What is the reduction half-reaction in the purification of silicon?

 A. $C(s) + 2 \, e^- \rightarrow CO(g)$
 B. $C(s) + 2 \, e^- + \frac{1}{2} \, O_2(g) \rightarrow CO(g)$
 C. $SiO_2(s) + 2 \, e^- \rightarrow Si(l) + O_2^{2-}(g)$
 D. $SiO_2(s) + 4 \, e^- \rightarrow Si(l) + 2 \, O^{2-}(g)$

19. Which reactions involve the oxidation of oxygen?

 A. The purification of gold, zinc, and silicon
 B. The purification of mercury
 C. The purification of gold, zinc, and mercury
 D. The purification of phosphorus

20. In the purification of mercury metal:

 A. mercury is reduced by one electron when HgO is heated.
 B. mercury is oxidized by two electrons when HgO is heated.
 C. mercury is oxidized by two electrons when HgS is treated with oxygen gas.
 D. sulfur is oxidized by six electrons when HgS is treated with oxygen gas.

To test the Nernst equation, a student titrates the cathode cell of a zinc-lead galvanic cell with potassium dichromate ($K_2Cr_2O_7$) under acidic conditions. The lead dication forms an insoluble precipitate ($PbCr_2O_7(s)$) with the dichromate dianion. As the lead concentration lowers, the cell potential decreases. Reaction 1 is the redox reaction of lead dication with zinc metal.

$$Pb^{2+}(aq) + Zn(s) \rightarrow Zn^{2+}(aq) + Pb(s)$$

Reaction 1

Figure 1 shows the titration apparatus and the two half-cells of the electrochemical cell. A voltmeter measures the potential difference throughout the duration of the reaction.

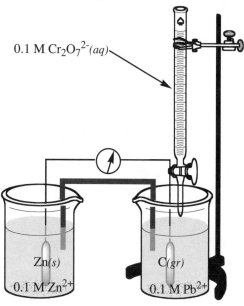

0.1 M $Cr_2O_7{}^{2-}(aq)$

$Zn(s)$

0.1 M Zn^{2+}

$C(gr)$

0.1 M Pb^{2+}

Figure 1

The voltage of the cell drops almost negligibly until just before the equivalence point, where it drops rapidly. Once the lead has been completely precipitated, excess dichromate anion can be reduced, as shown in Reaction 2.

$$14\ H^+(aq) + Cr_2O_7{}^{2-}(aq) + 3\ Zn(s) \rightarrow$$
$$3\ Zn^{2+}(aq) + 2\ Cr^{3+}(aq) + 7\ H_2O(l)$$

Reaction 2

The following voltage data can be used to determine the exact voltage at any point during the titration. Before equivalence, the voltage depends on the reaction of lead dication and zinc metal. After equivalence, the voltage depends on the reaction of dichromate anion and zinc metal.

$Pb^{2+}(aq) + 2\ e^- \rightarrow Pb(s)$	$E° = -0.13$ V
$Zn^{2+}(aq) + 2\ e^- \rightarrow Zn(s)$	$E° = -0.76$ V
$Cr_2O_7{}^{2-}(aq) + 14\ H^+(aq) + 3\ e^- \rightarrow 2\ Cr^{3+}(aq) + 7\ H_2O(l)$	$E° = +1.33$ V

Equation 1 can be used to determine the exact voltage at any point during the titration prior to the equivalence point. Equation 2 can be used to determine the exact voltage at any point during the titration after the equivalence point.

$$E_{obs} = E_{cell} - \frac{0.059}{n} \log \frac{[Zn^{2+}]}{[Pb^{2+}]}$$

Equation 1

$$E_{obs} = E_{cell} - \frac{0.059}{n} \log \frac{[Zn^{2+}]^3 [Cr^{3+}]^2}{[Cr_2O_7{}^{2-}]}$$

Equation 2

Figure 2 graphs the voltage as a function of time for the experiment.

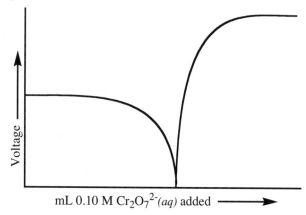

mL 0.10 M $Cr_2O_7{}^{2-}(aq)$ added

Figure 2

21. The reduced voltage prior to reaching the equivalence point can be attributed to which of the following?

   A. The precipitation of $Pb^{2+}(aq)$ from solution
   B. Competing reduction half-reactions between $Pb^{2+}(aq)$ and $Cr_2O_7{}^{2-}(aq)$
   C. A redox reaction with $Pb^{2+}(aq)$ and $Cr_2O_7{}^{2-}(aq)$
   D. Competing oxidation half-reactions between $Pb^{2+}(aq)$ and $Cr_2O_7{}^{2-}(aq)$

22. The higher maximum voltage following the equivalence point can be attributed to which of the following?

   A. $Pb^{2+}(aq)$ has a lower oxidation potential than $Cr_2O_7{}^{2-}(aq)$.
   B. $Cr_2O_7{}^{2-}(aq)$ has a lower oxidation potential than $Pb^{2+}(aq)$.
   C. $Pb^{2+}(aq)$ has a higher reduction potential than $Cr_2O_7{}^{2-}(aq)$.
   D. $Cr_2O_7{}^{2-}(aq)$ has a higher reduction potential than $Pb^{2+}(aq)$.

23. Given that zinc sulfate and lead sulfate are used in the reaction, what is the role of sulfate anion?

 A. To be oxidized
 B. To be reduced
 C. To precipitate excess dichromate
 D. To migrate through the salt bridge

24. Why should the circuit be left open until the start of the titration?

 A. To prevent the cell from charging voltage
 B. To prevent the cell from exchanging electrodes
 C. To prevent the lead and zinc from crossing through the salt bridge
 D. To prevent the cell from depleting voltage

25. What must be true about the zinc half-cell?

 A. It is the oxidation half-cell found at the anode.
 B. It is the oxidation half-cell found at the cathode.
 C. It is the reduction half-cell found at the anode.
 D. It is the reduction half-cell found at the cathode.

26. The observed voltage reaches a minimum when:

 A. $[Pb^{2+}]_{init} > [Cr_2O_7^{2-}]_{added}$.
 B. $[Pb^{2+}]_{init} = [Cr_2O_7^{2-}]_{added}$.
 C. mL 0.1 M Pb^{2+}_{init} > mL 0.1 M $Cr_2O_7^{2-}_{added}$.
 D. mL 0.1 M Pb^{2+}_{init} = mL 0.1 M $Cr_2O_7^{2-}_{added}$.

Passage V (Questions 27 - 33)

Oxidation-reduction titration can be used to ascertain the concentration of transition metal cations in solution. Visible spectroscopy, ultraviolet spectroscopy, and precipitation may also work. The optimal method is solution-dependent. A redox titration is similar to an acid-base titration, except that the titrant is an oxidizing or reducing agent. For instance, titanium +2 can be quantitatively oxidized by an oxidizing agent to form titanium +4. A balanced redox reaction is necessary to know the stoichiometric ratio of the titrant to the reactant in the solution.

A student fills three flasks with iron sulfate solution, so that each flask may be titrated by an oxidizing agent. The oxidation state of the iron is initially +2. After titration, the iron is oxidized to a +3 state. The oxidizing agent removes one electron from each iron dication. Iron sulfate is soluble in water, so it completely dissociates when mixed into water: The contents of each of the three flasks is listed in Figure 1.

 Flask 1: 1.52 grams $FeSO_4$ is added to enough water to make 100 mL solution.

 Flask 2: 1.52 grams $FeSO_4$ is added to enough water to make 200 mL solution.

 Flask 3: 3.04 grams $FeSO_4$ is added to enough water to make 100 mL solution.

Figure 1

The molecular mass of $FeSO_4$ is 152 grams per mole. A 20.00-mL aliquot from each of the three flasks is titrated with 0.020 M $KMnO_4(aq)$ solution in three separate titrations. The unbalanced equation for the oxidation-reduction reaction that takes place between permanganate anion and iron dication is shown in Reaction 1.

$$Fe^{2+}(aq) + MnO_4^-(aq) \rightarrow Fe^{3+}(aq) + MnO(s)$$

Reaction 1

$MnO_4^-(aq)$ is a purple solution, which causes some difficulty in reading the volume of titrant in the burette. The product $MnO(s)$ is a brown solid that precipitates from the solution. The $Fe^{2+}(aq)$ solution is clear. These titrations are monitored by color change. When the equivalence point is reached, the titration is stopped so the volume of titrant added can be recorded. The concentration of the initial iron dication solution can be calculated, from the molarity of the titrant solution. Conversely, the concentration of the titrant solution can be determined, if the concentration of the initial iron dication solution is known. Equation 1 is used to determine the concentration of either species, when only one concentration is known. Deviations from the formula are found with reactions that have different coefficients.

$$equiv \times M_{solution} \times V_{solution} = equiv \times M_{titrant} \times V_{titrant}$$

Equation 1

where equiv is equivalents, M is molarity, and V is volume.

27. What would indicate the endpoint of the titration of ferrous ion (Fe^{2+}) by permanganate (MnO_4^-)?

A. The clear solution turning and remaining brown
B. The brown solution turning and remaining clear
C. The violet solution turning and remaining clear
D. The clear solution turning and remaining violet

28. If a 20.00-mL sample from flask 2 requires a 17.50-mL aliquot of a $Na_2Cr_2O_7(aq)$ solution of unknown concentration to reach equivalence, then how much would a 20.00-mL sample from Flask 3 require?

A. A 70.00-mL aliquot of $Na_2Cr_2O_7(aq)$ solution
B. A 25.00-mL aliquot of $Na_2Cr_2O_7(aq)$ solution
C. A 17.50-mL aliquot of $Na_2Cr_2O_7(aq)$ solution
D. A 8.75-mL aliquot of $Na_2Cr_2O_7(aq)$ solution

29. Which of the following is the reducing agent in the titration of Flask 1 with $KMnO_4(aq)$ solution?

A. $KMnO_4(aq)$
B. $MnO(s)$
C. $Fe^{2+}(aq)$
D. $Fe^{3+}(aq)$

30. Which of the following is the oxidizing agent in the titration of Flask 2 with $Na_2Cr_2O_7(aq)$ solution?

A. $Na_2Cr_2O_7(aq)$
B. $Cr_2O_3(s)$
C. $Fe^{2+}(aq)$
D. $Fe^{3+}(aq)$

31. Which of the following is the ratio of $Na_2Cr_2O_7(aq)$ to $Fe^{3+}(aq)$ in the titration of Flask 2, where $Cr_2O_7^{2-}(aq)$ is reduced into $Cr_2O_3(s)$?

A. $1:1$
B. $1:3$
C. $2:3$
D. $1:6$

32. Given the values for the reduction half-cells of Fe^{2+} and Fe^{3+}, what is the E° for the oxidation half-reaction of the titration of Flask 1?

$$Fe^{3+} + 3e^- \rightarrow Fe \qquad -0.04 \text{ V}$$
$$Fe^{2+} + 2e^- \rightarrow Fe \qquad -0.44 \text{ V}$$

A. +0.76 V
B. +0.40 V
C. -0.40 V
D. -0.76 V

33. The BEST container for the titration would be made of which of the following materials?

A. Aluminum metal
B. Glass
C. Copper metal
D. Polyethylene

Passage VI (Questions 34 - 40)

Most precious metals can be found in nature in the form of an ore with an oxide coating. An ore is defined as an alloy of two or more metals homogeneously mixed. The oxide layer on the outside of the ore protects the inner core from oxidation. This occurs because metal in the core cannot transfer electrons through the oxide coating. To isolate selected precious metals, the ore is extracted in its entirety and then selectively treated to separate the metals, often in ion form.

Gold, for instance, is purified by first converting it to $AuCl_4^-$ and then selectively precipitating the $AuCl_4^-$ anion with some cation. The gold in the anion is next reduced to gold metal and thus is purified. The reduction of gold requires the application of current to the solution to plate out the gold onto the cathode (which must be an inert electrode from which gold can be removed easily).

Recently, scientists have aimed their research at techniques useful for mining precious metals from seawater. The plan involves running a microscopic net lined with sequestering agents that selectively bind target metals. The selectivity can be carried out by cation size or binding strength of the ligands in the sequestering agent.

Once the sequestering agent has bound the metal, it can be isolated and the metal can be released by lowering the pH drastically. The free precious metal cations can then be reduced by applying a current to the solution and plating the metal onto the cathode. Table 1 shows the standard reduction potentials for some precious metals in water:

$$Ag^+(aq) + 1\,e^- \rightarrow Ag(s)\ \ 0.80\ V$$
$$Pt^{2+}(aq) + 2\,e^- \rightarrow Pt(s)\ \ \ 1.20\ V$$
$$Au^{3+}(aq) + 3\,e^- \rightarrow Au(s)\ 1.50\ V$$

Table 1

34. Gold trication could be recovered in the form of gold metal by adding which of the following to the solution?

   A. $Cl_2(g)$
   B. $Ag^+(aq)$
   C. $Zn(s)$
   D. $Pt^{2+}(aq)$

35. Because the $Cl^-(aq)$ anion is NOT oxidized by the $Ag^+(aq)$ cation, it can be safely assumed that the reduction potential of $Cl_2(g)$ is which of the following?

   A. Less than -0.80 volts
   B. Between -0.80 and 0.0 volts
   C. Between 0.0 and 0.80 volts
   D. Greater than 0.80 volts

36. What is the oxidation state of gold in $AuCl_4^-$?

   A. -3
   B. 0
   C. +1
   D. +3

37. Since silver is in a column of the periodic table that expresses filled d-shell stability when electrons fill the orbitals, what electronic configuration is observed with silver cation (Ag^+)?

   A. $[Kr]5s^24d^8$
   B. $[Kr]5s^14d^9$
   C. $[Kr]5s^14d^{10}$
   D. $[Kr]4d^{10}$

38. A sequestering agent should contain which of the following structural features?

   A. Atoms with no lone pairs of electrons
   B. Atoms able to donate electron pairs
   C. Atoms without completed octet valences
   D. Atoms that are good Lewis acids

39. Which of the following is the mass percent of gold in $AuCl_4^-$?

   A. Less than 25%
   B. Between 25% and 50%
   C. Between 50% and 75%
   D. Greater than 75%

40. Which of the following reactions would produce the LOWEST (or most negative) voltage?

   A. $Ag^+(aq) + Cl^- \rightarrow Ag(s) + \frac{1}{2}Cl_2(g)$
   B. $Pt^{2+}(aq) + 2\,Cl^- \rightarrow Pt(s) + Cl_2(g)$
   C. $Au^{3+}(aq) + 3\,Cl^- \rightarrow Au(s) + \frac{3}{2}Cl_2(g)$
   D. All of the above reactions would require the same voltage.

GO ON TO THE NEXT PAGE

Passage VII (Questions 41 - 47)

The *galvanic cell*, by definition, is a cell utilizing a favorable redox reaction that releases energy in the form of electron flow. The cell is composed of two half-cells: an oxidation half-cell and a reduction half-cell. The oxidation half-reaction takes place in the anode half-cell, and overall electrons are released from the anode half-cell. The reduction half-reaction takes place in the cathode half-cell, and overall electrons are absorbed at the cathode half-cell. Figure 1 shows a standard galvanic cell.

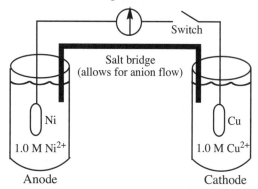

Figure 1

$$Cu^{2+}(aq) + Ni(s) \rightarrow Cu(s) + Ni^{2+}(aq)$$

Reaction 1

The overall voltage of the cell is the sum of the half-cell voltages for the two component reactions. Equation 1 shows this calculation.

$$E^{\circ}_{cell} = E^{\circ}_{red} + E^{\circ}_{ox}$$

Equation 1

Also by definition, a galvanic cell has a positive cell voltage overall. Reduction is defined as the gain of electrons, so reduction occurs at the cathode of a battery.

41. In the galvanic cell shown in Figure 1, oxidation occurs at:

A. the anode, because electrons flow from the anode to the cathode.

B. the cathode, because electrons flow from the anode to the cathode.

C. the anode, because electrons flow from the cathode to the anode.

D. the cathode, because electrons flow from the cathode to the anode.

42. Which of the following half-reactions could occur at the anode in a galvanic cell?

A. $Cl_2(g) + 2e^- \rightarrow 2 Cl^-(aq)$

B. $Na^+(g) + 1e^- \rightarrow Na(s)$

C. $VO_3^-(aq) + 3e^- \rightarrow VO(s)$

D. $Cr_2O_3(s) \rightarrow CrO_4^{2-}(aq) + 3e^-$

43. Which of the following combinations does NOT result in a galvanic cell when the reduction half-cell carries an E° value greater than zero?

A. $E^{\circ}_{oxidation} < 0$; $|E^{\circ}_{reduction}| > |E^{\circ}_{oxidation}|$

B. $E^{\circ}_{oxidation} > 0$; $|E^{\circ}_{reduction}| > |E^{\circ}_{oxidation}|$

C. $E^{\circ}_{oxidation} < 0$; $|E^{\circ}_{reduction}| < |E^{\circ}_{oxidation}|$

D. $E^{\circ}_{oxidation} > 0$; $|E^{\circ}_{reduction}| < |E^{\circ}_{oxidation}|$

44. What is NOT true about a galvanic cell?

A. The electron flow is from the anode to the cathode.

B. Reduction occurs at the cathode.

C. The voltage of the cell decreases as the cell runs in the discharging direction.

D. E_{cell} starts greater than zero and finishes when E_{cell} is less than zero.

45. The BEST initial composition for a galvanic cell would be a cathode half-cell containing a cation in a:

A. high oxidation state, and an anode half-cell containing a metal with a low ionization energy.

B. high oxidation state, and an anode half-cell containing a metal with a high ionization energy.

C. low oxidation state, and an anode half-cell containing a metal with a low ionization energy.

D. low oxidation state, and an anode half-cell containing a metal with a high ionization energy.

46. What is the ratio of reducing agent to oxidizing agent in the following reaction?

$$MnO_4^-(aq) + Al(s) \rightarrow MnO(s) + AlO_2^-(aq)$$

A. 3 : 5

B. 5 : 3

C. 2 : 3

D. 3 : 2

47. What must occur after the switch is closed in the cell shown in Figure 1?

I. Copper metal builds up on the cathode.

II. The overall cell voltage is greater than 0.00 V.

III. Anions flow through the salt bridge from the cathode to the anode.

A. I only

B. I and II only

C. II and III only

D. I, II, and III

GO ON TO THE NEXT PAGE

Passage VIII (Questions 48 - 54)

Photoelectric cells function by absorbing photons and converting photon energy into electrical flow (electricity). The electricity generated is then collected and stored as a potential difference in the form of a cell (battery). The electricity is generated when the photon strikes an ionizing plate (an electrode) and discharges an electron from the ionizing plate. The electron flows through the wire from one electrode to the other electrode where it is then stored. The potential builds up across the two plates. This potential difference is known as *capacitance*. A sample photoelectric cell is shown in Figure 1.

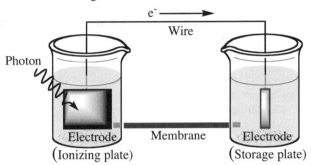

Figure 1

The incident photon must have an energy high enough to overcome the electrical potential for the cell; otherwise, the cell cannot build up charge difference. Cells are chosen with a negative (unfavorable) E° value so that upon the addition of the energy, they build up a charge that can discharge in a favorable manner. Equation 1 shows the conversion between the standard free energy and the standard cell voltage:

$$\Delta G° = -nFE°$$

where F = 96,500 C and $E° = E°_{red} + E°_{ox}$.

Equation 1

The efficiency of the cell is determined by comparing the energy of the incident photon relative to the stored energy of the cell. An efficient cell dissipates little or no energy.

48. An electrolytic cell:

A. produces energy by way of a favorable oxidation-reduction reaction.

B. produces energy by way of an unfavorable oxidation-reduction reaction.

C. stores energy by way of a favorable oxidation-reduction reaction.

D. stores energy by way of an unfavorable oxidation-reduction reaction.

49. For a photochemical cell to work, the energy of the photon absorbed must exceed:

A. the ΔG for oxidation at the anode.

B. the ΔG for the overall oxidation/reduction reaction.

C. the ionization potential for the anode.

D. the electron affinity for the cathode.

50. According to the diagram of the cell, photons of light directly cause which of the following?

A. The anode to be oxidized

B. The anode to be reduced

C. The cathode to be oxidized

D. The cathode to be reduced

51. The BEST material for the anode (ionizing plate) would be which of the following?

A. A metal

B. A metal oxide

C. A nonmetal

D. A nonmetal oxide

52. The overall conversion of energy in a photoelectric cell is from:

A. potential energy to electrical energy.

B. electrical energy to potential energy.

C. radiation energy to electrical energy.

D. radiation energy to potential energy.

53. When the cell discharges, it will:

A. dissipate the most energy initially, because it has the highest voltage at the start.

B. dissipate the least energy initially, because it has the highest voltage at the start.

C. dissipate a constant amount of energy, because the cell has a constant voltage throughout the discharging period.

D. dissipate an increasing amount of energy, because the anode is dissolving throughout the discharging period.

54. What is true about the current, I, at points a, b, and c in the following circuit?

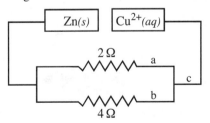

A. $I_a > I_b > I_c$

B. $I_c > I_b > I_a$

C. $I_c > I_a > I_b$

D. $I_b > I_c > I_a$

Dry cell batteries are common in many household products such as flashlights and radios. They contain no aqueous solution through which ions migrate, but instead contain a gelatinous paste of concentrated aqueous NH_4Cl. It is important that the electrons can easily flow through the membrane. Dry cell batteries are convenient because of their small size and long lifetime. A similar battery is the alkaline manganese cell, which exploits the same reaction, but in a basic medium. In a basic medium, the battery employs the following two half-cell reactions:

Anode: $Zn + 2\,OH^- \rightarrow ZnO(s) + H_2O + 2\,e^-$

Cathode: $MnO_2 + \frac{1}{2}H_2O + 1\,e^- \rightarrow \frac{1}{2}Mn_2O_3 + OH^-$

In lieu of manganese oxide, the cells can also use silver oxide and mercury oxide. In acidic medium, the dry cell battery employs the following two half-cell reactions.

Anode: $Zn \rightarrow Zn^{2+} + 2\,e^-$

Cathode: $MnO_2 + NH_4^+ + 1\,e^- \rightarrow \frac{1}{2}Mn_2O_3 + \frac{1}{2}H_2O + NH_3$

The overall cell potential (E°) for the dry cell battery is slightly greater than 1.50 V. The nickel-cadmium battery is a rechargeable battery as well. The nickel-cadmium battery (also known as the *nicad battery*) is found in calculators and electric shavers. The following two reactions are employed for the nickel-cadmium battery:

Anode: $Cd + 2\,OH^- \rightarrow Cd(OH)_2 + 2\,e^-$

Cathode: $NiOOH + H_2O + 1\,e^- \rightarrow Ni(OH)_2 + 1\,OH^-$

A typical nickel-cadmium (NiCad) battery has a fairly low voltage. The outer wall of the anode solution is initially the cadmium metal, but as the cell runs, the cadmium dissolves away. Figure 1 shows a cross section of a typical NiCad battery. As drawn, the outer casing contains zinc metal (in lieu of cadmium) in a basic potassium hydroxide solution. The cathode is made of HgO (NiO_2H in typical nicad batteries), which reduces on the surface of a stainless steel electrode. The electrons flow to the top of the cathode. The insulation holds the cell together.

Cathode

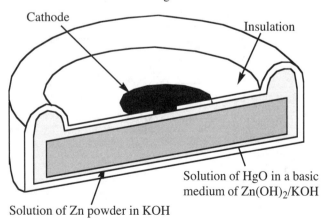

Insulation

Solution of HgO in a basic medium of $Zn(OH)_2$/KOH

Solution of Zn powder in KOH

Figure 1

All of the cells function in a similar manner, allowing substitutions to be made to achieve different voltages. The lifetime of a battery is determined by the quantity of species.

55. What is the overall balanced reaction for a nickel-cadmium battery?

A. $Cd + 2\,NiO_2H + 2\,OH^- \rightarrow Cd(OH)_2 + 2\,Ni(OH)_2$
B. $Cd + 2\,NiO_2H + 2\,H_2O \rightarrow Cd(OH)_2 + 2\,Ni(OH)_2$
C. $2\,Cd + NiO_2H + 2\,OH^- \rightarrow 2\,Cd(OH)_2 + Ni(OH)_2$
D. $2\,Cd + NiO_2H + 2\,H_2O \rightarrow 2\,Cd(OH)_2 + Ni(OH)_2$

56. What is the oxidation state change for manganese in the Zn/MnO_2 battery?

A. Mn goes from +4 to +6
B. Mn goes from +4 to +3
C. Mn goes from +2 to +6
D. Mn goes from +2 to +3

57. Which of the following reactions represents the cathode reaction in a zinc-mercury oxide battery at pH = 10?

A. $Zn \rightarrow Zn^{2+} + 2\,e^-$
B. $Zn + 2\,OH^- \rightarrow ZnO + H_2O + 2\,e^-$
C. $HgO + 2\,NH_4^+ + 2\,e^- \rightarrow Hg + H_2O + 2\,NH_3$
D. $HgO + H_2O + 2\,e^- \rightarrow Hg + 2\,OH^-$

58. Which of the following reactions CANNOT take place at the anode?

A. $2\,FeO + 2\,OH^- \rightarrow Fe_2O_3 + H_2O + 2\,e^-$
B. $Ag_2O + H_2O + 2\,e^- \rightarrow Ag + 2\,OH^-$
C. $Ti(OH)_2 + 2\,OH^- \rightarrow TiO_2 + H_2O + 2\,e^-$
D. $V_2O_3 + 4\,OH^- \rightarrow V_2O_5 + 2\,H_2O + 4\,e^-$

59. The electrons in a dry cell battery flow from:

A. the outer casing to the surface of the stainless steel cap.
B. one wall of the core to the other wall of the core.
C. bottom of the insulator to the top of the stainless steel cap.
D. from the stainless steel cap to the wall of the core.

60. What is observed with a NiCad battery over time?

A. Electrons build up in the anode.
B. Cadmium metal builds up in the anode.
C. Nickel hydroxide builds up in the anode.
D. Cadmium hydroxide builds up in the anode.

Passage X (Questions 61 - 67)

Pure gases can be obtained through a process known as *electrolysis*. Electrolysis cleaves compounds using an applied voltage. A typical example is the conversion of water liquid into hydrogen gas and oxygen gas. Electrolysis can also be used to form metals from cationic salts. Figure 1 is a schematic layout of an electrolysis cell used industrially to make chlorine gas from aqueous sodium chloride solution:

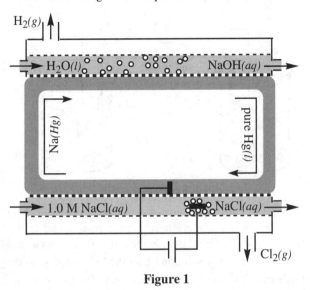

Figure 1

The oxidation of chloride anion must use less voltage than the oxidation of the oxygen of water; if it is to occur in water. In Figure 1, chloride is oxidized into chlorine gas at the anode in the NaCl(*aq*) solution (chlorine bubbles form at the anode). The cathode in the circulating mercury solution reduces sodium cation into sodium metal, which is dissolved in the mercury. Sodium metal circulates to the water where it is oxidized upon contact, reducing protons into hydrogen gas and leaving hydroxide as a side product. Hydrogen gas bubbles are collected.

Overall, sodium transfers electrons from the cathode of the applied voltage in the lower electrolytic region to the hydrogens of water in the upper galvanic region. The applied voltage must be high enough to reduce sodium cation and oxidize chloride anion. Heat energy is released when the sodium metal reduces the hydronium ion in water. The appropriate half-cell reactions for the electrolysis apparatus shown in Figure 1 are listed below:

$$Cl_2(g) + 2\,e^- \rightarrow 2\,Cl^-(aq) \qquad +1.36\ V$$

$$Na^+(aq) + 1\,e^- \rightarrow Na(s) \qquad -2.71\ V$$

$$H^+(aq) + 1\,e^- \rightarrow \frac{1}{2}H_2(g) \qquad 0.00\ V$$

61. Overall, what occurs in the cell in Figure 1?

   A. Na is oxidized, and Cl⁻ is reduced.

   B. Na is reduced, and Cl⁻ is oxidized.

   C. H^+ is oxidized, and Cl⁻ is reduced.

   D. H^+ is reduced, and Cl⁻ is oxidized.

62. What is true regarding the applied voltage in Figure 1?

   A. It must lie between 0 and 1.36 volts.

   B. It must lie between 1.36 and 2.71 volts.

   C. It must lie between 2.71 and 4.07 volts.

   D. It must be greater than 4.07 volts.

63. The overall reaction is:

   A. $NaCl(aq) + HCl(aq) \rightarrow H_2(g) + Na(s) + Cl_2(g)$

   B. $Na^+(aq) + H_2O(l) \rightarrow H_2(g) + Na(s) + O_2(g)$

   C. $NaCl(aq) + H_2O(l) \rightarrow H_2(g) + NaOH(aq) + Cl_2(g)$

   D. $NaCl(aq) + H_2(g) \rightarrow H_2O(l) + Na(s) + Cl_2(g)$

64. Which of the following statements describes sodium cation in the electrolysis cell?

   I. Sodium cation is more favorably reduced than hydronium cation.

   II. Sodium cation is reduced in the salt solution segment of the cell, because it can cross the membrane into mercury metal.

   III. The [Na^+] in the NaCl(*aq*) solution that enters the electrolytic cell is greater than the [Na^+] in the NaCl(*aq*) solution that leaves the cell.

   A. I only

   B. I and II only

   C. II and III only

   D. I, II, and III

65. Electron flow is defined as moving:

   A. from anode to cathode in both the battery and the electrolytic cell.

   B. from cathode to anode in both the battery and the electrolytic cell.

   C. from anode to cathode in the battery, and from the cathode to the anode in the electrolytic cell.

   D. from cathode to anode in the battery, and from the anode to the cathode in the electrolytic cell.

66. In an electrolytic cell, what must be TRUE about the cell and battery voltages?

   A. Both values are positive; $E_{battery} > E_{rx}$.

   B. Both values are positive; $E_{battery} < E_{rx}$.

   C. $E_{battery} > 0$ and $E_{rx} < 0$; $E_{battery} > |E_{rx}|$.

   D. $E_{battery} > 0$ and $E_{rx} < 0$; $E_{battery} < |E_{rx}|$.

GO ON TO THE NEXT PAGE

67. Which of the following is the STRONGEST reducing agent?

A. $Na^+(aq)$
B. $Na(s)$
C. $Cl^-(aq)$
D. $H_2(g)$

Passage XI (Questions 68 - 74)

A researcher sets up an electrochemical cell, Cell 1 in Figure 1 below, by placing a strip of zinc metal into a solution of 0.10 M $ZnSO_4(aq)$ in the left half-cell and a strip of copper metal into a solution of 0.10 M $CuSO_4(aq)$ in the right half-cell. The two metal strips are connected via a copper wire connected to a voltmeter. The solutions are then connected using a string soaked in $Na_2SO_4(aq)$.

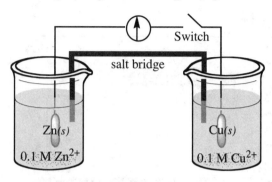

Figure 1

The researcher next creates a second cell, Cell 2 in Figure 2 below, by placing a strip of copper metal into a solution of 0.001 M $CuSO_4(aq)$ in the left half-cell and a strip of copper metal into a solution of 1.00 M $CuSO_4(aq)$ in the right half-cell. This is a *concentration cell*. The two sides are connected in the same manner as they were in Cell 1.

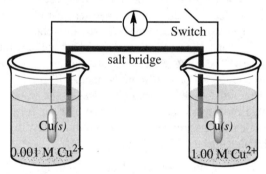

Figure 2

Concentration cells are driven force to equilibrate the concentration in the two half-cells. The driving force in Cell 1 is the standard cell potential. Listed in Table 1 below are the reduction potentials for selected standard half-cells:

Half-reaction	$E°_{cell}$
$Ag^+ + 1e^- \rightarrow Ag$	0.80 V
$Cu^{2+} + 2e^- \rightarrow Cu$	0.34 V
$Fe^{3+} + 3e^- \rightarrow Fe$	-0.04 V
$Ni^{2+} + 2e^- \rightarrow Ni$	-0.23 V
$Fe^{2+} + 2e^- \rightarrow Fe$	-0.44 V
$Cr^{3+} + 3e^- \rightarrow Cr$	-0.73 V
$Zn^{2+} + 2e^- \rightarrow Zn$	-0.76 V
$Al^{3+} + 3e^- \rightarrow Al$	-1.66 V

Table 1

GO ON TO THE NEXT PAGE

68. Which of the following statements correctly describes the anode and electron flow in Cell 1?

    A. The anode is the zinc electrode, and the electron flow is from right to left.

    B. The anode is the zinc electrode, and the electron flow is from left to right.

    C. The anode is the copper electrode, and the electron flow is from right to left.

    D. The anode is the copper electrode, and the electron flow is from left to right.

69. Cell 1 is BEST described as which of the following?

    A. An electrolytic cell
    B. A concentration cell
    C. A galvanic cell
    D. A charging cell

70. If the string in Cell 1 were replaced by a copper wire, then which of the following would be the new cell potential for Cell 1?

    A. 1.46 V
    B. 1.10 V
    C. 0.76 V
    D. 0.00 V

71. All of the following are observed, once the switch in Cell 2 is closed, EXCEPT:

    A. Electrons flow from left to right, gradually slowing, until to no electron flow is observed.

    B. The mass of the left copper electrode decreases, while the mass of the right copper electrode increases.

    C. The copper cation concentration in the right electrode decreases to a value of roughly 0.50 M.

    D. The copper cation concentration in the left electrode increases to a value of approximately 1.00 M.

72. Given that the cell potential can be calculated by the following formula, what is the cell potential in Cell 2?

$$E = E° - \frac{0.059}{n} \log Q$$

    A. 0.177 V
    B. 0.089 V
    C. 0.517 V
    D. 0.429 V

73. What is the standard cell potential for Cell 1?

    A. 1.10 V
    B. 0.42 V
    C. 2.20 V
    D. -0.42 V

74. What are the coefficients when the following equation is balanced?

$$H_2O(l) + ClO_3^-(aq) + Mg(s) \rightarrow$$
$$Cl^-(aq) + Mg^{2+}(aq) + OH^-(aq)$$

    A. $2:1:2 \rightarrow 1:2:4$
    B. $6:1:3 \rightarrow 1:3:3$
    C. $3:2:3 \rightarrow 2:3:6$
    D. $3:1:3 \rightarrow 1:3:6$

GO ON TO THE NEXT PAGE

Electrolysis is an industrial process that has two main usages. The first common usage is to produce very pure metals from oxides. Most metals are extracted from the earth in a casing of metal oxide. The second common usage is to produce very pure industrial gases, such as chlorine (used in the etching of silicon wafers). Both methods involve separating the cathode solution from the anode solution, and then isolating the products that form in each solution. A typical electrolysis apparatus is shown below in Figure 1:

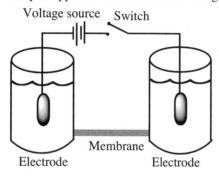

Figure 1

One of the common practices in industry is to plate both platinum metal and palladium metal onto graphite and charcoal. This metal-coated charcoal is used in catalytic converters, and as a hydrogenation catalyst in organic chemistry. Plating onto charcoal is possible because it conducts electricity. A piece of charcoal is used as the electrode in the cathode half-cell, where palladium dication or platinum dication is reduced. The same technique works for the purification of many materials. Table 1 shows half-cell reduction potentials, which can be used to determine the favorability of the overall reaction.

Reduction Half reaction	E°red
$Cl_2(g) + 2 e^- \rightarrow 2 Cl^-(aq)$	1.36 Volts
$Br_2(l) + 2 e^- \rightarrow 2 Br^-(aq)$	1.09 Volts
$Ag^+(aq) + 1 e^- \rightarrow Ag(s)$	0.80 Volts
$I_2(s) + 2 e^- \rightarrow 2 I^-(aq)$	0.54 Volts
$Cu^{2+}(aq) + 2 e^- \rightarrow Cu(s)$	0.34 Volts
$Ni^{2+}(aq) + 2 e^- \rightarrow Ni(s)$	-0.23 Volts
$Zn^{2+}(aq) + 2 e^- \rightarrow Zn(s)$	-0.76 Volts

Table 1

75. Why is palladium plated onto the surface of charcoal to form hydrogenation catalysts?

   A. To allow the palladium to dissolve better into the organic solvent

   B. To maximize the surface area of palladium, while keeping it easy to filter out from solution

   C. To enhance the reactivity of palladium by providing it with a larger supply of electrons

   D. To reduce the oxidation potential of palladium metal, so it lasts for a longer time

76. What problem can occur when a voltage greater than 1.86 volts is applied to an aqueous metal halide salt solution over a long duration of time?

   A. Hydrolysis of water to yield $H_3O^+(aq)$ and $OH^-(aq)$ occurs once the metal cation is completely reduced.

   B. Electrolysis of water to yield $H_2(g)$ and $O_2(g)$ occurs once the metal cation is completely reduced.

   C. The metal is further reduced into metallic anions.

   D. The halide is further oxidized into halogen cations.

77. The fact that Pd^{2+} can be reduced from $PdCl_2(aq)$, while Ni^{2+} must be reduced in the absence of water (using the molten salt form of $NiCl_2(aq)$, implies that the relative reduction potentials are:

   A. $2 H^+ \rightarrow H_2 > Ni^{2+} \rightarrow Ni > Pd^{2+} \rightarrow Pd$

   B. $Ni^{2+} \rightarrow Ni > 2 H^+ \rightarrow H_2 > Pd^{2+} \rightarrow Pd$

   C. $Pd^{2+} \rightarrow Pd > Ni^{2+} \rightarrow Ni > 2 H^+ \rightarrow H_2$

   D. $Pd^{2+} \rightarrow Pd > 2 H^+ \rightarrow H_2 > Ni^{2+} \rightarrow Ni$

78. Which of the following is NOT a desirable property for an electrode?

   A. It should be a good insulator.

   B. It should be inert chemically.

   C. It should have a high melting point.

   D. It should have minimal electrical resistance.

79. For the formation of copper metal from $CuCl_2(aq)$, what voltage must be applied to the solution?

   A. Any positive voltage

   B. A voltage of at least 0.34 V, but under 1.02 V

   C. A voltage of at least 1.02 V

   D. A voltage of at least 1.36 V

80. What is true about graphite and charcoal?

   A. Graphite cannot conduct electricity, because carbon has no d-orbitals.

   B. Graphite cannot conduct electricity, because carbon has no p-orbitals.

   C. Graphite conducts electricity through its σ-bonds.

   D. Graphite conducts electricity through its π-bonds.

81. Metal purification using which of the following salts would require the LEAST applied voltage?

   A. $AgCl(s)$

   B. $CuBr_2(s)$

   C. $NiBr_2(s)$

   D. $ZnCl_2(s)$

       GO ON TO THE NEXT PAGE

Passage XIII (Questions 82 - 87)

Galvanized steel is often referred to as *rustproof* steel. Despite iron in ordinary steel oxidizing quite rapidly, iron in galvanized steel does not oxidize to any notable extent. This is because galvanized steel has a metal that is more reactive than iron associated with it. The metal is referred to as a *sacrificial metal*. A sacrificial metal must have a greater standard oxidation potential than 0.44 V, the oxidation potential of iron to iron dication. Table 1 shows twelve standard half-reactions and their corresponding *emf* values.

Half-reaction	$E°_{half-rxn}$
$K \rightarrow K^+ + 1\,e^-$	2.92 V
$Na \rightarrow Na^+ + 1\,e^-$	2.71 V
$Mg \rightarrow Mg^{2+} + 2\,e^-$	2.37 V
$Al \rightarrow Al^{3+} + 3\,e^-$	1.66 V
$Au^{3+} + 3\,e^- \rightarrow Au$	1.50 V
$Pd^{2+} + 2\,e^- \rightarrow Pd$	0.99 V
$Ag^+ + 1\,e^- \rightarrow Ag$	0.80 V
$Zn \rightarrow Zn^{2+} + 2\,e^-$	0.76 V
$Cr \rightarrow Cr^{3+} + 3\,e^-$	0.73 V
$Fe \rightarrow Fe^{2+} + 2\,e^-$	0.44 V
$Cu^{2+} + 2\,e^- \rightarrow Cu$	0.34 V
$Ni \rightarrow Ni^{2+} + 2\,e^-$	0.23 V

Table 1

One potential problem that arises when choosing a sacrificial metal is that it can be too reactive. If the metal oxidizes too readily, then the surrounding air and moisture can destroy it prematurely. The ideal sacrificial metal is only slightly more reactive than iron.

82. A good material for galvanizing steel should have a low:

   A. oxidation potential.
   B. electron affinity.
   C. ionization energy.
   D. reduction potential.

83. Which of the following species is the STRONGEST oxidizing agent?

   A. Pd^{2+}
   B. Mg
   C. Al^{3+}
   D. Cu

84. Despite being a strong reducing agent, with a highly favorable oxidation potential, potassium metal is not a good sacrificial metal. How can this be explained?

   A. Potassium is too reactive; it reacts with atmospheric nitrogen and argon.
   B. Potassium is too reactive; it reacts with atmospheric oxygen and water.
   C. When potassium binds iron, it becomes chemically inert, and thus incapable of being oxidized.
   D. Potassium does not adhere to other metals.

85. What is the *emf* for the following oxidation-reduction reaction?

$$Fe^{2+} + Zn \rightarrow Fe + Zn^{2+}$$

   A. -1.20 V
   B. -0.32 V
   C. 0.32 V
   D. 1.20 V

86. In a voltaic cell involving copper and zinc half-reactions, what is true?

   I. Oxidation of zinc metal occurs at the cathode.
   II. Electrons flow to the electrode where copper plates out.
   III. The copper electrode increases in mass over the course of the reaction.

   A. I only
   B. II only
   C. I and II only
   D. II and III only

87. When zinc metal is exposed to the environment, it can act as:

   A. an oxidizing agent.
   B. a reducing agent.
   C. an oxophobe.
   D. an electron sponge.

     GO ON TO THE NEXT PAGE

A student sets up an experiment to determine the effects of the cell potential, concentration, and current on the degree of electroplating. In the first experiment, the student sets up six solutions with the following contents:

Solution I:	0.10 M $AgNO_3(aq)$
Solution II:	1.00 M $AgNO_3(aq)$
Solution III:	0.10 M $ZnSO_4(aq)$
Solution IV:	1.00 M $ZnSO_4(aq)$
Solution V:	0.10 M $CuSO_4(aq)$
Solution VI:	1.00 M $CuSO_4(aq)$

Into each solution, an inert electrode weighing exactly 5.00 grams is inserted. A steady current of electricity is applied to each electrode for the duration of one minute for all six solutions. The electrode is then removed and the mass is measured. The degree of plating can be determined by subtracting the original mass of the electrode from the final mass of the plated electrode. The mass for each electrode after it is removed is listed below:

Solution I:	6.187 grams
Solution II:	6.182 grams
Solution III:	5.360 grams
Solution IV:	5.358 grams
Solution V:	5.347 grams
Solution VI:	5.350 grams

The difference between the solutions in the mass after plating of the electrode is attributed to both the difference in molecular mass for each element, and the number of electrons required to reduce each cation. The degree of plating can be calculated, if the current and the duration of time are both known. The conversion from coulombs to moles involves Faraday's constant (96,500 coulombs per mole).

The procedure in this experiment can be used to form pure samples of metal. The metal coating adheres to the electrode until it is removed using the application of some force. This technique is used in the purification of gold. Electroplating is also used in the application of protective metal coatings to materials. Chromium can be applied to metal surfaces in this manner.

88. If an equal current is applied for an equal duration of time to separate flasks containing the aqueous ions Cu^{2+}, Zn^{2+}, Ag^+, and Au^{3+}, which ion yields the MOST precipitated metal by mass?

  A. Cu^{2+}
  B. Zn^{2+}
  C. Ag^+
  D. Au^{3+}

89. Why is it NOT possible to electroplate onto a plastic material?

  A. The plastic melts at the high temperatures required for electroplating.
  B. The plastic can be oxidized by the current.
  C. Plastic is an insulator and does not conduct electricity.
  D. Plastic is too malleable to allow for electroplating.

90. Which of the following graphs shows the relationship of mass as a function of time for Solutions I and IV?

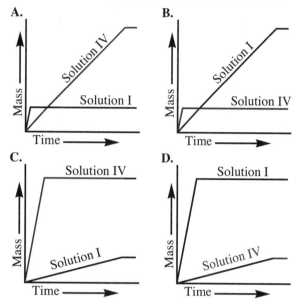

91. Electroplating results from:

  A. the oxidation of a metal into a cation.
  B. the reduction of a metal into a cation.
  C. the oxidation of a cation into a metal.
  D. the reduction of a cation into a metal.

92. Which of the following is a desirable property of a metal to be used to coat a structural beam that will be exposed to moisture?

  A. Its cation has a large positive reduction potential.
  B. The metal has a large positive reduction potential.
  C. Its cation has a large positive oxidation potential.
  D. The metal has a large positive oxidation potential.

93. Approximately what mass would be expected for a solution of Cd^{2+}, if it were exposed for one minute to the same current and electrode used in the experiment?

  A. A mass less than 5.347 grams
  B. A mass greater than 5.350 grams, but less than 5.358 grams
  C. A mass greater than 5.360 grams, but less than 6.182 grams
  D. A mass greater than 6.182 grams

   GO ON TO THE NEXT PAGE

94. Tarnish on silver is attributed to Ag_2S. Placing silver in an aluminum pan and adding aqueous baking soda ($NaHCO_3$) can remove the tarnish. Which of the following equations shows the reaction that occurs?

A. $Ag_2S(s) + 2\,NaHCO_3(aq)$
$$\rightarrow H_2(g) + 2\,Ag(s) + Na_2S(s)$$

B. $Ag_2S(s) + 2\,NaHCO_3(aq)$
$$\rightarrow CO_2(g) + 2\,Ag(s) + S(s)$$

C. $Ag_2S(s) + 2\,Al(s) \rightarrow 2\,Ag(s) + Al_2S(s)$

D. $3\,Ag_2S(s) + 2\,Al(s) \rightarrow 6\,Ag(s) + Al_2S_3(s)$

95. Given that $\Delta G° = -RT \ln K$ and $\Delta G° = -nFE°$, which of the following equations holds true?

A. $-RT \ln K = nFE°$

B. $\ln K = \dfrac{nFE°}{RT}$

C. $\ln K = -\dfrac{nFE°}{RT}$

D. $\ln K = \dfrac{RT}{nFE°}$

96. What are the coefficients for the following oxidation-reduction reaction?

$$Cr(s) + HI(aq) \rightarrow H_2(g) + CrI_3(s)$$

A. $2 : 6 : 3 : 2$

B. $2 : 6 : 3 : 4$

C. $2 : 3 : 3 : 2$

D. $4 : 6 : 3 : 4$

97. If a solution of 1.0 M $ZnCl_2$ were exposed to a 9.65-ampere current for 1,000 seconds, then how many grams of zinc metal would plate onto the cathode?

$\left(F = 96,500 \dfrac{\text{coulombs}}{\text{mole electrons}}\right)$

A. 3.269 grams Zn

B. 6.538 grams Zn

C. 9.807 grams Zn

D. 13.076 grams Zn

98. What is the cell potential for the following cell? The reduction potentials of nickel and magnesium are -0.23 V and -2.37 V, respectively.

$$Mg(s) + Ni^{2+}(aq) \rightarrow Ni(s) + Mg^{2+}(aq)$$

A. 5.20 V

B. 4.28 V

C. 2.60 V

D. 2.14 V

99. Which of the following graphs represents voltage as a function of time for a galvanic cell obeying the Nernst equation?

$$E = E° - \frac{0.059}{n} \log Q$$

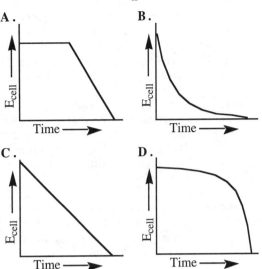

100. Aluminum metal is formed according to the Hall process. The reaction for the Hall process is drawn below:

$$2\,Al_2O_3(solution) + 3\,C(s) \rightarrow 4\,Al(s) + 3\,CO_2(g)$$

What must be true for this reaction?

A. Aluminum oxide is reduced.

B. Carbon is reduced.

C. Aluminum metal is oxidized.

D. Carbon dioxide is oxidized.

1. D	2. C	3. C	4. D	5. C
6. D	7. C	8. A	9. A	10. C
11. C	12. C	13. D	14. D	15. D
16. B	17. D	18. D	19. B	20. D
21. A	22. D	23. D	24. D	25. A
26. D	27. D	28. A	29. C	30. A
31. D	32. C	33. B	34. C	35. D
36. D	37. D	38. B	39. C	40. A
41. A	42. D	43. C	44. D	45. A
46. B	47. D	48. D	49. B	50. A
51. A	52. D	53. A	54. C	55. B
56. B	57. D	58. B	59. A	60. D
61. D	62. D	63. C	64. C	65. A
66. C	67. B	68. B	69. C	70. D
71. D	72. B	73. A	74. D	75. B
76. B	77. D	78. A	79. C	80. D
81. A	82. C	83. A	84. B	85. C
86. D	87. B	88. C	89. C	90. A
91. D	92. A	93. C	94. D	95. B
96. A	97. A	98. D	99. D	100. A

Electrochemistry Passage Answers

1. **Choice D is correct.** The loss of an electron from a compound is referred to as *oxidation*, so choice A is a valid answer. When an element loses one electron, the process is referred to as *ionization* (the ionization energy is the energy required to lose an electron if you recall), so choice B is valid. To convert an oxidation state from -1 to 0 requires losing an electron, because the new oxidation state is more positive (less negative). This makes choice C valid. The correct choice must be answer **D**. The electron affinity is the energy released when an element gains an electron, meaning that choice **D** does *not* involve the loss of an electron.

2. **Choice C is correct.** Potassium is less electronegative than sodium, so potassium gives off an electron more easily. This means that the oxidation potential for potassium is more positive than the oxidation potential for sodium. Chlorine is more electronegative than bromine, so chlorine gains an electron more easily. This means that the reduction potential for chlorine is more positive than the reduction potential for bromine. The best reaction (most favorable and with the largest cell voltage) is the reaction of potassium with chlorine. This makes choice **C** the best answer.

3. **Choice C is correct.** The oxidation states of hydrogen and oxygen are +1 and -2, respectively. The oxidation state of chlorine can be found by looking at the difference in the two compounds in question. In HCl, the oxidation state of chlorine must be -1, to keep the overall compound neutral. In HOCl, the oxidation state of chlorine must be +1, to keep the overall compound neutral. This makes choice **C** the correct answer choice.

4. **Choice D is correct.** From the periodic table, it can be determined that Rb has a lower ionization energy than either potassium (K) or sodium (Na). This results in a value for the ionization of Rb that is less than that of potassium or sodium, so it is less than either 495.9 or 418.7 kJ per mole. The best answer is choice **D**, less than 418.7 kJ per mole.

5. **Choice C is correct.** Because lithium is in the same column of the periodic table as sodium and potassium, the reaction of lithium with water should produce similar products, but with different energy. Both sodium and potassium when added to water produce metal hydroxide and hydrogen gas. No metal hydride forms, so choices B and D are eliminated. There is a reaction, so choice A is eliminated. Although both hydrogen gas and lithium hydroxide are produced, "only lithium hydroxide" is the best answer. Choose answer **C**.

6. **Choice D is correct.** Potassium metal is oxidized by the water, and because reducing agents get oxidized, potassium must be the reducing agent. This eliminates choices A and C. Water is a reactant, not hydrogen gas, so choice B is eliminated. The correct choice is answer choice **D**.

7. **Choice C is correct.** Metals have lower ionization energies than nonmetals, so metals are more easily oxidized. This can be confirmed from the highly positive reduction potentials of nonmetals and the highly positive oxidation potentials of metals. Statement I is therefore true. From the reactions listed, metals definitely form metal hydroxides. Several metals form the oxides when the water is removed. Although the passage does not provide enough information, calcium and magnesium are examples of metals that form both oxides and hydroxides in water. This makes statement II true. From the reactions of bromine and chlorine, it can be inferred that nonmetals do not form metal oxides and metal hydroxides. The best answer is choice **C**.

8. **Choice A is correct.** As base is added, the concentration of hydronium decreases. The passage provides the following equation: $\varepsilon_{observed} = \varepsilon°_{cell} - 0.0592 \log [H^+]$. As $[H^+]$ decreases, the pH increases, which eliminates choices B and D. As $[H^+]$ decreases, the $\log [H^+]$ (which equals -pH) gets more negative. This means a larger negative number is subtracted, thus making the number more positive. This makes the value of $\varepsilon_{observed}$ increase. Pick choice **A** today and smile tomorrow.

9. **Choice A is correct.** Reducing the pH requires making the solution more acidic. Increased acidity results from an increase in the $[H^+]$. Only the addition of HCl(*aq*) (choice **A**) would result in an increase in the $[H^+]$. Choose **A**. Answer choices B and C are bases, so when they are added to solution, the result is a decrease in the $[H^+]$. Choice D is a neutral salt, meaning that the only affect it has is to dilute the solution, which also results in a decrease in the $[H^+]$.

10. **Choice C is correct.** The pH of the solution is found using the equation: $pH = -\log[H^+]$. In this question, the concentration is 0.010 M, so $pH = -\log(.01) = -\log 10^{-2} = 2$. Pick choice **C** for optimum satisfaction.

11. **Choice C is correct.** The 0.285 volts *emf* is specific for the calomel reaction under standard conditions. Anything that changes the reaction or the conditions can vary the standard voltage. Using a weaker acid will reduce the amount of hydronium in solution, but this will not affect the calomel reaction. Choice A can be eliminated. If the resistance in the wire increases, then the current will drop, but the voltage of the reaction is independent of the wiring. Choice B can be eliminated. The number of pores on the bulb will affect how quickly the solution can equilibrate with the cell, but it will not change the reaction voltage. Choice D is eliminated. If the cation being reduced were to change, then it becomes a different reaction with a different voltage. This makes choice **C** the best answer.

12. **Choice C is correct.** From the equation in the passage, it can be seen that $Hg_2Cl_2(s)$ is gaining electrons, which is defined as reduction. This eliminates both choice B and choice D. In $Hg_2Cl_2(s)$, the oxidation state of mercury is +1, so mercury in the reactant has an oxidation state of +1 and 0 in the product. Mercury is the atom being reduced in the reduction half reaction. Chlorine has an oxidation state of -1 before and after the reaction. This means that chloride is simply a spectator ion, and it does not get involved in the oxidation-reduction reaction. In light of this revelation, the correct answer choice for this question must be choice **C**.

13. **Choice D is correct.** Again, Equation 1 from the passage must be used. $\varepsilon_{observed} = \varepsilon°_{cell} - 0.0592 \log[H^+]$ with the $\varepsilon_{observed}$ is 0.699V yields:

$$0.699 = 0.285 - .0592\left(\log[H^+]\right) \Rightarrow 0.414 = -.0592\left(\log[H^+]\right)$$

$$\Rightarrow \frac{0.414}{0.0592} = -\log[H+] = pH \therefore pH = \frac{0.414}{0.0592} = \frac{41.4}{5.92} \approx \frac{42}{6} = 7$$

The closest answer choice is 7, so you really should pick **D**.

14. **Choice D is correct.** A change in temperature always shifts the equilibrium of a reaction. The equilibrium of the reaction affects the $[H^+]$, so pH of the solution is affected by a change in the temperature. Choice A is a valid statement. Because the pH of the solution is dependent on the hydronium concentration ($[H_3O^+]$), a change in the volume of solvent changes the $[H_3O^+]$, and thus, changes the pH. Choice B is a valid statement. The degree to which a proton can dissociate into solution depends on the solvent, so the $[H_3O^+]$ and therefore pH vary with the type of solvent as well. Choice C is a valid statement. The solution is homogeneous, so no matter where the electrode probe is positioned in solution, it reads the same $[H_3O^+]$, so pH does *not* vary with position of the electrode. Choice **D** is an invalid statement, so it is the best choice.

Passage III (Questions 15 - 20)   Metallurgy

15. **Choice D is correct.** The cyanide anion is a ligand (lone pair donor) to the gold cation. The gold cation forms when oxygen gas oxidizes the gold metal. The cyanide ligand is simply acting as a Lewis base. The best answer is choice **D**.

16. **Choice B is correct.** The sum of the oxidation states of the atoms in the compound must add up to the overall charge on the compound. The cyanide ligand carries a -1 charge, so the gold cation must carry a +1, in order for the sum of the two cyanide ligands and one gold cation to have a -1 charge. The correct answer is choice **B**.

17. **Choice D is correct.** Sulfur goes from a -2 oxidation state in zinc sulfide to a +4 oxidation state in sulfur dioxide, so sulfur has been oxidized. This means that Statement I is not true. Zinc goes from a +2 oxidation state in zinc sulfide to an oxidation state of 0 in zinc metal, so zinc has been reduced. This means that Statement II is true. Oxygen gas gets reduced by oxidizing the sulfur in the first reaction, so oxygen gas is the oxidizing agent. This means that Statement III is true. The correct answer is choice **D**.

18. **Choice D is correct.** Silicon is reduced from an oxidation state of +4 to an oxidation state of 0. The silicon is therefore reduced by a total of four electrons, making choice **D** the only reasonable choice. The reaction does not need to be balanced; the four electrons are enough to distinguish the best answer.

19. **Choice B is correct.** Oxygen is only oxidized when heat is applied to mercury oxide. All of the reactions listed show oxygen in a reduced form in the final product, except when it exists as oxygen gas. The best answer is choice **B**.

20. **Choice D is correct.** Mercury is not oxidized in the first reaction; it remains with an oxidation state of +2. This eliminates choice C. Sulfur goes from -2 in HgS to +4 in SO_2, so sulfur is in fact oxidized by six electrons. This makes choice **D** the best answer. Mercury is reduced by two electrons in the second reaction, so choices A and B are both wrong.

Passage IV   (Questions 21 - 26)   Electrochemical Titration

21. **Choice A is correct.** As we read in the passage, the dichromate anion precipitates out of solution with lead dication as an ionic solid. As the concentration of Pb^{2+} decreases, the observed voltage for the cell decreases, because the denominator of the Q term in the Nernst equation becomes smaller, which makes the concentration term larger. The result is that the cell voltage decreases. This is best explained as choice **A**. The last three choices should be eliminated, because $Pb^{2+}(aq)$ and $Cr_2O_7^{2-}(aq)$ do not react with one another by any redox reaction, only precipitation.

22. **Choice D is correct.** The lead-zinc galvanic cell has an $\varepsilon°_{Cell}$ of -0.13 - (-0.76) = 0.63 V. The dichromate-zinc galvanic cell has an $\varepsilon°_{Cell}$ of 1.33 - (-0.76) = 2.09 V. Regardless of the concentration difference between the zinc cation and the other species in solution, the $\varepsilon°_{Cell}$ for the dichromate-zinc cell is so much greater than the lead-zinc cell that the $\varepsilon_{observed}$ has to be greater for the dichromate-zinc cell. The reason is that the reduction potential of dichromate (1.33 V) is much higher than the reduction potential of lead dication (-0.13 V). The best answer is choice **D**. Choices A and B can be eliminated, because dichromate ($Cr_2O_7^{2-}$) and lead dication (Pb^{2+}) do not oxidize, according to the data presented. Even if they do, their presence in the cathode half-cell requires that they undergo reduction rather than oxidation. From the data presented, choice **D** is true, while choice C is false.

23. **Choice D is correct.** The sulfate anion is a spectator ion that balances out the positive charge in each half-cell. The lead cation is reduced at the cathode so the Pb^{2+} concentration is decreased; while zinc metal is oxidized at the anode, so the Zn^{2+} concentration is increased. This means that the sulfate anion must flow from the cathode to the anode through the salt bridge to keep the net charge in each half-cell balanced. The best answer is therefore choice **D**. The spectator anions flow in the opposite direction of the electrons at the same charge per time. Because sulfate carries a -2 charge, the rate of sulfate migration through the salt bridge is half the rate of the electron flow (half the electrical current).

24. **Choice D is correct.** When the switch is closed, the circuit is complete, and the cell begins to produce electricity. As the cell produces electricity, the Pb^{2+} concentration will slowly decrease, so the amount of lead cation in solution is time dependent. This prevents the accurate measurement of the amount of lead present in the cathode half-cell, so determination of the exact equivalence is not possible. The faster equivalence can be reached will help to ensure a more accurate value. Given the answer choices, the best answer is choice **D**, because the voltage is depleted. Choice B is a throwaway choice, and regardless of whether the circuit is open or closed, the lead and zinc can possibly migrate through the salt bridge, eliminating choice C.

25. **Choice A is correct.** Zinc metal is being oxidized into zinc cation (zinc is losing electrons), so choices C and D are eliminated. Oxidation occurs at the anode, so choice **A** is the best answer. You should recall that oxidation occurs at the anode and reduction occurs at the cathode.

26. **Choice D is correct.** The observed voltage reaches a minimum when the concentrations of lead and dichromate are closest to zero. This occurs when the moles of Pb^{2+} present initially equals the moles of $Cr_2O_7^{2-}$ added. When volume is multiplied by molarity, the result is moles of solute. Only choice **D** lists when the moles of the two species are the same. Pick **D** and be a star-studded chem trooper.

Passage V   (Questions 27 - 33)   Redox Titration

27. **Choice D is correct.** The endpoint of titration occurs when the clear Fe^{2+} solution turns and remains purple from the excess $MnO_4^-(aq)$ in solution following the complete oxidation of Fe^{2+} by MnO_4^- ($KMnO_4$ is an oxidizing agent). MnO is a solid, so the solution does not turn brown, but a brown precipitate forms on the bottom of the flask. Over-titration with $KMnO_4$ results in the purple color remaining in solution. It turns clear only if the $KMnO_4$ reacts. The lingering of the purple color indicates that the reaction is complete. Choice **D** is the best answer.

28. **Choice A is correct.** Flask 3 has twice as much solute by weight and half the volume of solution compared to Flask 2. Relatively, as measured in grams per liter, the following is true:

$$M_{Flask\ 3} = \frac{Double\ the\ mass}{Half\ the\ volume} \times M_{Flask\ 2} = \frac{2}{\frac{1}{2}} \times M_{Flask\ 2} = 4 \times M_{Flask\ 2}$$

Flask 3 has four times the concentration of Flask 2, as measured in grams per liter. It is given that Flask 2 requires a 17.50-mL aliquot of $Na_2Cr_2O_7$(aq) to reach equivalence, so Flask 3 (containing 20.00 mL solution) requires four times the volume of titrant (4 x 17.50 mL) = 70.00 mL $Na_2Cr_2O_7$(aq) solution. Flask 3 requires a 70.00-mL aliquot, so choice **A** is the correct answer.

29. **Choice C is correct.** Since we know that $KMnO_4$ is the oxidizing agent in the reaction, Fe^{2+} must be the reducing agent. Based on this, you must choose **C**. The Fe^{2+} ion is oxidized to Fe^{3+}, so it causes reduction, thus defining itself as the reducing agent of the reaction.

30. **Choice A is correct.** In Flask 2, $FeSO_4$ is titrated with a $Na_2Cr_2O_7$(aq) solution. $Na_2Cr_2O_7$(aq) acts similarly to $KMnO_4$ and is also a great oxidizer, so it must be the oxidizing agent. Choose **A**.

31. **Choice D is correct.** First, you should write out the unbalanced equation:

$$Fe^{2+} + Na_2Cr_2O_7 \rightarrow Fe^{3+} + Cr_2O_3$$

From here, the first step is to balance the electrons in the two half-reactions. The ferrous (+2) cation loses one electron, while the dichromate gains three electrons per chromium (and thus six electrons per compound). To balance the electrons, the ferrous and ferric (+3) cations must both be multiplied by a factor of six.

$$6\ Fe^{2+} + 1\ Na_2Cr_2O_7 \rightarrow 6\ Fe^{3+} + 1\ Cr_2O_3$$

This solves the question and allows you to choose answer choice **D**.

On the MCAT, you should stop at this point and not waste time going further. Because this is a learning environment, however, we will continue to balance the reaction completely. From here, the next step is to balance the charges on each side of the reaction. The reactant side has a +12 net charge, while the product side has a +20 net charge. To balance the charges requires that an additional +8 be added to the reactant side of the equation. This is done by adding 8 H^+ to the left side of the reaction.

$$8\ H^+ + 6\ Fe^{2+} + 1\ Na_2Cr_2O_7 \quad \rightarrow \quad 6\ Fe^{3+} + 1\ Cr_2O_3 + 2\ Na^+$$
$$\text{overall charge} = +20 \qquad\qquad\qquad \text{overall charge} = +20$$

The final step is to balance the atoms in the equation. There are seven oxygen atoms on the reactant side and only three on the product side. The product side requires four more oxygen atoms, so to balance the atoms, 4 H_2O must be added to the product side:

$$8\ H^+ + 6\ Fe^{2+} + 1\ Na_2Cr_2O_7 \quad \rightarrow \quad 6\ Fe^{3+} + 1\ Cr_2O_3 + 2\ Na^+ + 4\ H_2O$$
$$\text{overall charge} = +20 \qquad\qquad\qquad\qquad \text{overall charge} = +20$$

The ratio of $Na_2Cr_2O_7$(aq) to Fe^{3+}(aq) is confirmed to be 1 : 6. This correlates to answer choice **D**. The ratio can be found quickly by comparing the oxidation and reduction counts. Fe is oxidized by one electron, while the chromium compounds are reduced by three electrons per chromium (from +6 to +3). Because there are two chromium atoms in $Na_2Cr_2O_7$, the total amount of electrons necessary to reduce the compound is six (2 × 3 electrons). This makes the ratio 1 : 6.

32. **Choice C is correct.** The oxidation half-reaction of Flask 1 is $Fe^{2+} \rightarrow Fe^{3+} + 1e^-$

Component reactions:
$$Fe^{2+} + 2e^- \rightarrow Fe \qquad -0.44\ V$$
$$Fe \rightarrow Fe^{3+} + 3e^- \qquad 0.04\ V$$

When the two reactions are added together, the overall oxidation half-reaction is found. This means that the $E°$ for the half-reaction can be found by summing the two voltages. $E° = -0.44 + 0.04 = -0.40$ V. Pick **C**.

33. **Choice B is correct.** The best container is made of the least reactive material. Glass (SiO_2) is already in a fully oxidized form, so it is unreactive with respect to oxidation-reduction chemistry. Glass is thus the best material in which to carry out the titration. Aluminum readily oxidizes, copper slowly oxidizes, and polyethylene oxidizes over time in air. The best answer is **B**.

34.   **Choice C is correct.** Gold trication (Au^{3+}) has a reduction potential of 1.50 V, so almost any compound that can be oxidized can reduce gold trication. The $Cl_2(g)$ has chlorine atoms with oxidation states of 0, so they won't be oxidized (lose electrons to be cations). Ag^+ is oxidized in its cation form, so Ag^+ cannot be oxidized any further. Pt^{2+} is already oxidized as it is, so it cannot be oxidized any further. The best choice is zinc metal ($Zn(s)$) which readily loses two electrons. Pick **C**.

35.   **Choice D is correct.** The reduction potential for silver cation is 0.80 volts. This means that because chloride anion is *not* oxidized to $Cl_2(g)$, the oxidation potential of Cl^- to $Cl_2(g)$ is less than -0.80 volts. Reversing this means that the reduction potential of $Cl_2(g)$ to Cl^- is greater than +0.80 volts, which is selection **D**.

36.   **Choice D is correct.** The chlorine atoms in the compound have an oxidation state of -1 each. This means that for the overall charge of the compound to be -1, the oxidation state of the gold must be +3 (4 (-1) + (+3) = -1). This makes choice **D** the best answer.

37.   **Choice D is correct.** Silver (Ag) has an electronic configuration of $[Kr]5s^1 4d^{10}$ when neutral because of the filled d-shell stability associated with the d^{10} electronic configuration. The electron is lost from the outermost shell when the silver becomes a cation. This would be the $5s^1$ electron that silver loses, which leaves an electronic configuration for Ag^+ of: $[Kr]4d^{10}$. Pick choice **D**.

38.   **Choice B is correct.** A sequestering agent must bind a metal cation, so it must be capable of donating a lone pair of electrons to a metal cation in a ligand fashion. Sequestering agents donate electron pairs, so they are Lewis bases. Atoms without filled octet valences can accept electrons, which make them good Lewis acids. This eliminates both choice C and choice D. Choice **B** is the best answer.

39.   **Choice C is correct.** The mass percent of Au in $AuCl_4^-$ can be solved as follows:

$$\frac{\text{Mass Au}}{\text{Mass } AuCl_4^-} = \frac{197}{197 + 4\,(35.5)} = \frac{197}{197 + 142} > \frac{1}{2}, \text{ eliminating choices A and B.}$$

$$\frac{197}{197 + 4\,(35.5)} = \frac{197}{339} < \frac{270}{360} = \frac{3}{4}, \text{ eliminating choice D.}$$

This leaves only choice **C**, which you should pick for best results. The actual value can be approximated as follows: $\frac{197}{339} = \frac{197}{333}$ - a little $= \frac{591}{999}$ - a little = 59% - a little.

40.   **Choice A is correct.** Because chlorine is oxidized in each answer choice, the question is really which cation has the lowest reduction potential, since the metal cations are reduced in each case. The lowest reduction potential, according to the chart, is found with Ag^+. This makes choice **A** the correct choice.

41.   **Choice A is correct.** In all galvanic cells, oxidation occurs at the anode, so electrons are lost from the anode and hence flow from the anode to the cathode. The best answer is choice **A**.

42.   **Choice D is correct.** Oxidation occurs at the anode, and the loss of electrons occurs with oxidation, so choice **D** must be the best answer. It is only in choice **D** that electrons are lost.

43.   **Choice C is correct.** In a galvanic cell, the $\varepsilon_{reduction} + \varepsilon_{oxidation}$ must be greater than 0 volts. If $\varepsilon_{oxidation}$ is greater than 0 volts, the overall voltage is positive, so choices B and D are galvanic cells, meaning they are eliminated. The only way that ε_{cell} can be less than zero when $\varepsilon_{reduction}$ is positive, is when $\varepsilon_{oxidation}$ is a negative value with a magnitude greater absolute value than $\varepsilon_{reduction}$. The best answer is choice **C**.

44.   **Choice D is correct.** In all cells, electron flow is from the anode to cathode, and reduction occurs at the cathode. This makes both choices A and B true in a galvanic cell, so they can be eliminated. Choice C is true according to the Nernst equation, because the cell eventually dies out once the voltage has dropped. The voltage never drops below zero, however, so choice **D** is *not* true. The best answer is choice **D**, because the cell stops when the voltage equals zero (not when it is less than zero).

45. **Choice A is correct.** The reduction of the cation in the cathode is most favorable when it starts at a high oxidation state (as it will have a strong desire to gain electrons). This eliminates choices C and D. The anode should contain a metal that is easily (favorably) oxidized, if the cell is to be galvanic. This corresponds to a metal with a low ionization energy. The best answer is thus choice **A**.

46. **Choice B is correct.** To answer this question, the reaction must first be balanced. The oxidation and reduction half-reactions are shown below.

$$\text{Oxidation: } Al(s) \rightarrow AlO_2^-(aq) + 3\,e^- \qquad\qquad \text{Reduction: } MnO_4^-(aq) + 5\,e^- \rightarrow MnO(s)$$

To balance the reaction from an electronic standpoint (at fifteen total electrons transferred in each half-reaction), $5\,Al(s)$ are needed to react with $3\,MnO_4^-(aq)$. Because $Al(s)$ is oxidized, it is the reducing agent, making $MnO_4^-(aq)$ the oxidizing agent (reactant that gets reduced). The ratio of reducing agent to oxidizing agent is therefore $5:3$. The best answer is choice **B**.

47. **Choice D is correct.** Reduction occurs at the cathode, so copper cations in solution plate out onto the surface of the electrode. This makes Statement I valid, which eliminates choice C. A galvanic cell by definition involves a favorable reaction that releases energy as it runs. The voltage of a favorable reaction is greater than 0.00 volts, so Statement II is valid. This eliminates choice A. To balance the flow of electron charge from anode to cathode, anions must flow from cathode (where the positive charge diminishes due to reduction) to the anode (where the positive charge increases due to oxidation) through the salt bridge. This makes Statement III true. Because all three statements are valid, the best answer is choice **D**.

Passage VIII   (Questions 48 - 54)   Photochemical Cell

48. **Choice D is correct.** By definition (and from the passage), electrolytic cells are unfavorable thermodynamically. Energy must be supplied for an electrolytic cell to run. The electrolytic cell can build up potential energy that can be harnessed later (the energy can be discharged in the form of a galvanic cell). The best answer is therefore answer **D**.

49. **Choice B is correct.** The first sentence of the second paragraph states that the energy of the photon must be high enough to overcome the electrical potential for the cell. This makes choice **B** correct. Choices A and C are the same answer just stated differently, so they cannot both be correct on a multiple-choice exam. The electron affinity for the cathode is usually favorable, so no energy should be required for the gain of an electron by the cathode. The total energy to move the electron comes from the photon and the affinity for the cathode (attraction to the storage plate).

50. **Choice A is correct.** Photons strike the ionizing plate and emit an electron. The ionizing plate loses an electron, so it has been oxidized. By definition, the anode loses electrons (gets oxidized), making choice **A** the best answer.

51. **Choice A is correct.** The best material is one that can be oxidized very easily. A nonmetal and nonmetal oxide do not readily lose electrons because of their high electron affinity (and electronegativity). A metal oxide is in a higher oxidation state than the metal, so metal oxides are less able to share their electrons than metals. Metal oxides have already been oxidized. The best answer for this question is a metal, choice **A**.

52. **Choice D is correct.** As is stated in the first paragraph of the passage, a photoelectric cell absorbs a photon, which then emits an electron that flows through a wire in the circuit, ultimately to be stored in a capacitor or battery. The overall process involves converting a photon into potential energy. A photon is electromagnetic radiation, so the best answer is choice **D**, the conversion of radiation into potential energy. Pick choice **D** if you want to be outstanding in electrochemistry.

53. **Choice A is correct.** If you believe the Nernst equation, then the voltage is constantly dissipating as a cell runs. The most energy is released initially, because that is when the voltage (joules per coulomb) is the greatest. This is best described by answer choice **A**. If you have any doubt about this, think about how a flashlight slowly becomes dimmer rather than brighter. The change in voltage is minimal, but nonetheless evident.

54. **Choice C is correct.** The chemical reaction in the circuit, as opposed to the traditional unequal parallel lines to symbolize voltage, power the circuit but are irrelevant to this question. The current at point c should be the greatest, because it has not been split to pass through the parallel resistors. The resistors are in parallel, so the current is split between the two resistors ($I_c = I_a + I_b$). The greater current flows through the pathway of lesser resistance. You may recall that current and resistance are inversely proportional to one another. The best answer is choice **C**, because the resistance is less through the resistor through which current a flows. I is equal to current.

55.   **Choice B is correct.** The two half reactions for the nickel-cadmium battery are given in the passage as:

Anode: $Cd + 2\ OH^- \rightarrow Cd(OH)_2 + 2\ e^-$

Cathode: $NiOOH + H_2O + 1\ e^- \rightarrow Ni(OH)_2 + 1\ OH^-$

To find the overall balanced equation, the number of electrons in each half-cell must be the same. In the oxidation half-cell, two electrons are produced, while in the reduction half-cell, only one electron is consumed. This means that the reduction half-cell must be multiplied by two. This yields the following two half-cells that upon addition yield the overall reaction:

Anode: $Cd + \text{2 OH}^- \rightarrow Cd(OH)_2 + \text{2 e}^-$

Cathode: $2\ NiOOH + 2\ H_2O + \text{2 e}^- \rightarrow 2\ Ni(OH)_2 + \text{2 OH}^-$

Overall: $Cd + 2\ NiOOH + 2\ H_2O \rightarrow Cd(OH)_2 + 2\ Ni(OH)_2$

The correct answer is choice **B**.

56.   **Choice B is correct.** In the reduction half-cell, MnO_2 is converted to Mn_2O_3. In MnO_2, the oxidation state of Mn is +4. In Mn_2O_3, the oxidation state of Mn is +3. These can be determined by assuming that the oxidation state of oxygen is -2 in all of the compounds. The oxidation state of Mn goes from +4 to +3. Because zinc is oxidized, manganese must be reduced, making choices A, C, and D incorrect. The correct choice is answer **B**. Only one electron is absorbed, so it should be reduced by one electron.

57.   **Choice D is correct.** Reduction takes place at the cathode, so choices A and B are immediately eliminated. Because at a pH equal to 10 the solution is basic, the correct answer must be choice **D**. Ammonium cation (NH_4^+) cannot exist at a pH of 10, because it has a pK_a value less than 10. It would exist as ammonia (NH_3) in a pH = 10 solution. The cell is basic, so choice **D** is best.

58.   **Choice B is correct.** Oxidation takes place at the anode, meaning that the reaction that *cannot* occur at the anode is a reduction half reaction. Reduction involves the gain of electrons, so the electrons are on the reactant side of the equation in reduction. In choice **B**, the reactant side of the equation shows electrons, meaning that electrons are gained in the reaction. Gaining electrons is the definition of reduction, so choice **B** cannot occur at the anode.

59.   **Choice A is correct.** The flow of electrons in any electrochemical cell is defined as being from the anode to the cathode (from the oxidation half-cell to the reduction half-cell). The trick to this question is therefore deciding where the anode and cathode actually are. The core of the dry cell battery carries out the oxidation half-reaction, while the stainless steel cap is the electrode on which manganese is reduced. In the battery drawing in Figure 1, the stainless steel cap is defined as the cathode. This means that the correct answer must have the electron flow going towards the stainless steel cap. This eliminates choices B and D. The insulator does not get involved in the reaction or the flow of electrons (hence the term "insulator"). This means that choice C is eliminated and makes the best answer (and only choice remaining) choice **A**. The electrons flow from the metal being reduced, which is found in the outer casing (as stated in the passage).

60.   **Choice D is correct.** Electrons do not build up in a cell; potential difference builds up. The electrons flow, but they do not exactly collect. Choice A is therefore eliminated. Cadmium is oxidized in the reaction, meaning that cadmium metal disappears and does not build up, whether it's at the anode or the cathode. Choice B is therefore eliminated. Nickel hydroxide is a product of the reaction, so nickel hydroxide builds up somewhere. Nickel hydroxide does not build up at the anode, however, because nickel hydroxide is formed from the reduction half-reaction, so it builds up at the cathode, according to the two half-cell equations. Choice C is therefore eliminated. Cadmium hydroxide is formed from the oxidation half-reaction, so it builds up at the anode. The best answer is choice **D**.

61.   **Choice D is correct.** In the electrolytic portion (lower half) of the overall cell, chlorine gas is released. This means that chloride anion loses an electron to form chlorine gas. Because Cl^- (chloride) is oxidized, choices A and C are eliminated. The sodium metal produced in the lower cell ultimately serves to reduce hydronium ion in water in the upper portion (galvanic section). Choice **D** is correct, because H^+ is reduced to $H_2(g)$ in the overall cell reaction.

62. **Choice D is correct.** The applied voltage promotes the unfavorable oxidation-reduction reaction that is taking place in the lower electrolytic portion of the electrolysis cell. The lower reduction and oxidation half-reactions are:

$Na^+(aq) + 1 e^- \rightarrow Na(l)$ with $\varepsilon_{reduction}$ = -2.71 V $Cl^-(aq) \rightarrow \frac{1}{2} Cl_2(g) + 1 e^-$ with $\varepsilon_{oxidation}$ = -1.36 V.

The overall voltage is -4.07 V, so a voltage greater than 4.07 V must be applied to force the unfavorable reaction to proceed. The best answer is choice **D**.

63. **Choice C is correct.** This question may seem tough at first, because the diagram in Figure 1 is daunting. But if you calming look at the arrows of what goes in and what comes out, you can get the answer. Both hydrogen gas ($H_2(g)$) and chlorine gas ($Cl_2(g)$) are released from the cell, so they must both be products of the overall reaction, which eliminates choices B and D. In the upper portion of the cell, $NaOH(aq)$ is produced and released from the solution, so it too must be a product of the reaction. This makes choice **C** the best answer.

64. **Choice C is correct.** Because the reduction potential of sodium cation is negative and the reduction potential of hydronium ion is zero (see the reaction voltages given in the passage), Statement I is a false statement. This actually eliminates choices A, B, and D, thereby making choice **C** the best answer by default. On the MCAT you may wish to pick choice **C** and move on. We'll consider the remaining to statements for completeness, but you should always be thinking about good test-taking habits. In the electrolytic portion of the cell, sodium metal is formed, because the electrons are delivered from the cathode into the mercury liquid, and sodium metal flows through mercury, while hydrogen gas does not. This makes Statement II a true statement. Because there are some sodium cations that are transferred to the upper cell to form NaOH, the [NaCl] entering the cell must be greater than the [NaCl] leaving the cell. This makes Statement III a true statement, and thus confirms that choice **C** is the best answer.

65. **Choice A is correct.** By definition, reduction occurs at the cathode and oxidation occurs at the anode, in a battery, a galvanic cell, and an electrolytic cell. Oxidation involves the loss of electrons, so electrons must flow away *from* the anode. Reduction involves gain of electrons, so electrons must flow *to* the cathode. Overall, the flow of electrons is always from anode to cathode, so choice **A** is the best answer. You make want to note that in physics they consider current to be the flow of imaginary positive charge in the opposite direction of the actual electron flow.

66. **Choice C is correct.** An electrolytic cell is defined as a cell that carries out an unfavorable reaction by applying an external voltage. This means that the reaction voltage is negative, so to have the reaction occur, the battery voltage must be positive, with the absolute value of the battery voltage greater than the absolute value of the voltage of the reaction. When the two values are summed, the cell voltage will be positive. The best answer is choice **C**.

67. **Choice B is correct.** The strongest reducing agent is the compound (or element) that is most easily oxidized. Sodium cation cannot give up an electron (because it would lose its noble gas electronic configuration), so choice A can be eliminated. The reactions in Table 1 are reductions, so the product formed from the least favorable reduction is the most favorably oxidized, and thus the strongest reducing agent. This makes choice **B** the best answer.

Passage XI   (Questions 68 - 74)   **Standard Cells**

68. **Choice B is correct.** The net reaction for Cell 1 is favorable, if the zinc electrode is oxidized and the copper electrode is reduced (an electrochemical cell is favorable when $E°_{cell}$ is positive). Thus, the electron flow must be from the Zn electrode (anode) to the Cu electrode (cathode). Because the copper electrode is not the anode, choice C and choice D are both eliminated. Since, by definition, electron flow is always from the anode to the cathode, and the Zn electrode (anode) is on the left, the electron flow must be from the left. Referring to the illustration of Cell 1 in the passage, the electron flow is from left to right, so, choice **B** is the correct answer.

69. **Choice C is correct.** Cell 1 does not use energy to produce chemical change, so it is not an electrolytic cell. The two half-cells do not differ in cation concentration, so it is not a concentration cell. The cell is set up so that energy from a spontaneous redox reaction is converted into electrical energy (electrical energy is discharged), which is a galvanic cell by definition. Pick **C**. "Nernst cell" is a fictitious term.

70. **Choice D is correct.** The cell would no longer be complete without the saturated aqueous salt string, which serves as a salt bridge to complete the circuit. Copper wire does not allow for the flow of sulfate anions from one half-cell to the other half-cell, so the cell potential is 0 volts. Pick **D**.

71. **Choice D is correct.** Cell 2 is a concentration cell, given the different concentrations in each half-cell. The electrons flow in such a way that the concentration of Cu^{2+} in each half-cell becomes equal over time. When electrons flow from the anode, the copper electrode dissolves into solution, resulting in an increased Cu^{2+} concentration in solution and a reduced mass of the electrode. This means that the half-cell with the lower concentration of Cu^{2+} is the anode, and the half-cell with the greater concentration of Cu^{2+} is the cathode. The half-cell on the left is less concentrated (making it the anode), so electrons flow from the left to the right as drawn. This makes choice A a valid statement, so it is eliminated. The left copper electrode dissolves away and thus decreases in mass, while the right copper electrode plates out and thus increases in mass. This makes choice B a valid statement, so it is eliminated. In a concentration cell, the electrons flow from the less concentrated half-cell to the more concentrated half-cell, until the two cells have equal Cu^{2+} concentration. The electrons flow from the half-cell with 0.001 M Cu^{2+} to the half-cell with 1.00 M Cu^{2+}. The Cu^{2+} ions in the 1.00 M solution get reduced. The Cu^{2+} concentration decrease from 1.00 M until both cells are equally concentrated. The final concentration is the average of the two initial concentrations, which is 0.5005 M Cu^{2+}. This makes choice C a valid statement and choice **D** an incorrect statement, so choice **D** is the best answer.

72. **Choice B is correct.** You are given the equation $\varepsilon = \varepsilon^\circ - \dfrac{0.059}{n} \log Q$, where $Q = \dfrac{[\text{Anode}]}{[\text{Cathode}]}$.

$$Q = \frac{0.001 \text{ M}}{1.000 \text{ M}} = 0.001, \ n = 2 \text{ moles of electrons, and } \varepsilon^\circ = 0$$

Plugging the values into the equation yields:

$$\varepsilon = \varepsilon^\circ - \frac{0.059}{n} \log Q = 0 - \frac{0.059}{2} \log (.001) = (-0.0295)(-3) = 0.0885 \text{ V}$$

The cell potential in Cell 2 (the concentration cell) is calculated to be 0.089 V, so choice **B** is the best answer.

73. **Choice A is correct.** The half-reactions are listed as reduction reactions in the table, so be sure to change the sign for zinc oxidation from positive to negative. The largest positive cell potential for Cell 1 is obtained when the zinc is oxidized and the copper cation is reduced. In a cell, there must always be both a reduction half-reaction and an oxidation half-reaction. The numerical value for E°_{cell} is calculated from the following equations and half-cell potentials:

$$
\begin{array}{ll}
Cu^{2+} + 2e^- \rightarrow Cu & +0.34 \text{ V} \\
Zn \rightarrow Zn^{2+} + 2e^- & \underline{+0.76 \text{ V}} \\
 & +1.10 \text{ V}
\end{array}
$$

The cell potential of Cell 1 is therefore 1.10 V, answer choice **A**.

74. **Choice D is correct.** Starting with $H_2O + ClO_3^- + Mg \rightarrow Cl^- + Mg^{2+} + OH^-$, first balance the electrons either through the bridge method or the half-cell method. Magnesium goes from an oxidation state of 0 to +2, so 2 electrons are lost. Chlorine goes from an oxidation state of +5 to -1, so 6 electrons are gained. This needs to be balanced so that there are 3 magnesiums for every 1 chlorine.

$$? \ H_2O + 1 \ ClO_3^- + 3 \ Mg \rightarrow 1 \ Cl^- + 3 \ Mg^{2+} + ? \ OH^-$$

Choices A and C are eliminated, because they do not have the correct ratio of magnesiums to chlorines. After the electrons, the charges must be balanced. The overall charge on the left side is -1 due to the chlorate anion, and the overall charge on the right side is +5 due to the three magnesium cations and one chloride anion.

$$? \ H_2O + 1 \ ClO_3^- + 3 \ Mg \quad \rightarrow \quad 1 \ Cl^- + 3 \ Mg^{2+} + ? \ OH^-$$
$$\text{overall charge} = -1 \qquad\qquad \text{overall charge} = +5$$

To balance charge, six hydroxide anions are added to the right side of the equation. This eliminates answer choice B, narrowing the answer down to choice **D**. The last step of the balancing, if you wish to go on (although you could stop here), is to balance the atoms. To balance atoms, water is added to the left side of the reaction.

$$? \ H_2O + 1 \ ClO_3^- + 3 \ Mg \quad \rightarrow \quad 1 \ Cl^- + 3 \ Mg^{2+} + 6 \ OH^-$$
$$\text{overall charge} = -1 \qquad\qquad \text{overall charge} = -1$$

There are six oxygen atoms on the right, and only three on the left, so three waters must be added to the left side of the equation. Adding three waters results in the following balanced equation:

$$3 \ H_2O + 1 \ ClO_3^- + 3 \ Mg \rightarrow 1 \ Cl^- + 3 \ Mg^{2+} + 6 \ OH^-$$

The coefficients of the balanced equation are $3:1:3 \rightarrow 1:3:6$, so choice **D** is the best answer.

75. **Choice B is correct.** Palladium metal is neutral, and it does not dissolve into organic solvent. This eliminates choice A. By plating palladium onto the surface of carbon, the surface area is maximized, and thus the reactivity is most efficient. This could also have been achieved by powdering the palladium, but that would have allowed the palladium to pass through pores in the catalytic converter through which the exhaust gas flows. The larger carbon-palladium chunk would not pass through the filtering system, so it doesn't inadvertently get discarded in the exhaust. Choice **B** is the best answer. Carbon does not supply electrons (it does not ionize readily), so choice C can be eliminated. Palladium metal hopefully does not oxidize, but because carbon does not readily undergo oxidation in the presence of the exhaust gas, it cannot help to limit the oxidation of palladium. Choice D can be eliminated.

76. **Choice B is correct.** The addition of voltage does not form hydronium and hydroxide ions, because both oxygen and hydrogen carry the same oxidation states as they do in water. This means that no redox chemistry transpired, so voltage was not necessary. Choice A can be eliminated. The further reduction of metals to anions and halogens to cations is not realistic, so choices C and D are throwaway answers. The addition of 1.86 volts can cause the reduction of protons to hydrogen gas and the reduction of oxygen within water to oxygen gas. This makes choice **B** the correct answer.

77. **Choice D is correct.** Because palladium dication can be reduced in the presence of protons (H^+), it must be easier (and thus more favorable) to reduce Pd^{2+} than H^+. This eliminates choices A and B. Because nickel dication cannot be reduced in the presence of protons (H^+), it must be harder (and thus less favorable) to reduce Ni^{2+} than H^+. This eliminates choice C and makes choice **D** the best answer.

78. **Choice A is correct.** The role of the electrode is to facilitate the transfer electrons between solutions, and provide a surface on which cations can acquire electrons and plate out as neutral atoms. As a result, an electrode must be able to conduct electricity, so it must **not** be a good insulator. This makes choice **A** the "**not** true" statement. An ideal electrode should simply transfer electrons, and it should not be involved in the reaction in any manner. This means that the electrode should be inert, eliminating choice B. A high melting point is ideal for an electrode, so that it does not melt into solution during the process. This eliminates choice C. As the resistance decreases, the current (electrical conductivity) increases, making the electrode better at delivering electrons to the cations. This eliminates choice D.

79. **Choice C is correct.** The voltage associated with the conversion of copper chloride to copper metal and chlorine gas is 0.34 volts for the reduction of copper cation into copper metal plus -1.36 volts for the oxidation of chloride anion into chlorine gas, resulting in an overall cell voltage of -1.02 volts. This means that at least 1.02 volts must be added for the reaction to occur, so choices A and B can be eliminated. However, if the voltage added is greater than 1.36 volts, then the reduction of hydronium (protons) to hydrogen gas may also be observed. To avoid getting this unwanted side reaction, the applied voltage should be less than 1.36 volts. This makes the best answer choice **C**.

80. **Choice D is correct.** Carbon does not have d-orbitals, so choice A is partially correct; but because it is used as an electrode, it must be able to conduct electricity. This eliminates choice A. Carbon does have p-orbitals, so choice B is definitely incorrect and can be eliminated. Electricity is conducted through the π-network of graphite, because of the delocalized nature of the π-electrons through the highly conjugated network. This makes choice **D** the best answer.

81. **Choice A is correct.** The standard voltage of the reaction ($\varepsilon°_{rx}$) can be found by summing the standard reduction potential for the cation reduction half-reaction ($\varepsilon°_{red}$) and the standard oxidation potential for the anion oxidation half-reaction ($\varepsilon°_{ox}$). The overall reaction (cell) with the least negative voltage is the one that will require the lowest applied voltage to go in the electrolytic direction. The voltages for each of the oxidation-reduction reactions are as follows:

Choice **A**:	For AgCl;	$0.80 + (-1.36) = -0.56$
Choice **B**:	For $CuBr_2$;	$0.34 + (-1.09) = -0.75$
Choice **C**:	For $NiBr_2$;	$-0.23 + (-1.09) = -1.32$
Choice **D**:	For $ZnCl_2$;	$-0.76 + (-1.36) = -2.12$

The lowest value is associated with the silver chloride, making choice **A** the best answer.

82. **Choice C is correct**. A good material for galvanizing steel should be easier to oxidize than iron. This means that our focus is on losing an electron, rather than gaining one. This eliminates choices B and D, which both refer to the gain of an electron. In fact, a material with a low electron affinity would also have a low reduction potential, so choices B and D could have been eliminated because they are complimentary answers. If a material has a low oxidation potential, that means it is difficult to oxidize it, which would imply that it would not oxidize as easily as iron. The material would not be a sacrificial metal in that case, which eliminates choice A. The ideal material should be easy to ionize, which means it must have a low ionization energy. Choice **C** is the best answer.

83. **Choice A is correct**. An oxidizing agent is the reactant that gets reduced in an oxidation-reduction reaction. This means that the best answer must be the compound that can most readily gain electrons. Magnesium, Mg, will readily lose electrons, but that makes it a reducing agent. Choice B is eliminated. Using similar logic, choice D is also eliminated. Although copper may not readily lose its electrons, it certainly won't gain electrons to become an anion. To decide between the two remaining choices, Pd^{2+} and Al^{3+}, we must look at Table 1. The reduction of Pd^{2+} is more favorable than the reduction of Al^{3+} (an $E°_{red}$ of +0.99 V is more favorable than an $E°_{red}$ of -1.66 V). The best answer is choice **A**.

84. **Choice B is correct**. The passage states that a good sacrificial metal should be only slightly more reactive than the metal it is protecting, to avoid having it oxidize in the atmosphere. According to Table 1, potassium metal has an oxidation potential of 2.92 volts, which makes it highly reactive. Potassium metal is too reactive. Choices C and D can be eliminated at this juncture, because potassium being a poor sacrificial metal has nothing to do with its being neutered by iron or an inability to adhere to a surface. The concern is that potassium metal can readily oxidize in the air. This is due to it reacting with oxygen gas and water vapor in the air, not with inert gases such as nitrogen and argon. The best answer is choice **B**.

85. **Choice C is correct**. To solve this question requires using the values listed in Table 1. In the reaction, Fe^{2+} is being reduced and zinc metal is being oxidized. The reduction of Fe^{2+} to Fe has a standard *emf* of -0.44 V. The oxidation of Zn to Zn^{2+} has a standard *emf* of +0.76 V (the negative of its reduction potential). The standard *emf* for the reaction is found by summing the two half-reaction *emf* values ($E°_{cell} = E°_{red} + E°_{ox}$). In this case, the overall cell voltage (*emf*) is -0.44 V + 0.76 V = 0.32 V, choice **C**.

86. **Choice D is correct**. A voltaic cell is one that is overall favorable, and therefore has a positive *emf* value. In a voltaic cell involving copper and zinc half-reactions, Cu^{2+} is reduced into Cu and Zn is oxidized into Zn^{2+}. This results in an $E°_{red}$ of +0.34 V for the copper half-reaction and an $E°_{ox}$ of +0.76 V for the zinc half-reaction. The overall cell voltage is 1.10 volts, so it is in fact voltaic. By definition, oxidation occurs at the anode. So even though zinc metal is oxidized in the favorable reaction, it occurs at the anode and not the cathode. This makes Statement I invalid, which eliminates choices A and C. By default, Statement II must be valid (given that it is found in the two remaining answer choices). It is true that electrons flow to the cathode, where reduction takes place. Reduction results in the plating out of a material (in this case copper metal), so Statement II is in fact valid. This means that the buildup of copper metal increases the electrode's mass over time. Statement III is a valid statement, making choice **D** the best answer.

87. **Choice B is correct**. When zinc metal is exposed to the environment, it can be oxidized into zinc cation. Being that it gets oxidized, we can refer to it as a reducing agent rather than an oxidizing agent. This eliminates choice A and makes choice **B** the best answer. Zinc will turn into zinc oxide, which would lead one to refer to it as oxophilic, not oxophobic. Choice C is eliminated. Given that zinc is being oxidized, it is releasing electrons, not absorbing them. Zinc metal is not an electron sponge, so choice D is eliminated.

88. **Choice C is correct**. Because the charge on the silver cation is +1, twice as many moles of silver metal (Ag) form as both copper metal (Cu) and zinc metal (Zn). Three times as many moles of silver metal (Ag) form as gold metal (Au). To find the mass formed, the moles formed must be multiplied by the atomic mass of the element. The answer choice with the greatest value from moles times molecular mass is the correct answer choice. Silver has an atomic mass of 107.9, and it requires one electron per ion, so one mole of electrons produces 107.9 grams of silver. Copper has an atomic mass of 63.5, but it requires two electrons per ion, so only 31.75 grams form from one mole of electrons. Zinc has an atomic mass of 65.4, but it requires two electrons per ion, so only 32.7 grams form from one mole of electrons. Gold has an atomic mass of 197.0, but it requires three electrons per ion, so only 65.67 grams form from one mole of electrons. The greatest mass results from the silver cation, so choice **C** is the best answer.

89. **Choice C is correct.** To carry out electroplating, a current must run through some material suspended in a solution of ions. The charge builds up on the surface of the material where ions are reduced and thus can precipitate (onto the surface of the metal). If the material does not conduct electricity, charge cannot build up on its surface. Plastic is an insulator, not a conductor of electricity, making choice **C** the best answer. Choice A should have been eliminated, because high temperatures are not required for electroplating. Choice B should be eliminated, because a current of electrons causes reduction, not oxidation. Choice D should have been eliminated, because malleability does not effect electroplating.

90. **Choice A is correct.** Because Solution I has a lower concentration of metal than Solution IV, Solution I finishes before Solution IV. This means that either choice **A** or choice D is the correct choice. Silver has a greater mass than zinc, and it requires only one electron for complete reduction, so the electrode of Solution I has a greater initial increase in mass per unit time than solution IV. This can be seen in choice **A** where Solution I shows a steeper slope than Solution IV.

91. **Choice D is correct.** Electroplating results from the conversion of cations in solution into precipitated metal atoms. To convert a cation to a neutral element, electrons must be added. The gain of electrons is defined as reduction, so choice **D** best describes the process.

92. **Choice A is correct.** A good protective metal coating is one that does not oxidize away. This means that it must be unfavorable for the metal to oxidize away, which would imply that the metal has negative oxidation potential. A negative oxidation potential for the metal would result in a positive reduction potential for the cation (the reverse reaction). This is answer choice **A**. This also explains why choice D is eliminated. Choice B is incorrect, because the reduction of a metal to an anion is not known to occur. This not only would not be a desirable property, but it would not be practical. A large positive oxidation potential for its cation just means that the cation can further be oxidized, making choice C a bad choice.

93. **Choice C is correct.** In the experiment, the cation solutions are exposed to the current for one minute. Like zinc and copper, cadmium cation (Cd^{2+}) takes two electrons to be reduced. Because cadmium has an atomic mass greater than that of both copper and zinc, the mass of the electrode is greater than the electrodes for Solutions III, IV, V, and VI. The electrode has a mass greater than 5.360 grams (the mass of the heavier zinc plated electrode), which eliminates choices A and B. To form the same mass as the silver cation, cadmium would have to have twice the atomic mass of silver. The atomic mass of cadmium is less than twice the atomic mass of silver, so the electrode has a mass less than 6.182 grams (the mass of the lighter silver plated electrode). This eliminates choice D. The best answer is choice **C**.

| Questions 94 - 100 | Not Based on a Descriptive Passage |

94. **Choice D is correct.** Choice A can be eliminated, because both the H^+ and the Ag^+ are reduced in the reaction as given, and nothing is oxidized. An oxidation-reduction reaction must have both an oxidation half-reaction and a reduction half-reaction. If choice B were true, then tarnish could never occur, because the reduction of silver would be carried out by the sulfide anion it binds. Choice C is eliminated, because Al cannot exist in a +1 oxidation state. The correct answer is choice **D**, because the oxidation state of aluminum (which was oxidized) is +3. Pick choice **D** and feel happy.

95. **Choice B is correct.** Setting the two equation equal to each other yields: -RT ln K = - nFε°. This becomes RT ln K = nFε° once the negative signs have been eliminated. Choices A and C are therefore wrong. Dividing both sides by RT yields choice **B**: $\ln K = \dfrac{nF\varepsilon°}{RT}$.

96. **Choice A is correct.** By simply balancing the atoms in the equation, we find that the coefficients should be 2 : 6 : 3 : 2, so choose **A**. Sometimes it is easier to balance by inspection than to balance by the redox method. A simple guideline to follow is: If the molecules are all uncharged, balance by inspection.

97. **Choice A is correct.** First, convert the current units into coulombs: C = amps × sec. = (9.65 amps)(1000 sec) = 9650 C. One mole of electrons carries a charge of one faraday (F), which equals 96,500 coulombs (C), and each mole of Zn dication requires two moles of electrons to be reduced to zinc metal. The molecular weight of Zn is 65.38 g. By substitution:

$$9650\ C\left(\frac{1\ mole\ e^-}{96,500\ C}\right)\left(\frac{1\ mole\ Zn}{2\ mole\ e^-}\right)\left(\frac{65.38\ grams\ Zn}{1\ mole\ Zn}\right) = 3.269\ g\ Zn$$

Choice **A** is the correct answer.

98. **Choice D is correct.** Magnesium is oxidized, and nickel dication is reduced. The half-reactions for the given cell are as follows:

$$Mg \rightarrow Mg^{2+} + 2e^- \qquad\qquad 2.37\ V$$
$$Ni^{2+} + 2e^- \rightarrow Ni \qquad\qquad -0.23\ V$$

Because Mg is oxidized, not reduced, the value for the reduction potential must be reversed to +2.37 V. The cell potential is 2.37 + (-0.23) = 2.14 V. Choice **D** is the best answer.

99. **Choice D is correct.** The Nernst equation shows logarithmic decay of the voltage. The log value is multiplied by a small term, making the decay insignificant until the last few moments of the decay. This is best shown in choice **D**. Choice A is close, but the linear decay at the end is inaccurate.

100. **Choice A is correct.** Because aluminum and carbon dioxide are products in the reaction, choices C and D are eliminated. Carbon is oxidized to carbon dioxide, and aluminum oxide (Al_2O_3) is reduced to aluminum metal. The best answer is choice **A**.

Notes

General Chemistry Bubble Sheet
(Make five copies, one for each section of the book.)

1. Ⓐ Ⓑ Ⓒ Ⓓ	37. Ⓐ Ⓑ Ⓒ Ⓓ	73. Ⓐ Ⓑ Ⓒ Ⓓ
2. Ⓐ Ⓑ Ⓒ Ⓓ	38. Ⓐ Ⓑ Ⓒ Ⓓ	74. Ⓐ Ⓑ Ⓒ Ⓓ
3. Ⓐ Ⓑ Ⓒ Ⓓ	39. Ⓐ Ⓑ Ⓒ Ⓓ	75. Ⓐ Ⓑ Ⓒ Ⓓ
4. Ⓐ Ⓑ Ⓒ Ⓓ	40. Ⓐ Ⓑ Ⓒ Ⓓ	76. Ⓐ Ⓑ Ⓒ Ⓓ
5. Ⓐ Ⓑ Ⓒ Ⓓ	41. Ⓐ Ⓑ Ⓒ Ⓓ	77. Ⓐ Ⓑ Ⓒ Ⓓ
6. Ⓐ Ⓑ Ⓒ Ⓓ	42. Ⓐ Ⓑ Ⓒ Ⓓ	78. Ⓐ Ⓑ Ⓒ Ⓓ
7. Ⓐ Ⓑ Ⓒ Ⓓ	43. Ⓐ Ⓑ Ⓒ Ⓓ	79. Ⓐ Ⓑ Ⓒ Ⓓ
8. Ⓐ Ⓑ Ⓒ Ⓓ	44. Ⓐ Ⓑ Ⓒ Ⓓ	80. Ⓐ Ⓑ Ⓒ Ⓓ
9. Ⓐ Ⓑ Ⓒ Ⓓ	45. Ⓐ Ⓑ Ⓒ Ⓓ	81. Ⓐ Ⓑ Ⓒ Ⓓ
10. Ⓐ Ⓑ Ⓒ Ⓓ	46. Ⓐ Ⓑ Ⓒ Ⓓ	82. Ⓐ Ⓑ Ⓒ Ⓓ
11. Ⓐ Ⓑ Ⓒ Ⓓ	47. Ⓐ Ⓑ Ⓒ Ⓓ	83. Ⓐ Ⓑ Ⓒ Ⓓ
12. Ⓐ Ⓑ Ⓒ Ⓓ	48. Ⓐ Ⓑ Ⓒ Ⓓ	84. Ⓐ Ⓑ Ⓒ Ⓓ
13. Ⓐ Ⓑ Ⓒ Ⓓ	49. Ⓐ Ⓑ Ⓒ Ⓓ	85. Ⓐ Ⓑ Ⓒ Ⓓ
14. Ⓐ Ⓑ Ⓒ Ⓓ	50. Ⓐ Ⓑ Ⓒ Ⓓ	86. Ⓐ Ⓑ Ⓒ Ⓓ
15. Ⓐ Ⓑ Ⓒ Ⓓ	51. Ⓐ Ⓑ Ⓒ Ⓓ	87. Ⓐ Ⓑ Ⓒ Ⓓ
16. Ⓐ Ⓑ Ⓒ Ⓓ	52. Ⓐ Ⓑ Ⓒ Ⓓ	88. Ⓐ Ⓑ Ⓒ Ⓓ
17. Ⓐ Ⓑ Ⓒ Ⓓ	53. Ⓐ Ⓑ Ⓒ Ⓓ	89. Ⓐ Ⓑ Ⓒ Ⓓ
18. Ⓐ Ⓑ Ⓒ Ⓓ	54. Ⓐ Ⓑ Ⓒ Ⓓ	90. Ⓐ Ⓑ Ⓒ Ⓓ
19. Ⓐ Ⓑ Ⓒ Ⓓ	55. Ⓐ Ⓑ Ⓒ Ⓓ	91. Ⓐ Ⓑ Ⓒ Ⓓ
20. Ⓐ Ⓑ Ⓒ Ⓓ	56. Ⓐ Ⓑ Ⓒ Ⓓ	92. Ⓐ Ⓑ Ⓒ Ⓓ
21. Ⓐ Ⓑ Ⓒ Ⓓ	57. Ⓐ Ⓑ Ⓒ Ⓓ	93. Ⓐ Ⓑ Ⓒ Ⓓ
22. Ⓐ Ⓑ Ⓒ Ⓓ	58. Ⓐ Ⓑ Ⓒ Ⓓ	94. Ⓐ Ⓑ Ⓒ Ⓓ
23. Ⓐ Ⓑ Ⓒ Ⓓ	59. Ⓐ Ⓑ Ⓒ Ⓓ	95. Ⓐ Ⓑ Ⓒ Ⓓ
24. Ⓐ Ⓑ Ⓒ Ⓓ	60. Ⓐ Ⓑ Ⓒ Ⓓ	96. Ⓐ Ⓑ Ⓒ Ⓓ
25. Ⓐ Ⓑ Ⓒ Ⓓ	61. Ⓐ Ⓑ Ⓒ Ⓓ	97. Ⓐ Ⓑ Ⓒ Ⓓ
26. Ⓐ Ⓑ Ⓒ Ⓓ	62. Ⓐ Ⓑ Ⓒ Ⓓ	98. Ⓐ Ⓑ Ⓒ Ⓓ
27. Ⓐ Ⓑ Ⓒ Ⓓ	63. Ⓐ Ⓑ Ⓒ Ⓓ	99. Ⓐ Ⓑ Ⓒ Ⓓ
28. Ⓐ Ⓑ Ⓒ Ⓓ	64. Ⓐ Ⓑ Ⓒ Ⓓ	100. Ⓐ Ⓑ Ⓒ Ⓓ
29. Ⓐ Ⓑ Ⓒ Ⓓ	65. Ⓐ Ⓑ Ⓒ Ⓓ	
30. Ⓐ Ⓑ Ⓒ Ⓓ	66. Ⓐ Ⓑ Ⓒ Ⓓ	
31. Ⓐ Ⓑ Ⓒ Ⓓ	67. Ⓐ Ⓑ Ⓒ Ⓓ	☐ Chemistry Section
32. Ⓐ Ⓑ Ⓒ Ⓓ	68. Ⓐ Ⓑ Ⓒ Ⓓ	
33. Ⓐ Ⓑ Ⓒ Ⓓ	69. Ⓐ Ⓑ Ⓒ Ⓓ	☐ Raw Score
34. Ⓐ Ⓑ Ⓒ Ⓓ	70. Ⓐ Ⓑ Ⓒ Ⓓ	
35. Ⓐ Ⓑ Ⓒ Ⓓ	71. Ⓐ Ⓑ Ⓒ Ⓓ	☐ Estimated Scaled Score
36. Ⓐ Ⓑ Ⓒ Ⓓ	72. Ⓐ Ⓑ Ⓒ Ⓓ	